WHAT IS SCIENCE?

TWELVE EMINENT SCIENTISTS
AND PHILOSOPHERS EXPLAIN
THEIR VARIOUS FIELDS
TO THE LAYMAN

Edited by James R. Newman

SIMON AND SCHUSTER
NEW YORK • 1955

SECOND PRINTING

LIBRARY OF CONGRESS CATALOG CARD NUMBER: 55–11042
MANUFACTURED IN THE UNITED STATES OF AMERICA
BY H. WOLFF BOOK MFG. CO., INC., NEW YORK

Contents

INTRODUCTION *James R. Newman* vii

SCIENCE AND HUMAN LIFE *Bertrand Russell* 6

MATHEMATICS AND LOGIC *Sir Edmund Taylor Whittaker* 24

ASTRONOMY AND COSMOLOGY *Hermann Bondi* 66

PHYSICS *Edward U. Condon* 102

CHEMISTRY *John Read* 154

BIOCHEMISTRY *Ernest Baldwin* 198

BIOLOGY *Warder Clyde Allee* 231

EVOLUTION AND GENETICS *Julian Huxley* 256

PSYCHOLOGY *Edwin G. Boring* 294

ANTHROPOLOGY *Clyde Kluckhohn* 319

PSYCHOANALYSIS *Erich Fromm* 362

SCIENCE AS FORESIGHT *Jacob Bronowski* 385

Bibliography 437

Index 459

Introduction

Twelve scientists and philosophers have contributed freshly written essays to this symposium on science and the scientific outlook. The book is addressed to the general reader.

There is no want of literature on what science has done, or is expected to do tomorrow, to increase man's control over nature. While these achievements and hopes are discussed in the present volume, they are not its principal concern. Its emphasis is rather on the nature of scientific knowledge, on the scientific method, on science as an intellectual pursuit; in short, the book attempts to answer the question: What is science? Another matter examined in these pages is the bearing of science on society. It is a commonplace that science is not wisdom; that it may save us from the pox but not from our own folly. But like many other commonplaces this one is not very helpful. Indeed, it is a source of much mischief because it promotes the cause of fashionable philosophies which assert that, since science cannot provide answers for all human problems, it is not a safe guide in dealing with any of them. We all agree that science has changed civilization and will continue to change it if there is a civilization left. But we do not agree—and on this point scientists no less than other thoughtful men fall out among themselves—as to how knowledge can be used for good ends and what are the responsibilities of its discoverers to see that it is not used for bad ends. Science cannot resolve these issues but scientists have no right to evade them. Several of the authors of this symposium have dealt with the subject at length; Lord Russell has devoted his entire essay to it.

Though written for persons without special training, the pieces in this book are not always easy. Neither is modern science. A decent respect for the reader requires that he be told when a subject admits of no further simplification; the contributors, I am glad to say, have not pretended to explain what cannot here be explained. Nevertheless, every effort has been made to speak plainly, to refrain from jargon and nebulous profundities, to enlighten rather than to astound. Although some areas are too difficult for any deep explorations in these pages, the nature of the problem, the aims of its investigators and the instruments they use, have been made clear. Thus if it has not always been possible to escort him through it, the reader has at least been given many fresh and exciting glimpses of the promised land.

Some of the contributors provided abundant material for the preparation of biographical sketches and lists of suggested readings. In other instances, especially where the authors have been excessively self-effacing, I have had to rely upon the biographical scraps of conventional reference books—which have not always been very lively or illuminating. I wish to express my appreciation for the valuable editorial assistance of my old friend and associate Robert Hatch. I am most thankful for help generously given by Dr. J. Bronowski and Professor Ernest Nagel.

The authors of this book have succeeded, I believe, in giving an unusually rich and illuminating picture of scientific thinking. They have offered thoughtful opinions on the possibilities and the limitations of science, what it can contribute to civilization and what other ingredients are required to assure the progress—or perhaps one should say, survival—of society. I hope this book helps to a more balanced view both of science and human values. I hope it helps counteract the malicious doctrines, flourishing again in this age of insecurity, which belittle science and reason, exhort men to consult their hearts instead of their heads, depreciate the lessons of experience and proclaim the higher truth emanating from inner voices. "Science," said Adam Smith, "is the great antidote to the poison of enthusiasm and superstition." An ailing world would do well to reach for the right bottle in the medicine cabinet.

JAMES R. NEWMAN

SCIENCE AND HUMAN LIFE

BERTRAND RUSSELL

about

Bertrand Russell

Bertrand Arthur William Russell was born at Trelleck, in Monmouthshire, England on May 18, 1872. His father was Viscount Amberley, his mother, Kate Stanley, daughter of Baron Stanley of Alderley. Both parents died before Russell was four years old and he was brought up by his grandmother, Countess Russell, a woman of strong opinions and puritanical principles. Her elevated outlook on social matters, her indifference to money—"only possible," as Russell says, "to those who have always had it"—and to other conventional earmarks of success, her "belief in private judgment and the supremacy of the individual conscience"—all had a profound influence on the formation of Russell's character.

Russell was tutored at home until he was 18; he then went to Cambridge where he concentrated on mathematics and philosophy. Among his teachers was Alfred North Whitehead who played a central part in the younger man's mental development, became his friend and later collaborated with him in the writing of the Principia Mathematica, one of the great intellectual achievements of the twentieth century.

After graduating from Cambridge Russell spent several years abroad, visited America in 1896, and in 1898 returned to Trinity College, Cambridge, as a lecturer and fellow. His first book, German Social Democracy, appeared in 1896; other early writings include An Essay on the Foundations of Geometry (1897) and his admirable *monograph,* A Critical Exposition of the Philosophy of Leibniz (1900).

Russell describes 1900 as "the most important year in my intellectual life." He went that year with Whitehead to the International Congress of Philosophy in Paris where he listened to the Italian logician Peano give an account of his system of symbolic logic. This experience stimulated Russell's own interest in the field and led to two of his major works, The Principles of Mathematics *(1903) and the* Principia Mathematica *(1910-1913).*

Although Russell's primary interests for many years were philosophy and the foundations of mathematics, he was at all times deeply concerned with politics and the problems of society. He was active in that famous organization for the advancement of socialism, the Fabian Society, and was a close friend of Sidney and Beatrice Webb. At one time he considered standing for Parliament, but because he declined to conceal his agnosticism could not win party support for his candidacy. An outspoken opposition to conscription brought him into difficulties during the First World War. He was fined and dismissed from his college post. In 1918 he was imprisoned for six months because he had written a pamphlet accusing the American Army of "intimidating strikers" at home, which was regarded as "likely to prejudice His Majesty's relations with the United States of America." While in jail he wrote his Introduction to Mathematical Philosophy, *first published in 1919. By the time Russell was released the governor of the prison must have felt that he had had quite enough of mathematical philosophers: he had been required, though unable to comprehend it, to read the manuscript of Russell's book for possible seditious tendencies.*

In 1920 Russell made a trip to Russia, where he met Lenin, Trotsky and Gorki. From this visit came The Practice and Theory of Bolshevism *(1920), in which Russell praised the fundamental ideas of communism but warned against the excesses of those who held power and were determined at all costs to put the ideas into practice. He spent a year in China (1920-21), with whose people he developed a close bond of sympathy. Looking back on this visit in 1943, he wrote: "I loved the Chinese, but it was obvious that the resistance to hostile militarisms must destroy much of what was best in their* civilization." After this trip he returned to teaching and lecturing in England and the United States. His voluminous writings on general questions brought his name to the attention of a wide audience. Between 1920 and 1940 he published many books and more than 200 articles on mathematical, philosophical, scientific, political and social subjects. No other contemporary philosopher ranged over so broad a field or stood so high in popular esteem. Among his principal works are Mysticism and Logic (1918), a brilliant and eloquent collection of essays; The Analysis of Mind (1921); The Prospects of Industrial Civilization (1923), a study of socialism written in collaboration with his second wife, Dora Russell; The ABC of Relativity (1925); The Analysis of Matter (1927); An Outline of Philosophy (1927), perhaps the best of modern introductions to philosophical thought; Marriage and Morals (1929); The Scientific Outlook (1931); Education and the Social Order (1932); Freedom and Organization (1934); Power (1938), regarded as one of the most trenchant of analyses of the theory of the state; An Inquiry into Meaning and Truth (1940), the William James lectures at Harvard University; History of Western Philosophy (1946); Human Knowledge (1948); Unpopular Essays (1950); The Impact of Science on Society (1951); Human Society in Ethics and Politics (1955).

Russell has made many visits to the United States, his longest stay being from 1938 to 1944. During this period he lectured at the University of Chicago, at the University of California in Los Angeles, at Harvard and at the Barnes Foundation at Merion, Pennsylvania. He was appointed a professor of philosophy at the College of the City of New York, but the appointment was revoked by court order when an anguished lady brought suit to have the appointment annulled on the ground of Russell's "advocacy of free love." On his return to England in 1944 Russell was again appointed to a fellowship at Trinity College. He continued to write, lecture and express himself vigorously on topics ranging from epistemology to the catastrophic consequences of modern warfare. He has received almost every distinction his country can award, including the Order of Merit, and in 1950 was awarded the Nobel prize in literature. Russell writes with such incandescent clarity, wit and incisiveness that, regardless of theme, all his works are literary achievements.

Russell is 83 years old and in excellent health. He writes with as much sting as he did 60 years ago. He remains a magnificent nonconformist, kindly, tolerant and skeptical in outlook—the values he has always cherished. "I should like," he said a couple of years ago, "to live another ten years, provided there is not another world war meanwhile. If there is, there will be something to be said for being dead."

It is a privilege to bring to the readers of this book the words of one who in mind and spirit embodies the highest good of our civilization.

SCIENCE AND HUMAN LIFE

BERTRAND RUSSELL

Science and the techniques to which it has given rise have changed human life during the last hundred and fifty years more than it had been changed since men took to agriculture, and the changes that are being wrought by science continue at an increasing speed. There is no sign of any new stability to be attained on some scientific plateau. On the contrary, there is every reason to think that the revolutionary possibilities of science extend immeasurably beyond what has so far been realized. Can the human race adjust itself quickly enough to these vertiginous transformations, or will it, as innumerable former species have done, perish from lack of adaptability? The dinosaurs were, in their day, the lords of creation, and if there had been philosophers among them not one would have foreseen that the whole race might perish. But they became extinct because they could not adapt themselves to a world without swamps. In the case of man and science, there is a wholly new factor, namely that man himself is creating the changes of environment to which he will have to adjust himself with unprecedented rapidity. But, although man through his scientific skill is the cause of the changes of environment, most of these changes are not willed by human beings. Although they come about through human agencies, they have, or at any rate have had so far, something of the inexorable inevitability of natural forces. Whether Nature dried up the swamps or men deliberately drained them, makes little difference as regards the ultimate result. Whether men will be able to survive the changes of environment that their own skill has brought about is an open question. If the answer is in the affirmative, it will be known some day; if not, not. If the answer is to be in the affirmative, men will have to apply scientific ways of thinking to themselves and their institutions. They cannot continue to hope, as all politicians hitherto have, that in a world where everything has changed, the political and social habits of the eighteenth century can remain inviolate. Not only will men of science have to grapple with the sciences that deal with man, but—and this is a far more difficult matter—they will have to persuade the world to listen to what they have discovered. If they cannot succeed in this difficult enterprise, man will destroy himself by his halfway cleverness. I am told that, if he were out of the way, the future would lie with rats. I hope they will find it a pleasant world, but I am glad I shall not be there.

But let us pass from these generalities to more specific questions.

One of the most obvious problems raised by a scientific technique is that of the exhaustion of the soil and of raw materials. This subject has been much discussed, and some governments have actually taken some steps to prevent the denudation of the soil. But I doubt whether, as yet, the good done by these measures is outweighing the harm done in less careful regions. Food, however, is such an obvious necessity that the problem is bound to receive increasing attention as population pressure makes it more urgent. Whether this increased attention will do good or harm in the long run is, I fear, questionable. By a spendthrift use of fertilizers, food production in the present can be increased at the cost of food production in the future. Can you imagine a politician going to his constituents and saying: "Ladies and gentlemen, it is in your power to have abundance of food for the next thirty years, but the measures that will give you this abundance will cause scarcity for your grandchildren. I am therefore proposing measures to insure frugality in the present in order to avoid famine in the somewhat distant future." Is it possible to believe that a politician who said this would win elections against one less addicted to foresight? I hardly think so, unless the general level of political intelligence and virtue can be very considerably increased.

The question of raw materials is more difficult and complex than the question of food. The raw materials required at one stage of technique are different from those required at another. It may be that by the time the world's supply of oil is exhausted, atomic power will have taken its place. But to this sort of process there is a limit, though not an easily assignable one. At present there is a race for uranium, and it would seem likely that before very long there will be no easily accessible source of uranium. If, when that happens, the world has come to depend upon nuclear energy as its main source of power, the result may be devastating. All such speculations are of course very questionable, since new techniques may always make it possible to dispense with formerly necessary raw materials. But we cannot get away from the broad fact that we are living upon the world's capital of stored energy and are transforming the energy at a continually increasing rate into forms in which it cannot be utilized. Such a manner of life can hardly be stable, but must sooner or later bring the penalty that lies in wait for those who live on capital.

In primitive times, when the human population of the globe was small, such problems did not arise. Agriculture, it is true, was practiced in ways that exhausted the soil for a time, but there were usually new vacant lands available; and if there were not, the corpses of enemies sufficed as fertilizers. The system was "conservative" in the physicists' sense. That is to say, energy on the whole accumulated as fast as it was used. Now, this is not the case; and, so far as one can see, it will never be the case while scientific technique continues.

All this however, you may say, is distant and doubtful: we have more pressing matters to consider. This is true, and I will proceed to consider some of them.

The problem which most preoccupies the public mind at the present moment is that of scientific warfare. It has become evident that, if scientific skill is allowed free scope, the human race will be exterminated, if not in the next war, then in the next but one or the next but two—at any rate at no very distant date. To this problem there are two possible reactions: there are those who say, "let us create social institutions which will make large-scale war impossible"; there are others who say, "let us not allow war to become *too* scientific. We cannot perhaps go back to bows and arrows, but let us at any rate agree with our enemies that, if we fight them, both sides will fight inefficiently." For my part, I favor the former answer, since I cannot see that either side could be expected to observe an agreement not to use modern weapons if once war had broken out. It is on this ground that I do not think that there will long continue to be human beings unless methods are found of permanently preventing large-scale wars. But this is a serious question as to which I will say no more at the moment. I shall return to it presently.

The substitution of machines for human labor raises problems which are likely to become acute in the not very distant future. These problems are not new. They began with the Industrial Revolution, which ruined large numbers of skilled and industrious handicraftsmen, inflicting upon them hardships that they had in no way deserved and that they bitterly resented. But their troubles were transitory: they died; and such of their children as survived sought other occupations. The sufferers had no political power and were not able to offer any effective resistance to "progress." Nowadays, in democratic countries, the political situation is different and wage earners cannot be expected to submit tamely to starvation. But if we are to believe Norbert Wiener's book on cybernetics—and I see no reason why we should not—it should soon be possible to keep up the existing level of production with a very much smaller number of workers. The more economical methods, one may suppose, would be introduced during a war while the workers were at the front, if such a war were not quickly ended by H-bomb extermination, and when the survivors returned their former jobs would no longer be available. The social discontent resulting from such a situation would be very grave. It could be dealt with in a totalitarian country, but a democracy could only deal with it by radical changes in its social philosophy and even in its ethics. Work has been thought to be a duty, but in such a situation there would be little work to do and duty would have to take new forms.

Changes in political philosophy are necessary for several reasons. One of the most important is that modern techniques make society more organic in the sense that its parts are more interdependent and an injury to one individual or group is more likely than it formerly was to cause injury to other individuals or groups. It is easier to kill a man than to kill a sponge because he is more highly organized and more centralized. In like manner it is easier to inflict vital damage upon a scientific community than upon a community of nomads or scattered peasants. This increase of interdependence makes it necessary to limit freedom in various ways which liberals in the past considered undesirable. There are two spheres in which such limitation is especially necessary: the one is in economics; and the other, in the relations between states.

Take economics first. Suppose, as is not improbable, that most of the power used in industry comes to be distributed from a fairly small number of atomic power-stations, and suppose that the men working in these stations retained the right to strike. They could completely paralyze the industrial life of a nation and could levy almost unlimited blackmail in the form of demands for higher wages. No community would tolerate such a state of affairs. The workers in power-stations would have to have understudies like actors in a theater, and the forces of the state would have to be employed if necessary to enable the understudies to replace workers on strike. Another example, which war has already brought to the fore, is the supply and use of raw materials. Whenever raw materials are scarce their distribution has to be controlled and not left to the free play of unfettered economic forces. Scarcity of this sort has hitherto been thought of as a transitory phenomenon due to the needs and ravages of war. But it is likely to remain, in regard to many essentials, a normal condition of highly developed industry. Some central authority for the allocation of raw materials must therefore be expected as a necessary limitation of economic freedom. Another unavoidable limitation comes from the vastness of some obviously desirable enterprises. To bring fertility to the interior of Australia and to parts of Siberia is almost certainly possible, but only by an expenditure far beyond the capacity of private enterprise. One may expect that the progress of science will increase the number of such possible enterprises. Perhaps it will be possible in time to make the Sahara rainy, or even to make northern Canada warm. But, if such things become possible, they will be possible only for whole communities and not for private corporations.

Even more important than the limitations of economic liberty are the limitations on the liberty of states. The liberal doctrine of nationality, which was preached by liberals before 1848 and embodied in the Treaty of Versailles by President Wilson, had its justification as a protest against alien domination. But to allow *complete* liberty to any national state is just as anarchic as it would be to allow complete liberty to an individual. There are things which an individual must not do because the criminal law forbids them. The law and the police are in most cases strong enough to prevent such things from being done: murderers are a very small percentage of the population of any civilized country. But the relations between states are not governed by law and cannot be until there is a supranational armed force strong enough to enforce the decisions of a supranational authority. In the past, although the wars resulting from international anarchy caused much suffering and destruction, mankind was able to survive them, and, on the whole, the risks of war were thought less irksome than the controls that would be necessary to prevent it. This is ceasing to be true. The risks of war have become so great that the continued exist-ence of our species either has become or soon will become incom-patible with the new methods of scientific destruction.

The new dangers resulting from our more organic society call for certain changes in the kind of character that is admired. The bold buccaneer, or the great conqueror such as Alexander or Napoleon, has been admired and is still admired although the world can no longer afford this type of character. We come here upon a difficulty. It is a good thing that people should be adventurous and that there should be scope for individual enterprise; but the adventure and en-terprise, if they are not to bring total disaster, must steer clear of cer-tain fields in which they were formerly possible. You may still, with-out harm to your fellow men, wish to be the first man to reach the moon. You may wish to be a great poet or a great composer or a man who advances the boundaries of scientific knowledge. Such ad-venture injures no one. But if Napoleon is your ideal, you must be restrained. Certain kinds of anarchic self-assertion, which are splen-did in the literature of tragedy, have come to involve too much risk. A motorist alone on an empty road may drive as he pleases, but in crowded traffic he must obey the rules. More and more the lives of individuals come to resemble the motorist in traffic rather than the lonely driver in an empty desert.

I come at last to a question which is causing considerable concern and perplexity to many men of science, namely: what is their social duty toward this new world that they have been creating? I do not think this question is easy or simple. The pure man of science, as such, is concerned with the advancement of knowledge, and in his professional moments he takes it for granted that the advancement of knowledge is desirable. But inevitably he finds himself casting his pearls before swine. Men who do not understand his scientific work can utilize the knowledge that he provides. The new techniques to which it gives rise often have totally unexpected effects. The men who decide what use shall be made of the new techniques are not necessarily possessed of any exceptional degree of wisdom. They are mainly politicians whose professional skill consists in knowing how to play upon the emotions of masses of men. The emotions which easily sway masses are very seldom the best of which the individuals composing the masses are capable. And so the scientist finds that he has unintentionally placed new powers in the hands of reckless men. He may easily come to doubt, in moments of depression or overwork, whether the world would not be a happier place if science did not exist. He knows that science gives power and that the power which it gives could be used to increase human welfare; but he knows also that very often it is used, not so, but in the very opposite direction. Is he on this account to view himself as an unintentional malefactor?

I do not think so. I think we must retain the belief that scientific knowledge is one of the glories of man. I will not maintain that knowledge can never do harm. I think such general propositions can almost always be refuted by well-chosen examples. What I will maintain—and maintain vigorously—is that knowledge is very much more often useful than harmful and that fear of knowledge is very much more often harmful than useful. Suppose you are a scientific pioneer and you make some discovery of great scientific importance, and suppose you say to yourself, "I am afraid this discovery will do harm": you know that other people are likely to make the same discovery if they are allowed suitable opportunities for research; you must therefore, if you do not wish the discovery to become public, either discourage your sort of research or control publication by a board of censors. Nine times out of ten, the board of censors will object to knowledge that is in fact useful—e.g., knowledge concerning contraceptives—rather than to knowledge that would in fact be harmful. It is very difficult to foresee the social effects of new knowledge, and it is very easy from the sheer force of habit to shrink from new knowledge such as might promote new kinds of behavior.

Apart from the more general duties of scientists toward society, they have a quite special and exceptional duty in the present critical condition of the world. All men of science who have studied thermonuclear warfare are aware of two superlatively important facts: first, that whatever agreements may have been reached to the contrary, thermonuclear weapons will certainly be employed by both sides in a world war; second, that if such weapons are employed there can be no hope of victory for either side, but only of universal destruction involving, quite possibly, the end of all human and animal life and almost certainly, failing that, a complete reversion to barbarism. A great war with thermonuclear weapons will not produce a universal victory of communism. It will also not produce the sort of world desired by the Western Powers. Nor will it give opportunity for the independent flourishing of Southeast Asia or Africa. Radioactive clouds, borne by the wind, will not respect frontiers and will ignore the legal rights of neutrals. In view of this prospect, there is one matter upon which the interests of the whole world coincide. Whether you are a Communist or an anti-Communist, an inhabitant of Asia or Europe or America, a white, brown, yellow or black man, your interests are exactly the same as those of the rest of the human race. Your paramount interest, if you are aware of the situation, must be to preserve the existence of mankind by preventing a great war. It is clearly the duty of men of science to bring the facts home, as far as lies in their power, to the governments and peoples of both East and West. This is no easy task. The governments of both East and West, whether from ignorance or from motives of prestige, are engaged in trying to persuade their populations that thermonuclear weapons will destroy the enemy but not themselves. *The Red Star*, the official military organ of the Soviet government, published several articles on methods of defense against thermonuclear weapons. These articles were so absurd that one could hardly believe their authors to be sincere. It seemed obvious that the purpose of the articles was to deceive people in Russia as to the perils to which they would be exposed. I am afraid that the schemes for civil defense put forward in America and Britain are equally misleading. I hope that this is because the authorities are ignorant and not because they are dishonest.

Clearly, scientists both of the East and of the West have an imperative duty: namely, the duty of bringing home to the protagonists the fact that the time is past for swashbuckling and boasting and campaigns of bluff which, if the bluff is called, can end only in utter disaster. I have been glad to see a lead given by a small number of men of science of the highest eminence, representing many countries and all creeds, Americans, Western Europeans, Poles and Japanese. I have rejoiced to see these men issue a clear statement as to what is likely to happen in a great war; and I should wish them to invite all other men of science, in all countries, to subscribe to this statement.

I am aware that this will involve a certain degree of heroism and self-sacrifice. But there will be a reward which brave men should find sufficient: the reward of preserving uprightness and self-respect in the face of danger. These virtues are common in battle, and men of science should be able to show them also in a conflict with ignorance and ferocity. Science has fought great fights in former centuries against the embattled forces of obscurantism. In the nineteenth century it seemed as though science were victorious, but the victory is in danger of proving illusory. If science is to do its duty by mankind, men of science must once again face martyrdom and obloquy and the accusation of indifference to moral values. Perhaps their prestige may suffice to save them from the worst penalties for their courage, but of this we cannot be confident. What we can say with confidence is that it is not worth while to prolong a slavish and cowardly existence for a few miserable years while those who know the magnitude of the impending catastrophe wait for that radioactive death that is in store for them as well as for others.

A difficult readjustment in the scientists' conception of duty is imperatively necessary. As Lord Adrian said in his address to the British Association, "Unless we are ready to give up some of our old loyalties, we may be forced into a fight which might end the human race." This matter of loyalty is the crux. Hitherto, in the East and in the West alike, most scientists, like most other people, have felt that loyalty to their own state is paramount. They have no longer a right to feel this. Loyalty to the human race must take its place. Everyone in the West will at once admit this as regards Soviet scientists. We are shocked that Kapitza, who was Rutherford's favorite pupil, was willing, when the Soviet government refused him permission to return to Cambridge, to place his scientific skill at the disposal of those who wished to spread communism by means of H-bombs. We do not so readily apprehend a similar failure of duty on our own side. I do not wish to be thought to suggest treachery, since that is only a transference of loyalty to another national state; I am suggesting a very different thing: that scientists the world over should join in enlightening mankind as to the perils of a great war and in devising methods for its prevention. I urge with all the emphasis at my disposal that this is the duty of scientists in East and West alike. It is a difficult duty, and one likely to entail penalties for those who perform it. But, after all, it is the labors of scientists which have caused the danger and on this account, if on no other, scientists must do everything in their power to save mankind from the madness which they have made possible.

Science from the dawn of history, and probably longer, has been intimately associated with war. I imagine that when our ancestors descended from the trees they were victorious over the arboreal conservatives because flints were sharper than coconuts. To come to more recent times, Archimedes was respected for his scientific defense of Syracuse against the Romans; Leonardo obtained employment under the Duke of Milan because of his skill in fortification, though he did mention in a postscript that he could also paint a bit; Galileo similarly derived an income from the Grand Duke of Tuscany because of his skill in calculating the trajectories of projectiles. In the French Revolution, those scientists who were not guillotined devoted themselves to making new explosives. There is therefore no departure from tradition in the present-day scientists' manufacture of A-bombs and H-bombs. All that is new is the extent of their destructive skill.

I do not think that men of science can cease to regard the disinterested pursuit of knowledge as their primary duty. It is true that new knowledge and new skills are sometimes harmful in their effects, but scientists cannot profitably take account of this fact since the effects are impossible to foresee. We cannot blame Columbus because the discovery of the Western Hemisphere spread throughout the Eastern Hemisphere an appallingly devastating plague. Nor can we blame James Watt for the Dust Bowl, although if there had been no steam engines and no railways the West would not have been so carelessly or so quickly cultivated. To see that knowledge is wisely used is primarily the duty of statesmen, not of men of science; but it is part of the duty of men of science to see that important knowledge is widely disseminated and is not falsified in the interests of this or that propaganda.

Scientific knowledge has its dangers; but so has every great thing. And over and beyond the dangers with which it threatens the present, it opens up as nothing else can the vision of a possible happy world, a world without poverty, without war, with little illness. And, what is perhaps more than all, when science has mastered the forces which mold human character, it will be able to produce populations in which few suffer from destructive fierceness and in which the great majority regard other people, not as competitors to be feared, but as helpers in a common task. Science has only recently begun to apply itself to human beings, except in their purely physical aspect. Such science as exists in psychology and anthropology has hardly begun to affect political behavior or private ethics. The minds of men remain attuned to a world that is fast disappearing. The changes in our physical environment require, if they are to bring well-being, correlative changes in our beliefs and habits. If we cannot effect these changes, we shall suffer the fate of the dinosaurs who could not live on dry land. I think it is the duty of science—I do not say of every individual man of science—to study the means by which we can adapt ourselves to the new world. There are certain things that the world quite obviously needs: tentativeness, as opposed to dogmatism, in our beliefs; an expectation of co-operation, rather than competition, in social relations; a lessening of envy and collective hatred. These are things which education could produce without much difficulty. They are not things adequately sought in the education of the present day.

It is to progress in the human sciences that we must look to undo the evils which have resulted from a knowledge of the physical world hastily and superficially acquired by populations unconscious of the changes in themselves that the new knowledge has made imperative. The road to a happier world than any known in the past lies open before us if atavistic destructive passions can be kept in leash while the necessary adaptations are made. Fears are inevitable in our time, but hopes are equally rational and far more likely to bear good fruit. We must learn to think rather less of the dangers to be avoided than of the good that will lie within our grasp if we can believe in it and let it dominate our thoughts. Science, whatever unpleasant consequences it may have by the way, is in its very nature a liberator, a liberator of bondage to physical nature and, in time to come, a liberator from the weight of destructive passions. We are on the threshold of utter disaster or unprecedentedly glorious achievement. No previous age has been fraught with problems so momentous; and it is to science that we must look for a happy issue.

MATHEMATICS AND

LOGIC

SIR EDMUND TAYLOR WHITTAKER

about

Sir Edmund Taylor Whittaker

Sir Edmund Whittaker, one of the world's foremost mathematicians, has had a distinguished professional career reaching back into the last century. Few men still living have known intimately and worked together with so many of those who made the revolution of modern science. The following autobiographical sketch contains historical side lights which will, I believe, delight the reader and give him information not otherwise obtainable.

"I was born at Southport, England, on October 24, 1873, the son of John Whittaker and Selina, daughter of Edmund Taylor, M.D. At the age of eleven I was sent away from home to the Manchester Grammar School. I was on the classical side, which meant that three-fifths of my time was devoted to Latin and Greek. In the lower forms, where the study was purely linguistic, I did well, but my lack of interest in poetry and drama caused a falling-off when I was promoted to the upper school, and I was glad to escape by electing to specialize in mathematics. Only after I had left school did I discover the field of Latin and Greek learning that really appealed to me— ancient and medieval theology, philosophy and science.

"I gained an entrance scholarship to Trinity College, Cambridge in 1891, and was elected a Fellow of Trinity in 1896 and put on the lecturing staff. Among my pupils at Trinity in 1896-1906 were the well-known mathematicians G. H. Hardy, Sir James Jeans, Harry

Bateman, Sir Arthur Eddington, J. E. Littlewood, G. N. Watson, H. W. Turnbull, and Sir Geoffrey Taylor.

"The professor of pure mathematics at this time was A. R. Forsyth, a sociable and hospitable man who liked entertaining mathematicians from the continent of Europe. I lived in the next rooms to him in college and was always invited to meet them: and in this way I came to know Felix Klein, who was a frequent visitor and for whom I had a great admiration and affection, and also Henri Poincaré and G. Mittag-Leffler.

"In 1898, 1899 and 1900 I acted as one of the secretaries of the mathematical and physical section of the British Association for the Advancement of Science. This was a valuable experience for such a young man, for I was brought into close contact with the great mathematical and experimental physicists of the older generation—Lord Kelvin, Lord Rayleigh, Sir George Stokes and G. F. FitzGerald; and those of the generation still in its prime—Sir J. J. Thomson, Sir Joseph Larmor, Sir Arthur Schuster and Sir Oliver Lodge; and my own contemporaries, such as Lord Rutherford.

"I became a Fellow of the Royal Astonomical Society in 1898 and was appointed one of its secretaries in 1901. Here again I was brought into contact with many senior men of great distinction, particularly Sir William Huggins, who first applied spectroscopy to the stars, and Sir Norman Lockyer, and with others who though not famous astronomers were celebrated in other ways—notably Admiral Sir Erasmus Ommaney, who was a very old man when I knew him but attended the meetings regularly; he had fought (I presume as a midshipman) at the battle of Navarino in 1827, when the Turkish fleet was destroyed by an allied fleet under Codrington, and Greece was liberated.

"I left Trinity in 1906 on being appointed Royal Astronomer of Ireland—the office held in 1827-1865 by Sir William Rowan Hamilton, the discoverer of quaternions and of Hamiltonian methods in optics and dynamics. My most distinguished pupil in Dublin was Eamon de Valera, who has never ceased to follow mathematics as a recreation from his political activities. About the end of my time in Ireland he was a candidate for a vacant chair of mathematics in Galway: I was asked my opinion and said that he was a man who would go far—*a prediction fulfilled in a way I did not at the time anticipate.*

"In 1912 I was elected to the historic chair of mathematics in the University of Edinburgh, which had been occupied in 1674-1675 by Gregory and in 1725-1746 by Maclaurin. The epitaph composed for Maclaurin by Johnson when he and Boswell visited Scotland is still to be read in Greyfriars Kirkyard, and tells how Maclaurin was elected to the chair electus ipso Newtono suadente.

"In Edinburgh from 1912 to 1946 I had many undergraduate and postgraduate pupils who afterwards rose to distinction; two boys who came up from school together one year, and later became Fellows of the Royal Society, were W. V. D. Hodge, who now holds the Lowndean chair of Geometry at Cambridge, and my son J. M. Whittaker, now vice-chancellor of the University of Sheffield. I gave many lectures or courses of lectures at other universities which were afterwards printed: The Rouse Ball and Tarner lectures at Cambridge, the Herbert Spencer lectureship at Oxford, the Donnellan lectureship in Dublin, the Riddell lectureship at Durham (Newcastle), the Selby lectureship at Cardiff, the Hitchcock professorship at the University of California, the Bruce-Preller lectureship at the Royal Society of Edinburgh, the Larmor lectureship at the Royal Irish Academy, and the Guthrie lectureship of the Physical Society.

"In connection with the Edinburgh chair, I may mention the institution in 1914 of what was, so far as I know, the first university mathematical laboratory, which incorporated in mathematical teaching the theory of computation as known to professional astronomers.

"From other universities I received the honorary degrees of LL. D. (St. Andrews and California) and Sc. D. (Dublin, National University of Ireland, Manchester, Birmingham and London).

"I was elected F.R.S. in 1905, served on the Council and was awarded the Sylvester and Copley medals. With the Royal Society of Edinburgh I had continuous contact, being president in 1939-1944. At the end of my tenure of the presidency, a bronze portrait head, executed by Mr. Benno Schotz, R.S.A., was subscribed for by the Fellows and placed in the Society's house. I was president of the Mathematical Association in 1920-21, of the Mathematical and Physical Section of the British Association in 1927, and of the London Mathematical Society in 1928-1929, being awarded its De Morgan Medal in 1935.

"I am an Honorary Fellow or Foreign Member of many national academies or mathematical societies and of my old college, Trinity, and H. H. Pope Pius XI appointed me a member of the pontifical Academy of Sciences and conferred on me the Cross pro Ecclesia et Pontifice."

Sir Edmund's many writings include Modern Analysis (*in collaboration with* G. N. Watson), Treatise on Analytical Dynamics, Theory of Optical Instruments, History of the Theories of Aether and Electricity, The Calculus of Observations, The Beginning and End of the World, *and his* Tarner Lectures, From Euclid to Eddington. *He is held in as high regard for his works on the philosophy and history of science as for those on purely mathematical subjects.*

Whittaker was knighted in 1945. Now in his 82nd year he continues with remarkable vigor to pursue his writings and researches. The second volume of his History of the Theories of Aether and Electricity, *a monumental history of the whole of theoretical physics was published in 1953. He is at work on the third volume which will take the story up to 1950. The following essay is a tour de force, surveying modern mathematics and logic, showing how they evolved from the mathematical interests of the past and describing some of the main problems mathematicians are working on today. I know of no one else who could have covered this vast field in such brief space, much less have made the discussion accessible in large part to the ordinary intelligent reader.*

MATHEMATICS AND LOGIC

SIR EDMUND TAYLOR WHITTAKER

The First Mathematicians

Mathematics is in this book regarded as a kind of science. But there is a great difference between mathematics and the other recognized branches of science, as can be seen when we examine the nature of a typical mathematical theorem. Take for instance this, which was originally enunciated in the eighteenth century by Edward Waring of Cambridge: "Every positive whole number can be represented as the sum of at most nine cubes." With Waring this was really no more than a guess based on observation of a great number of particular cases; but evidently mere observation cannot furnish a *proof* that the theorem is true in general, and indeed a strict proof of this theorem was not known until more than a century later. Let us see how the notion of a science that depends on logical proof came into being.

Historians are generally agreed that this development originated with the Greek philosophers of the sixth and fifth centuries before Christ. To be sure, the arts of calculation and measurement had made considerable progress before this, amongst the ancient Babylonians and Egyptians, who were able to solve numerical problems beyond the powers of most modern schoolboys; but the procedure which is characteristic of mathematics as we know it, the *proving* of theorems, was introduced by the Greeks.

The records are scanty, and generally later in date by some centu-

24

ries than the events referred to. But there can be no doubt that the movement began in the fringe of Greek settlements along the coast of Asia Minor, which were in contact with the older civilizations of the East, and were at the time enjoying peace and prosperity. The new principle that was central in their philosophy was the conviction that the world has a unity; in a polytheistic society they were essentially monotheists, and they held that science is of one pattern. The first of them whose name has come down to us, Thales of Miletus (640?-546 B.C.) taught that all matter is essentially one, that it consists, in fact, of modifications of water. His successor, Anaximander, the second head of the school, opened wider possibilities by asserting only that there is one primitive formless substance everywhere present, out of which all things were made.

Thales is credited with the discovery of the mathematical theorem that "the angle in a semicircle is a right angle." This differs in character from the geometrical facts known to the ancient Egyptians, which had been concerned with areas. Thales seems to have been the first thinker to make lines and curves (which are abstractions) fundamental. For him, the theorem was probably a simple fact of observation. He would be familiar with wall decorations in which rectangles were inscribed in circles: a diagonal of a rectangle is also a diagonal of the corresponding circle, and the right angle formed by two sides of the rectangle is therefore the angle standing on a diameter, i.e., it is the angle in a semicircle.

The Place of Logic in Geometry

The disciples of Thales based their doctrine of physics on the assumption of a single ever-present medium which could undergo modifications. So far as the relations of physical objects with each other were concerned, they knew little beyond the experimental arts of surveying and measuring which they had inherited from the Egyptians and Babylonians. The Greeks of the next generation, however, developed this primitive geometry into an independent science, in which the whole corpus of the properties of figures in space, such as the theorem that the angle in a semicircle is a right angle, were deduced logically from a limited number of principles which were regarded as obviously true and so could be assumed: such as that *if equals are added to equals, the sums are equal* and *the whole is greater than its parts*. These principles were given the name of *common notions* (*koinai ennoiai*), and later of axioms (*axiōmata*).

This *rational geometry* was discovered not by the philosophers of Asia Minor (who disappear from history no', long after the fall of Miletus in 494 B.C., but by another school which sprang up in the Greek settlements in southern Italy, and which took the name of *Pythagoreans* from its founder Pythagoras (582?-aft. 507 B.C.). The famous theorem, that in a right-angled triangle the sum of the squares of the sides containing the right angle is equal to the square of the hypotenuse, is called by his name, probably with justice, though the Babylonians had methods of finding the length of the hypotenuse which doubtfully suggest some knowledge of it. It may seem strange that a proposition whose proof (as given in modern textbooks) is comparatively difficult, should have become known at such an early stage in the history of the subject; but it must be explained that the Pythagoreans had inherited from the pyramid-builders of Egypt the notion of *similarity in figures*, and that Pythagoras' theorem can be proved very easily when this notion is used. Thus, if ACB is a triangle right-angled at C, and CK is perpendicular to AB, then the triangle ACB is the sum of the triangles ACK and CKB. But these are three similar triangles, and their areas are proportional to the areas of any other figures erected on the corresponding sides, which are similar to each other, in particular to the squares on these sides: whence immediately we have $AC^2 + CB^2 = AB^2$.

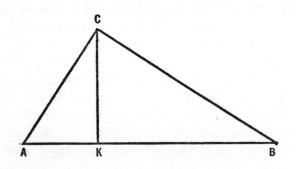

The new field of rational geometry was recognized as one in which progress was possible indefinitely; and practically the whole of the geometry now studied in schools was discovered by the Pythagoreans between 550 B.C. and 400 B.C.

To Thales' principle, that different kinds of matter are portions of a primitive universal matter, Pythagoras adjoined another principle, namely that the differences between different kinds of matter are due to differences in geometrical structure, or form. Thus the smallest constituent elements of fire, earth, air, and water, were respectively a tetrahedron, a cube, an octahedron, and an icosahedron. This belief led to much investigation on the theory of the regular solid bodies, which is the underlying subject of the great work in which the Pythagorean geometry was eventually set forth, the *Elements* of Euclid.*

The Discovery of Irrationals

The Pythagoreans held that the principles of unity, in terms of which the cosmos was explicable, were ultimately expressible by means of *numbers*; and they attempted to treat geometry numerically, by regarding a geometrical point as analogous to the unit of number— *a unit which has position*, as they put it. A point differs from the unit of number only in the additional characteristic that it has location; a line twice as long as another line was supposed to be formed of twice as many points. Thus space was regarded as composed of separate indivisible points, and time of separate instants; for when the Greeks spoke of number, they always meant *whole* number. A prospect was now opened up of understanding all nature under the aspect of countable quantity. This view was confirmed by a striking discovery made by Pythagoras himself, namely that if a musical note is produced by the vibration of a stretched string, then by halving the length of the string we obtain a note which is an octave above

---

* For the important contributions made by the Babylonians to algebra and geometry the reader is referred to an admirable survey of ancient mathematics incorporating the researches of the past 25 years, especially on cuneiform tablets: B. L. Van der Waerden, *Science Awakening*, Groningen (Holland), 1955.—*Ed.*

the first note, and by reducing the length to two-thirds of its original value we obtain a note which is at an interval of a fifth above it. Thus structure, expressible by numerical relations, came to be regarded as the fundamental principle of the universe.

In carrying out the program based on this idea, however, the Pythagoreans came upon difficulties. For instance, they asked, what is the ratio of the number of points in the side of a square to the number of points in the diagonal? Let this ratio be $m : n$ where m and n are whole numbers having no common factor. Then since the square of the diagonal is, by Pythagoras' theorem, twice the square of the side, we have $n^2 = 2m^2$. From this equation it follows that n is an even number, say $n = 2p$, where p is a whole number. Therefore $m^2 = 2p^2$, so m also is even, and therefore m and n have a common factor, contrary to hypothesis. Hence the ratio of the number of points in the side of a square to the number of points in the diagonal cannot be expressed as a ratio of whole numbers: we have made the discovery of *irrational numbers*. Since ratios such as this could exist in geometry but could not exist in the arithmetic of whole numbers, the Pythagoreans concluded that continuous magnitude cannot be composed of units of the same character as itself, or in other words, that geometry is a more general science than arithmetic.

The Paradoxes of Zeno

The logical difficulty created by the discovery of irrationals was soon supplemented by others, which the Greek philosophers of the fifth century B.C. constructed in their attempts to understand some of the fundamental notions of mathematics.

Let a ball be bouncing on a floor, and suppose that whenever it hits the floor it bounces back again, and remains in the air for half as long a time as on the preceding bounce. Will it ever stop bouncing?

If the duration of the first bounce is taken as 1, then the durations of the succeeding bounces are $\frac{1}{2}$, $\frac{1}{4}$, $\frac{1}{8}$, etc., and the sum of these durations is $1 + \frac{1}{2} + \frac{1}{4} + \frac{1}{8} + \cdots$. Now let these durations be represented on a line: if C is the middle point of a line AB and if D

is the middle point of *CB*, *E* the middle point of *DB*, *F* the middle point of *EB*, and so on, then if $AC = 1$,

A   C   D   E F B

we have $CD = \frac{1}{2}$, $DE = \frac{1}{4}$, $EF = \frac{1}{8}$, etc., and the whole length AB is

$$1 + \frac{1}{2} + \frac{1}{4} + \frac{1}{8} + \cdots .$$

But the whole length is 2. So *after a time 2, the bouncing will have stopped*, a fact which is perhaps at first sight difficult to understand when we reflect that whenever the ball comes down, it goes up again.

A famous paradox, due to Zeno (490?-435 B.C.) is that of the race between Achilles and the tortoise. The tortoise runs (say) one-tenth as fast as Achilles, but has a start of (say) 100 yards. By the time Achilles has run this 100 yards and is at the place the tortoise started from, the tortoise is 10 yards ahead: when Achilles has covered this 10 yards, the tortoise is 1 yard ahead: and so on forever— Achilles never catches up. This conclusion is obviously contrary to common sense. But we may remark that if Achilles is required to ring a bell every time he reaches the spot last occupied by the tortoise, then there will be an infinite number of such occasions, and the time required for the overtaking will indeed be infinite. The point is, that a finite stretch of space can be divided into an infinite number of intervals, and if those intervals are noted in review one by one, then the time required for the review is infinite.

The Beginnings of Solid Geometry in the Atomistic School

About the end of the fifth century B.C., some philosophers, of whom the most celebrated was a Thracian named Democritus, accepted the existence of empty space (which had been denied by the school to which Zeno belonged) and taught that the physical world is composed of an infinite number of small hard indivisible bodies (the *atoms*) which move in the void. All sensible bodies are composed of groupings of atoms. This notion was applied in order to calculate the volume of a cone or pyramid. The pyramid was conceived as a pile of shot, arranged in layers parallel to the base, the quantity of shot in any layer being proportional to the area of the layer and so to the square of the distance of the layer from the vertex of the pyramid. Then by summing the layers, it was found that the volume of the cone or pyramid is one-third the volume of a prism of the same height and base.

The Parallel Axiom

When the Greek philosophers based mathematics on axioms, they believed axioms to be true statements, whose truth was so obvious that they could be accepted without proof. One of the axioms they used, however, was felt to be not perfectly obvious, and for over twenty centuries attempts were made to prove it, by deducing it from other axioms which could be more readily admitted. This *parallel axiom,* as it is called, was stated by Euclid thus: *if a straight line falling on two straight lines makes the interior angles on the same side less than two right angles, the two straight lines, if produced indefinitely, meet on that side on which are the angles less than two right angles.*

Euclid himself seems to have had some hesitation about it, for he avoided using it in his first 28 propositions. He wished, however, to study *parallel* lines (that is, lines which are in the same plane, and, being produced ever so far both ways, do not meet), and he found that a theory of parallel lines could not be constructed without this axiom or something equivalent to it.

The Greeks, although they did not really doubt the truth of the parallel axiom, constructed arguments which seemed to disprove it. Thus, let *AB* be a straight line falling on two straight lines *AK, BL,* and making the interior angles on the same side *KAB, LBA,* together less than two right angles. On *AK* take *AC* = 1/2 *AB* and on *BL* take *BD* = 1/2 *AB*. Then the lines *AK, BL,* cannot meet

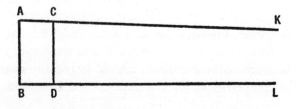

within the ranges AC, BD, since if they did, two sides of a triangle would be less than the third side. We now have the line CD falling on the two straight lines CK, DL, and making the interior angles on the same side less than two right angles, so we can repeat the argument. By repeating it indefinitely often, we can conclude that the two lines AK, BL, will never meet. The fallacy in the argument is of course the same as in the paradox of Achilles and the tortoise. Namely, the distance from A to the meeting-point is by this process divided into an infinite number of segments; if we consider the operation of forming these segments one by one in turn, we shall never come to the end of the process.

Many axioms have been proposed at different times as substitutes for the parallel axiom, capable of leading logically to the theory of parallels; one such axiom consists in affirming the existence of triangles *similar* to each other, but of different sizes; and another axiom consists in the statement that *two straight lines which intersect one another cannot both be parallel to the same straight line.* Either of these two substitutes seems to be more obviously true than Euclid's parallel axiom; but early in the eighteenth century an Italian Jesuit named Saccheri (1667-1733) thought of what seemed a still better plan, namely to prove Euclid's original parallel axiom by showing that a denial of its truth leads to a *reductio ad absurdum.* He carried out this program and showed that when the parallel axiom is not assumed, a logical system of geometry can be obtained, which however differs in many respects from the geometry universally believed to be true: for instance, the sum of the angles of a triangle is not equal to two right angles. Saccheri considered that by arriving at this result he had achieved his aim of obtaining a *reductio ad absurdum* and thereby had shown that the parallel axiom is true. He never for one moment imagined that the system he had found could be proposed as an alternative to Euclidean geometry for the description of actual space.

The Geometry of Astronomical Space

In the nineteenth century however, some doubts were expressed as to whether the properties of space were represented everywhere and at all times by the geometry of Euclid. "The geometer of to-day," wrote W. K. Clifford (1845-1879), "knows nothing about the nature of the actually existing space at an infinite distance: he knows nothing about the properties of the present space in a past or future eternity."

Let us look into this question by considering a triangle in astronomical space, having its vertices, say, at the sun and two of the most distant nebulae, and having as its sides the paths of light-rays between these vertices. Then at each of the three vertices there will be an angle between the two sides that meet there. Have we any reason to believe that the sum of these three angles at the vertices will be equal to two right angles? Obviously it is not practicable to submit the matter to the test of observation; and we can find no *logical* reason for believing that the sum must *necessarily* be two right angles, since Saccheri's work showed that Euclidean geometry is not a logical necessity. Euclidean geometry is certainly valid, to a very close degree of approximation, for the triangles that we can observe in the limited space of a terrestrial laboratory. In their case its departure from truth is imperceptible, but for much larger triangles we must admit that neither logic nor observation gives us any decision.

We must therefore regard it as possible that in the astronomical triangle the sum of the three angles may be different from two right angles. We must recognize that empty space may have properties affecting measurements of size, distance, and the like: *in astronomical space the geometry is possibly not Euclidean.*

A language has been invented by mathematicians to describe this state of affairs. We know that the geometry of figures drawn on a curved surface, for instance the surface of a sphere, is different from the geometry of figures drawn in a plane, which is Euclidean; and this suggests a way of speaking about a three-dimensional space in which the geometry of solid bodies is not Euclidean: we say that in such a case, the *space* is *curved*. Astronomical space, then, may have a small *curvature*. This has long been recognized as a possibility, but it was not until the present century that the idea was developed into a definite quantitative theory. In 1929 the American astronomer E. P. Hubble announced as an observational fact that the spectral lines of the most distant nebulae are displaced toward the red end of the spectrum, by amounts which are proportional to the distance of the nebulae. This red-displacement was interpreted to mean that the nebulae were receding from us with velocities proportional to their distances; in fact, that the whole universe was expanding, all distances continually increasing proportionally to their magnitudes. Combining this with the results of theoretical investigation, Eddington in 1930 published a mathematical theory of the nature of space, in which he supposed that astronomical space is not Euclidean, and that the deviation from Euclidean character depends not only on the size of the geometrical configuration considered, but also on the time that has elapsed since the creation of the world. This, which is known as the *theory of the expanding universe*, was generally accepted and developed for the next 23 years. Values were found for the total mass, extent, and curvature of the universe; but in 1953 a new explanation of the red-displacement was proposed by E. Finlay-Freundlich, and the question is still under discussion.

General Relativity

The deviations from Euclidean properties which have just been considered have a uniform character over vast regions of space. According to the theory of *General Relativity*, there are also deviations which vary considerably within quite small distances, and which are due to the presence of ordinary gravitating matter. Something of the kind was conjectured by the Irish mathematical physicist G. F. Fitzgerald when toward the end of the nineteenth century he said, "Gravity is probably due to a change of structure in the ether, produced by the presence of matter." Perhaps he thought of the change of structure as being something like change in specific inductive capacity or permeability. However, Einstein in 1915 published a definite mathematical theory, in which gravitational effects were attributed to a change in the curvature of the world, due to the presence of matter; and he showed that by this hypothesis it was possible to account for a peculiarity of the orbit of the planet Mercury which was not explained by the older Newtonian theory.

The Non-Euclidean Geometries

We shall now describe some of the features of the *non-Euclidean geometries* that are obtained by assuming the parallel axiom to be untrue for geometry in the plane.

If we consider a straight line CD and a point P not on it, then either:

(1) it may be impossible to draw any straight line through P that does not intersect CD. The geometry is then said to be *elliptic*.

(2) or it may be possible to draw an infinite number of straight lines through P that do not intersect CD. The geometry is then said to be *hyperbolic*.

Between these possibilities there is an intermediate case, in which it is possible to draw one and only one line through P which does not intersect CD: this case corresponds to ordinary Euclidean geometry.

In elliptic geometry the sum of the angles of a triangle is always greater than two right angles. Every straight line, when it attains a certain length, returns into itself like the equator on a sphere, so the lengths of all straight lines are finite, and the greatest possible distance apart of two points is half this length. The perpendiculars to a straight line at all the points on it meet in a point.

In hyperbolic geometry, the sum of the three angles of a triangle is always less than two right angles; and indeed, the greater the area of the triangle, the smaller is the sum of its angles. If we consider a straight line CD, and a point P outside it, then we can draw two straight lines through P, PA and PB, which are not in the same straight line, with the properties that (1) any line through P which lies entirely outside the angle APB does not intersect the line CD, (2) any line through P which is inside the angle APB intersects the line CD at a point at a finite distance from P, (3) the two lines

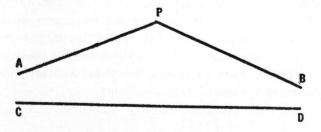

PA, *PB*, tend asymptotically at one end of the line *CD* at infinity, so we may say they intersect it at infinity and are more or less analogous to Euclidean parallels: they are, in fact, called *parallels* to the line *CD* drawn through the point *P*. Lines which are parallel to each other at any point are parallel along their whole length, but *parallels are not equidistant*: the distance between them tends to zero at one end and to infinity at the other.

Topology

The opinion that the material universe is formed of atoms, which are eternal and unchangeable, had been held by many of the ancient Greek philosophers and was generally accepted by European physicists in the nineteenth century. An attempt to account for it mathematically was made in 1887 by William Thomson (Lord Kelvin), who after seeing a display of smoke-rings in a friend's laboratory, pointed out that if the atoms of matter are constituted of vortex rings in a perfect fluid, then the conservation of matter can be immediately explained, and the mutual interaction of atoms can be illustrated. In 1876 P. G. Tait of Edinburgh, having the idea that different kinds of atoms might correspond to different kinds of knotted vortex rings, took up the study of knots as geometrical forms. This is a problem of a new kind, since we are not interested in the precise description of the curve of the cord, but only in the essential distinction between one kind of knot and another—the reef-knot, the bowline, the clove hitch, the fisherman's bend, etc. The transformations which change the curve of the cord but do not change the essential character of the knot were specially studied. Relations of this kind, i.e., relations which are described by such words as "external to," "right-handed," "linked with," "intersecting," "surrounding," "connected by a channel with," etc., are called *topological*, and the study of topological relations in general is called *topology*.

Another topological problem which was studied in the early days of the subject arose in connection with the flow of an electric current through a linear network of conductors. The network is a set of points (vertices) connected together in pairs by conductors. We can inquire what is the greatest number of conductors that can be removed from the network in such a way as to leave all the vertices connected together in one linear series by the remaining conductors. The number as obtained is of importance in the general problem of flow through the network.

The New Views of Axioms

It has long been realized that the axioms stated by Euclid are in-sufficient as a basis for Euclidean geometry; he tacitly assumes many others which are not in his list. Among these may be mentioned *axioms of association,* such as "if two different points of a straight line are in a plane, then all the points of the straight line are in the plane"; *axioms of order,* such as "of three different points lying on a straight line, one and only one lies between the other two"; and *axioms of congruence,* which assert the uniqueness of something —that there is only one distinct geometrical figure with certain prop-erties: thus, a triangle is uniquely determined by two adjacent sides and the included angle.

Questions arise also regarding the use made of diagrams in geo-metrical proofs. In an edition of Euclid the diagrams are accurately drawn, and their topological features, which may be seen by inspec-tion, are often essential to the proof. Thus let a diagram be drawn representing any triangle *ABC* with the line *AE* bisecting its angle *A* and the line *DE* perpendicular to its side *BC* at its middle point; if this is carelessly drawn, the point *E* of the intersection of *AE* and *DE* might be placed *inside* the triangle—a topological error. But in that case, drawing perpendiculars *EL* to *AB* and *EK* to *AC*, we can

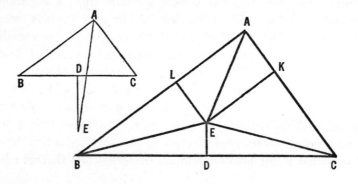

easily show that the triangles *LEB* and *KEC* are equal in all respects, and also the triangles *EBD* and *ECD* are equal in all respects, thus the angles *ABC* and *ACB* are equal, and the triangle *ABC* is isosceles. *Thus a wrong topological understanding has led to a proof that every triangle is isosceles.* The axioms must therefore be such as to guard against any erroneous topological assumptions. A rigorously logical deduction of Euclidean geometry is a formidable affair.

It is of course obvious that the theorems of geometry were *discovered* long before strict logical proofs were found for them. Archimedes, the greatest of the Greek mathematicians, distinguishes between *investigating* theorems (*theōrein*) and *proving them rigorously* (*apodeiknunai*).

When it was realized that the parallel axiom is not universally and eternally true, opinion changed about the place of axioms in mathematics. It now came to be accepted that the business of the mathematician is to deduce the logical consequences of the axioms he assumes at the basis of his work, *without regard to whether these axioms are true or not*; their truth or falsehood is the concern of another type of man of science—a physicist or a philosopher. Thus the horizon of the geometer was widened; instead of inquiring into the structure of actual space, he studied various different types of geometry defined respectively by their axioms: Euclidean and non-Euclidean geometries and also geometries with a finite total number of points, and what are called *non-Archimedean* and *non-Desarguesian* geometries. A non-Archimedean geometry is one which denies the "axiom of Archimedes," namely that if two segments are given, there is always a multiple of the smaller that exceeds the larger. A non-Desarguesian geometry is one in which the theorem of Desargues is not true, namely that if two triangles be such that the straight lines joining their vertices in pairs are concurrent, then the intersections of pairs of corresponding sides lie on a straight line.

The Dangers of Intuition

The recognition that an axiom is a statement which is assumed, without any necessary belief in its truth, brought a great relief to mathematicians; for intuition had led the older workers to believe in the truth of many particular assertions which were shown in the latter part of the nineteenth century to be false. The following is an example. We may for the present purpose define a *continuous* plane curve to be one in which, as we pass along the curve from a point *P* to a neighboring point *Q*, the length of the perpendicular from a point on the curve to any fixed straight line passes through all the values intermediate between the values that it has at *P* and *Q*. Now it is obvious that a continuous curve will, in general, have a tangent at every point. But this is not always the case, as can be shown by the following construction. Take a straight line of any length, divide it into three equal parts, and on the middle part as base erect an equilateral triangle. Delete the base of the triangle, so we are left

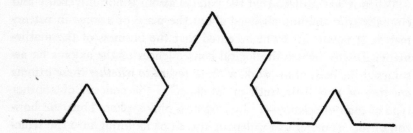

with four segments of equal length forming a broken line. Divide each of these four segments into three equal parts, and as before erect an equilateral triangle on the middle part of each segment, and then delete the bases of these triangles, so now we have a broken line of 16 segments. Repeating this process indefinitely, we arrive in the limit at a broken line which is a definite curve, but has no tangent at any point. Examples of this kind made it impossible to accept the view generally held by Kantian philosophers, that mathematics is concerned with those conceptions which are obtained by direct intuition of space and time.

The Plan of a Rigorous Geometry

Euclid attempted to specify the subject matter of geometry by definitions such as "a *point* is that which has no parts," and "a *straight line* is a line which lies evenly with the points on itself." Neither of these definitions is made use of in his subsequent work; and indeed, the first is clearly worthless, since there exist many things besides points which have no parts, while the second is obscure.

In a modern rigorous geometry, the point and the straight line are generally accepted as *undefined notions*, so that the pattern of a branch of mathematics is now:

(1) enumeration of the *primitive concepts* in terms of which all the other concepts are to be defined

(2) *definitions* (i.e. short names for complexes of ideas)

(3) *axioms*, or fundamental propositions which are assumed without proof. It is necessary to show that they are *compatible* with each other (i.e. by combining them we cannot arrive at a contradiction) and *independent* of each other (i.e. no one of them can be deduced from the others). The compatibility is often proved by translating the assumptions into the domain of numbers, when any inconsistency would appear in arithmetical form; and the independence may be proved (as the independence of the parallel axiom was proved) by leaving out each assumption in turn and showing that a consistent system can be obtained without it.

(4) *existence-theorems*. The discovery of irrationals led the Pythagoreans to see the necessity for these. Does there exist a five-sided polygon whose angles are all right angles? The Greek method of proving the existence of any particular geometrical entity was to give a construction for it; thus, before making use of the notion of the middle point of a line, Euclid proves, by constructing it, that a line possesses a middle point. *The "problems" of Euclid's Elements are really existence-theorems.*

(5) *deductions*, which are the body and purpose of the work.

Space Time

Until the end of the nineteenth century it was believed that the universe was occupied by *space*, which had three dimensions, so that a point of it was specified by the length, breadth and height of its displacement from some point taken as origin. It was supposed that space was always the same, consisting of the same points in the same positions. Whoever might be observing it, two different observers, in motion relative to each other, would see precisely the same space. In order to specify the position of a particle at any time, it was necessary therefore to know only the three co-ordinates of the space-point at which it was situated, and the time. The way of measuring time was supposed to be the same for the whole universe. Events happening at different points of space were said to be *simultaneous* if the time co-ordinates of the two points were the same.

This scheme collapsed in the early years of the present century, when the theory of relativity was discovered and it was shown that *observers who are in motion relative to each other do not see the same space.* If we consider a particular observer, moving in any way, then *for him* each particle in the universe will have three definite space co-ordinates and a definite time co-ordinate; but for a different observer, moving relatively to him, both the space co-ordinates and the time co-ordinates of the particle will in general be changed. When we label every point-event of space with its co-ordinates (x, y, z) as recognized by a particular observer, and also with its time t as recognized by this observer, then all point-events are specified by the four co-ordinates (t, x, y, z), just as all points in ordinary space are specified by three co-ordinates (x, y, z). We speak of this fourfold aggregate of point-events as a *four-dimensional manifold,* which is called *space time.* If a value of t is specified, the points (t, x, y, z) which have this value of t form a three-dimensional manifold with coordinates (x, y, z), and this manifold represents a *space* formed of the points which are *simultaneous* for the observer whose time is t. The problem is to find a set of equations

$$t' = t' \,(t,x,y,z): x' = x' \,(t,x,y,z): y' = y' \,(t,x,y,z): z' = z' \,(t,x,y,z)$$

which rearranges the fourfold of point-events (t,x,y,z) so as to convert the spaces which are simultaneous for one observer into the spaces which are simultaneous for another observer.

Numbers

Although numbers have been in use since the earliest ages, it was not until the last quarter of the nineteenth century that any satisfactory philosophical explanation was given of what they are.

Number is a property not of physical objects in themselves, but of collections or *classes* of objects. We must begin by explaining what we mean by saying that two classes have *the same* number. If we have a group of husbands and wives, and if we know that each husband has one wife and each wife has one husband, then we can affirm that the number of husbands is the same as the number of wives, even though we do not know what that number is. In other words, two classes between whose respective members a *one-to-one correspondence* can be set up, have *the same number*: to be precise, the same *cardinal* number, for a distinction is drawn between cardinal and ordinal numbers; ordinal numbers are defined only by reference to sets whose elements are arranged in serial order. This definition applies equally well whether the number is finite or not. Thus if two rays OAC, OBD, proceeding from a point O, cut off segments AB and CD from two straight lines, then we can set up a one-to-one correspondence between the points P of AB and the points Q of CD by radii OPQ, and we can say that AB has the same number of points as CD.

We can, however, draw lines from another point Z to A and B; suppose that these lines cut the line CD in points E and F. Then the number of points in EF is the same as the number of points in AB, and therefore the same as the number of points in CD.

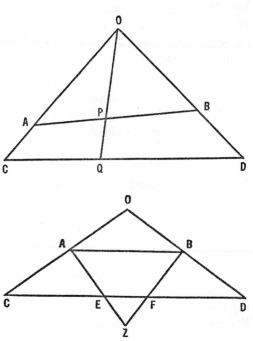

We see therefore that *in the case of infinite collections, the number of the whole is not necessarily greater than the number of the parts;* and indeed, a *transfinite* number may be defined as the number of a collection which can be put into one-to-one correspondence with a part of itself: for example, the positive integers have a one-to-one correspondence with their squares; and, therefore, the number of the integers is equal to the number of their squares, although the squares form only a part of the whole collection of integers.

The cardinal numbers can be arranged in order by use of the notions of *greater* and *less*, which can be thus defined: a cardinal *m* is greater than a cardinal *n* if there is a class which has *m* members and has a part which has *n* members, but there is no class which has *n* members and has a part which has *m* members.

The addition and multiplication of two numbers can be readily defined. If A and B are two collections whose cardinal numbers are *a* and *b*, then a class C formed by combining the collections A and B has for cardinal number the *sum* $a + b$. If we form a new collection, of which each element consists of one element taken from A, paired with one element taken from B, and if these pairs are taken in all possible ways, then the cardinal number of the new collection is the *product ab*. It is readily seen that sums and products so defined satisfy

$$\text{the associative law} \quad a\,(bc) = (ab)\,c$$
$$\text{the commutative law} \quad ab = ba$$
$$\text{and the distributive law} \quad a\,(b + c) = ab + ac$$

Transfinite Numbers

Until seventy years ago, infinity was a somewhat vague, general concept, and mathematicians did not know that transfinite numbers of different magnitudes could be accurately defined and distinguished. Let us consider some examples of them.

Take first the *rational* numbers, which are the fractions representing the ratio of one whole number to another. They can be written in a rectangular array thus:

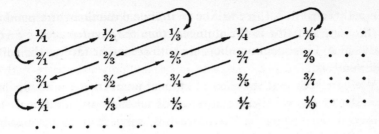

They may now be arranged in a single order by taking the diagonals of this array in turn, thus:

$$\tfrac{1}{1}, \tfrac{2}{1}, \tfrac{1}{2}, \tfrac{3}{1}, \tfrac{2}{3}, \tfrac{1}{3}, \tfrac{4}{1}, \tfrac{3}{2}, \tfrac{2}{5}, \tfrac{1}{4}, \tfrac{5}{1}, \tfrac{4}{3}, \tfrac{3}{4}, \tfrac{2}{7}, \tfrac{1}{5}, \cdots$$

When they are thus ordered, they can be put in a one-to-one correspondence with the natural numbers

$$1, 2, 3, 4, 5, 6, 7, \cdots.$$

Any collection which can be put in a one-to-one correspondence with the natural numbers is said to be *denumerable*. Thus the *rational numbers form a denumerable or countable set*. The cardinal number of a denumerable set is the smallest transfinite cardinal number, and is denoted by *Aleph-zero,*

Now let the rational numbers be arranged in order of magnitude and suppose that at a certain place in the order a division or *cut* is made, which causes the numbers to fall into two classes (e.g. all the rational numbers whose squares are less than 2 and all the rational numbers whose squares are greater than 2), which we shall call the *left class* and the *right class,* such that every rational number in the left class is smaller than every rational number in the right class. It may be that the right class has a least member, which will of course be a rational number, say p; or it may be that the left class has a greatest number, which will be a rational number, say q. In these cases the cut is said to be made by a rational number, p or q as the case may be. But if the left class has no greatest member and the right class has no least member, then the cut is still regarded as being made by a number; but this will be a number of a new class, which is called an *irrational number.* Thus if the left and right classes are the rational numbers whose squares are respectively less and greater than 2, since there is no rational number whose square is exactly equal to 2, there will be an irrational number corresponding to the cut, and this is the number commonly represented by $\sqrt{2}$. Rational and irrational numbers are both comprehended in the name *real numbers*.

We have seen that the class of rational numbers is countable; but the class of real numbers, composed of rationals and irrationals together, is *not* countable. To prove this, suppose it to be possible that all the real numbers from 0 to 1 could be arranged in order as 1st, 2nd, 3rd, . . . etc., say n_1, n_2, n_3, . . . Suppose that these numbers are represented in the ordinary denary scale as decimals. Then we can form a new decimal in the following way: take its first digit to be any digit (from 0 to 9) different from the first digit of n_1; take its second digit to be any digit different from the second digit of n_2; take its third digit to be any digit different from the third digit of n_3; and so on. The number thus formed differs from all the numbers previously enumerated and it is a real number between 0 and 1; so the original enumeration cannot have contained all the real numbers between 0 and 1. By this *reductio ad absurdum* we see that *the set of real numbers from 0 to 1 is not denumerable*.

The set of real numbers is called the *arithmetic continuum*; by what has just been proved, the transfinite cardinal number of the arithmetic continuum is not Aleph-zero, but a greater transfinite number, which is denoted by c.

The arithmetic continuum has been constructed arithmetically, without any dependence on time and space, the two notions of the continuum with which we are intuitively familiar. If we are to assume that the arithmetic continuum is equivalent to the linear continuum, so that the motion of a particle along the line is an exact image of a numerical variable increasing from one value to another, it is evident that we must introduce an axiom, namely that there is a single point on the line corresponding to every single real number. Of course we are not bound to assume this axiom. We may assume that several points, forming an infinitesimal segment, separate the right and left classes in the proposition by which irrational numbers were defined. On this assumption, the axiom of Archimedes, to which reference was made on page 37, would not be true.

If the Pythagorean conception of the line as made up of unit points had been correct, the ratio of any two segments of the line would have been a rational number, and there would have been no room for irrationals.

The Number of Points in a Three-Dimensional Space

One would naturally expect that the number of points in a three-dimensional region, such as the interior of a cube of side unity, would be infinitely greater than the number of points on a segment of a line, say one of the edges of the cube. But, surprisingly, this is not the case: the points in the cube can be made to correspond, point by point, with the points in its edge.

For take three of the edges, meeting at one corner, as axes of co-ordinates x, y, z, so that for points in the cube we have three co-ordinates all between 0 and 1. A point on an edge can be specified by a single co-ordinate w between 0 and 1. Now let the co-ordinate w, which represents a particular point on the edge be expressed as a decimal, adding 0's at the end so as to make it an unending decimal. Take the 1st, 4th, 7th, etc. digits of w, and write down a decimal x of which these are the successive digits. Similarly write down y, consisting of the 2nd, 5th, 8th, . . . digits of w, and write down z, consisting of the 3rd, 6th, 9th, . . . digits. The point of space whose co-ordinates (x, y, z) are thus determined corresponds uniquely to the value of w; thus, there is a one-to-one correspondence between the points on the edge and the points inside the cube, and therefore they have the same number.

Imaginary Quantities

A work written by an Egyptian priest more than a thousand years before Christ, with the alluring title "Directions for knowing all dark things," explains how to solve various numerical problems, such as "What is the number which, when its seventh part is added to it, becomes 24?" The ancient Babylonians also proposed arithmetical puzzles, and were acquainted with arithmetic and geometric progressions. But algebra as a science can scarcely be said to have existed before the introduction of negative numbers in the early centuries of the Christian era, although results that are now commonly obtained by algebraic methods had long been known.

The solution of the quadratic equation—in algebraic notation

$$ax^2 + bx + c = 0$$

was achieved in geometrical form by the Greek mathematicians. If the quadratic has no roots which are real numbers, it possesses algebraic roots of the form $x + y\sqrt{-1}$ where x and y are real: that is, roots that are *complex quantities*. But the geometrical preoccupations of the Greeks led to their attention being devoted entirely to real roots, and solutions involving the "imaginary" quantity $\sqrt{-1}$ were dismissed by everybody before the sixteenth century as nonexistent.

In the Renaissance, however, the Italian mathematicians discovered the solution of the cubic equation

$$x^3 + qx + r = 0 \quad ;$$

their formula gave for instance the solution of the equation

$$x^3 - 15x - 4 = 0$$

as

$$x = \sqrt[3]{(2 + 11\sqrt{-1})} + \sqrt[3]{(2 - 11\sqrt{-1})}.$$

In order to evaluate this, we note that

$$2 + 11\sqrt{-1} = (2 + \sqrt{-1})^3, \text{ and } 2 - 11\sqrt{-1} = (2 - \sqrt{-1})^3.$$

So we have the root expressed in the form

$$x = 2 + \sqrt{-1} + 2 - \sqrt{-1}$$

or

$$x = 4.$$

We have thus found a real root of the cubic, by a calculation *which cannot avoid using* $\sqrt{-1}$; and, this discovery compelled the mathematicians to face the question of the status of imaginary quantities. For a long time their attitude was one of mystification: the imaginary was, they said, *inter Ens et non-Ens amphibium* ("an amphibian between Being and non-Being").

Later it was shown to possess many important properties. Thus, many theorems were found to be true only when the numbers concerned were no longer restricted to be real: for instance, the theorem that every algebraic equation of degree n has n roots is true in general only when complex roots are taken into account. But conservatism died hard. In the latter part of the eighteenth century an English mathematician, Francis Maseres, who had been *senior wrangler* at Cambridge in 1752, published several tracts on algebra and theory of equations in which he refused to allow the use of "impossible" quantities.

Today, imaginary quantities are of great importance; in fact, the extensive and most useful *Theory of Functions of a Complex Variable* is wholly concerned with functions which depend on the quantity $x + y \sqrt{-1}$. It is a strange fact that as mathematics grows more abstract, it becomes more effective as a tool for dealing with the concrete —a point that was often stressed by the philosopher A. N. Whitehead. As an example, one may cite the very abstract *theory of groups*, which has many applications in the modern quantum-mechanical physics.

System of Numeration

The choice of the number 10 as the basis of our system of numeration is due to our having ten fingers; among primitive peoples the set of fingers, in which ten objects are presented in a definite order, was the natural aid to counting. Modern systems of numeration depend on the notion of place-value, with the use of the symbol zero, a plan which seems to have been introduced about 500 A.D.: thus the number 5207.345 means

$$5.10^3 + 2.10^2 + 0.10 + 7 + \tfrac{3}{10} + \tfrac{4}{10}^2 + \tfrac{5}{10}^3.$$

While the historical reason for the use of a decimal system is readily intelligible, it must be said that an octonary system, based on the number 8 (so that 5207.345 would mean

$$5.8^3 + 2.8^2 + 0.8 + 7 + \tfrac{3}{8} + \tfrac{4}{8}^2 + \tfrac{5}{8}^3)$$

would be more convenient. The multiplication table of the octonary system would call for only half as great an effort as is required in the decimal system; and, the most natural way of dealing with fractions is to bisect again and again, as is done for instance with brokers' prices on the stock exchange. It is perhaps unfortunate that our remote ancestors, when using their fingers for counting, included the thumbs.

Another system of numeration, which has become prominent in recent years, owing to its use in the modern electronic calculating machines, is to express numbers in "the scale of 2," or the "binary scale," in which 10110.01101 would mean

$$2^4 + 0 + 2^2 + 2 + 0 + 0 + \tfrac{1}{2}^2 + \tfrac{1}{2}^3 + 0 + \tfrac{1}{2}^5.$$

Symbolic Logic

Long ago Leibnitz, in the course of his life as a diplomat, sometimes found himself required to devise a formula for the settlement of a dispute, such that each of the contending parties could be induced to sign it, with the mental reservation that he was bound only by his own interpretation of its ambiguities. Equivocation, such as was practiced in this connection, was, as Leibnitz well knew, impossible in mathematics, where every symbol and every equation has a unique and definite meaning. And the contrast led him to speculate on the possibility of constructing a symbolism or ideography, like that of algebra, capable of doing what ordinary language cannot do, that is, to represent ideas and their connections without introducing undetected assumptions and ambiguities. He therefore conceived the idea of a logical calculus, in which the elementary operations of the process of reasoning would be represented by symbols—an alphabet of thought, so to speak—and envisaged a distant future when philosophical and theological discussions would be conducted by its means, and would reach conclusions as incontrovertible as those of mathematics. Perhaps this was too much to hope, but the actual achievements of mathematical logic have been amazing. Logic, when its power has been augmented by the introduction of symbolic methods, is capable of leading from elementary premises of extreme simplicity to conclusions far beyond the reach of the unaided reason.

The first outstanding contribution to the subject was made by George Boole, for the latter part of his life, professor in Cork, who published a sketch of his theory in 1847, and a fuller account in 1854, in his book *An Investigation of the Laws of Thought*. In this system, a letter such as x denotes a *class* or collection of individual things to which some common name can be applied: for instance, x might represent the class of all doctors. We can also regard x as a symbol of operation, namely, the operation which selects, from the totality of objects in the world, those objects which are doctors. Now let y denote some other class, say the class of all women. Then the product xy must represent the result of first selecting all women, and then selecting from them those who are doctors; that is, xy represents all women doctors, all the individuals who belong both to the class x and to the class y. When, in ordinary language, a noun is qualified by an adjective, as in "feminine doctor," we must understand the idea represented by this product.

Now consider the case when the class y is the same as the class x. In this case, the combination xy expresses no more than either of the symbols taken alone would do, so $xy = x$, or (since y is the same as x) $x^2 = x$. In ordinary algebra, the equation $x^2 = x$ is true when x has either of the values zero and unity, but in Boolean algebra all symbols obey this law.

Let us now take up the question of addition. The class $x + y$ is defined to consist of all the individuals who belong to *one at least* of the classes x and y, whether the classes overlap or not.

The symbol used for zero in ordinary algebra is used in Boolean algebra to denote the class that has no members, the null class: obviously we must have

$$x \cdot 0 = 0 \quad \text{and} \quad x + 0 = x,$$

as in ordinary algebra.

The symbol 1 is used to denote the class consisting of everything, or the "universe of discourse": it has the properties

$$x \cdot 1 = x \quad \text{and} \quad x + 1 = 1.$$

Lastly, the minus sign must be introduced: the symbol $-x$ is defined to be the class consisting of those members of 1 which do not belong to x, so that

$$- x + x = 1 \quad \text{and} \quad x\,(- x) = 0.$$

So far, we have interpreted Boolean algebra as an algebra of classes; but, we may take the classes to be classes of cases in which certain propositions are true, and this led to an interpretation of it as an algebra of propositions. If x and y are propositions, their product would represent simultaneous affirmation, so xy would be the proposition which asserts "both x and y": the sum would denote alternative affirmation, so $x + y$ would be the proposition "either x or y or both." The minus sign would represent "it is not true that," so $- x$ would be the proposition contrary to x: the equation $x = 1$ would imply that x is true, while the equation $- x = 1$, which is equivalent to $x = 0$, would signify that x is false. The equation $- x + x = 1$ would now represent the logical principle of the excluded middle, that every proposition is either true or false, and the equation $x \cdot (- x) = 0$ would represent the principle of contradiction.

Peano's Symbolism

Boole used only the ordinary algebraic symbols: the symbol x, which in ordinary algebra represents multiplication, may be said to correspond in Boolean algebra to the word *and*, while the symbol of addition, $+$, corresponds to *or*, and the symbol of a negative quantity, $-$, corresponds to *not*. The great development of such ideas took place in the last years of the nineteenth century, when Giuseppe Peano, professor at the University of Turin, invented a new ideography for use in symbolic logic. He introduced new symbols to represent other logical notions, such as "is contained in," "the aggregate of all x's such that," "there exists," "is a," "the only," etc. For example, the phrase "is the same thing as" is represented by the sign $=$, while the symbol $\cap$ between two classes indicates the aggregate of individuals who belong to both classes (the *product* of Boole's algebra). One of the elementary processes of logic consists in deducing from two propositions, containing a common element or middle term, a conclusion connecting the two remaining terms. This corresponds to the process of elimination in algebra and may be performed in a way roughly analogous to it. The parallelism of logic and algebra is indeed far reaching: for instance, the logical distinction between categorical propositions and conditional propositions corresponds closely to the algebraical distinction between identities and equations. Again, the inequalities of algebra have their analogues in logic. Consider, for instance, the statement that if a proposition *a* implies a proposition *b*, and *b* implies a proposition *c*, then *a* implies *c*. This bears an obvious resemblance to the algebraical theorem that if *a* is less than *b*, and *b* is less than *c*, then *a* is less than *c*. It is useful to have a symbol which represents logical implication or inclusion, and all modern forms of symbolic logic do in fact employ one or two, one in the calculus of propositions and one in the calculus of classes. This however, does not represent an independent concept, but can be defined in terms of the logical product; for the statement that *a* is included in, or implies, *b*, is equivalent to the statement that the logical product of *a* and *b* is equal to *a*.

Peano's ideograms represent the constitutive elements of all the other notions in logic, just as the chemical atoms are the constitutive elements of all substances in chemistry; and they are capable of replacing ordinary language completely for the purposes of any deductive theory.

The Developments of Whitehead and Russell

In 1900 A. N. Whitehead and Bertrand Russell, both of Cambridge, went to Paris to attend the congresses in mathematics and philosophy which were being held in connection with the International Exhibition of that year. At the Philosophical Congress they heard an account of Peano's system and saw that it was vastly superior to anything of the kind that had been known previously. They resolved to devote themselves for years to come to its development, and, in particular, to try to settle by its means the vexed question of the foundations of mathematics.

The thesis which they now set out to examine, and if possible to prove, was that *mathematics is a part of logic*: it is the science concerned with the logical deduction of consequences from the general premises of all reasoning, so that a separate "philosophy of mathematics" simply does not exist. This of course contradicts the Kantian doctrine that mathematical proofs depend on a priori forms of intuition, so that, for example, the diagram is an essential part of geometrical reasoning. Whitehead and Russell soon succeeded in proving that the cardinal numbers 1, 2, 3, . . . can be defined in terms of concepts which belong to pure logic, such as *class, implication, negation,* and which can be represented by Peano ideograms. From this first success they advanced to the investigations published in the three colossal volumes of *Principia Mathematica,* which appeared in 1910-1913 and contain altogether just under 2,000 pages.

It was admitted that for mathematical purposes certain axioms must be adjoined to those that are usually found in treatises on logic, e.g., the intuition of the unending series of natural numbers, which leads to the principle of mathematical induction; but this extension of logic did not affect the main position.

The growth of logic, which had been at a standstill for the two thousand years from Aristotle to Boole, has progressed with amazing vitality from Boole to the present day. It is remarkable that some of the errors of Aristotle remained undetected until the recent developments. Consider, for instance, his doctrine that "in universal statement the affirmative premise is necessarily convertible as a particular statement, so that for example from the premise *all dragons are winged creatures,* follows the consequence *some winged creatures are dragons.* The premise is unquestioned, but Aristotle's deduction from it asserts the existence of dragons. Now it is evident that the existence of dragons cannot be deduced by pure reason and, therefore, Aristotle's general principle must be wrong. The most important advance, however, was not the detection of the errors of the old logic, but the removal of its limitations. The Aristotelian system in effect took into account only subject-predicate types of propositions, and failed to deal satisfactorily with reasoning in which relations were involved, such as "If there is a descendant, there must be an ancestor." It was not possible to reduce to an Aristotelian syllogism the inference that if *most* have coats and *most* have waistcoats, then *some* must have both coats and waistcoats. In this and other respects the subject has become enlarged to such an extent that only a comparatively small part of any modern treatise is devoted to the traditional logic.

Whitehead and Russell's work may without exaggeration be described as the foundation of the modern renaissance in logic, which, as the successive volumes of the *Journal of Symbolic Logic* show, is now chiefly centered in America. A notable feature of it is the development of what Hilbert has called *metamathematics*, that is, of theorems *about* theorems. An example is the result found in 1931 by Gödel, that there are some propositions of mathematics which, though they have a meaning, cannot be either proved or disproved by means of any system based on axioms, such as that of *Principia Mathematica*.

Russell's Paradox

The advantages of an ideography as compared with ordinary language are strikingly evident in the discussion of certain contradictions which have threatened to invalidate reasoning, such as a famous paradox that was discovered fifty years ago by Bertrand Russell. He remarked that in the case of e.g., the class whose members are all thinkable concepts, the class, being itself a thinkable concept, is one of its own members. This is not the case with e.g., the class of all blue objects, since this class is not itself blue. We can therefore say that those classes which do not contain themselves as one of their members form a particular kind of classes. The aggregate of these classes constitutes a new class which we shall call *x*. Let us put this definition in the two forms:

Form A. A class which contains itself as a member is not a member of *x*.

Form B. A class which does not contain itself as a member is a member of *x*. Now if *x* were a member of itself, then by A it would not be a member of itself, so we should have a contradiction; while if *x* were not a member of itself, then by B it would be a member of itself, which is again a contradiction. Thus on either supposition we arrive at a contradiction, which appears to be insoluble by any kind of verbal explanation.

Now let us look at the matter from the point of view of symbolism. The contradiction that "x is an x" is equivalent to "x is not an x" was obtained essentially by substituting x for y in the statement that (1) y is a class (2) y is an x, is equivalent to "y is not a y." This substitution, however, is not, as it stands, an operation performed on the fundamental logical symbols in accordance with the rules which are laid down for operating on them; for, x is not itself one of the elementary ideograms, but is an abbreviation, a single letter standing proxy for a complex of ideas. Now all abbreviations, however convenient, are from the logical point of view superfluous; and an argument involving them is not valid unless, at every stage of it, the proxy symbols can be replaced by the full expressions for which they stand. In order therefore to be sure that what has been done is correct from the point of view of symbolic logic, we must translate the whole argument, and in particular the operation of substituting x for y, into the language of the elementary ideograms and the operations that are permissible with them, so that all explicit mention of x will have been eliminated from the proof. When, however, we try to do this, we find that we cannot. *It is not possible to state Russell's paradox in the form of an assertion composed solely of the elementary ideograms.* This shows that if we had from the beginning avoided the use of ordinary speech or of proxy symbols and conducted all our investigations according to the strict precepts of ideography, then Russell's paradox would never have emerged. It can be obtained by argumentation in words, or it can be obtained by a quasi-symbolic argument in which an operation is permitted which is untranslatable into pure symbolic logic; but it cannot be obtained by any process which is restricted to using throughout nothing but the elementary ideograms and the operations that are recognized as permissible with them, and which express both the final result and all intermediate equations in terms of them exclusively. Thus Russell's paradox, being inexpressible in symbolic logic, is really meaningless, and we need not concern ourselves with it further. The contradiction which appears in it is not inherent in logic, but originates in the imperfections of language and of abbreviated symbolism.

The Intuitionists

The Whitehead-Russell doctrine that mathematics is based on logic is opposed by a school led by the Dutch mathematician L. E. J. Brouwer and the German Hermann Weyl, and known as *intuitionists*, who maintain the contrary view, that logic is based on mathematics. The series of natural numbers is held to be given intuitively and to be the foundation of all mathematics, so that numbers are not derived, as Russell supposed, from logic. Their system contains a new feature which may be explained thus.

Let it be asked whether, in the development of π as a decimal fraction, there is a place where a particular digit, say 5, occurs ten times in succession. It is of course conceivable that by performing the actual development we might come upon such a succession; or it is conceivable that a general proof might show that it cannot happen; but these two solutions evidently do not exhaust all the possibilities. Under these circumstances, Brouwer and Weyl decline to pronounce the disjunctive judgment of existence, that the development of π as a decimal either does or does not include a succession of ten 5's; in other words, they assert that the logical principle of the *excluded middle*, that every proposition is either true or false, is not valid in domains where a conclusion one way or the other cannot be reached in a finite number of steps. They replace the notion of *true* by *verifiable* and call propositions *false* only if their contradictory is verifiable. This position leads them to abandon the attempt to justify large parts of traditional mathematics: in particular, they reject all proofs by *reductio ad absurdum* (which generally depend on the law of the excluded middle) and all propositions involving infinite collections or infinite series. The disastrous consequences to mathematical analysis of adopting such a position have prevented it from gaining any general acceptance, but it is not easy to disprove.

Probability

In 1654 some one proposed to Blaise Pascal the following problem: a game between two players of equal skill is discontinued for some reason before it is finished: given the scores attained at the time of the stoppage, and the full score required for a win, in what proportion should the stakes be divided? Pascal communicated the problem to his friend Pierre de Fermat, and the two in finding the solution created the *theory of probability*.

Like any other branch of pure mathematics, the theory of probability begins with undefined notions, and axioms. We consider a *trial*, such as drawing a card out of a pack, in which different possible *events* (the drawing of particular cards) might occur, and we introduce the undefined notion of *probability*, which may be described as a numerical measure of *quantity of belief* that one particular event will happen, i.e., that some named card will be drawn. The axiom on which the theory is based may be stated thus: *In a given trial let* A *and* B *be two events which cannot possibly happen together; then the probability that either* A *or* B *will happen is the sum of the probabilities of their happening separately.*

Thus in tossing a coin, let x be the probability of heads and y the probability of tails. Then on account of the symmetry of the coin we may assume that $x = y$. Moreover, from the axiom we see that $x + y$ is the probability that either heads or tails will fall; but this latter is a certainty, to which we give our entire belief. It is convenient to measure entire belief by the number unity: so we have

$$x = y \qquad x + y = 1$$

and therefore $x = y = \frac{1}{2}$. *The probability of heads in a single toss of a coin is* $\frac{1}{2}$.

In practically all the calculations that we can make, some use is made of a property of symmetry: thus, a die is a cube, symmetrical with respect to all its six faces, so the probability that when cast it will show a particular specified face is $\frac{1}{6}$; a pack has 52 cards which are equally likely to be drawn, so the probability of drawing, say, the ace of spades, is $\frac{1}{52}$.

The axiom can readily be extended in the form: *the probability of an event is the ratio of the number of favorable cases to the number of possible cases, when all cases are supposed* (generally for reasons of symmetry) *to be equally likely*. Thus, suppose an old man has only two teeth: what is the probability that they will meet? In this case, whatever position one of the teeth occupies, there are 31 possible positions for the other tooth, and of these only one is favorable. There-the required probability is $\frac{1}{31}$.

It is, however, easy to make mistakes through not taking sufficient care in enumerating the equally likely cases. Thus, take the following argument, which appeared in a recent book: "The sum of an odd number and an even number is an odd number, while the sum of two odd numbers is an even number, and so is the sum of two even numbers. Hence if two numbers are chosen at random, the probability that their sum will be even is twice the probability that it will be odd." The error here comes from not recognizing that there are *four* equally likely cases, namely, OO, OE, EO, EE; of these, two are favorable to an even sum and two to an odd sum, so the probabilities of an odd and an even sum are really equal.

A well-known problem is that of the "Yarborough," i.e., the probability that a hand, which is obtained when an ordinary pack of cards is dealt between four players, should contain no card higher than a nine. The probability is nearly $\frac{1}{1828}$; a former Earl of Yarborough is said to have done very well for himself by betting 1000 to 1 against its happening.

Although the difficulty of probability problems as regards mathematical symbolism is usually not great, they are often very puzzling logically. The reader may like to try the following: given an assertion, A, which has the probability a, what does that probability become, when it is made known that there is a probability m that B is a necessary consequence of A, B having the probability b? [1]

A problem which has some bearing on the credibility of evidence is the following: let p be the a priori probability of an event which a witness has asserted to have happened; and let the a priori probabilities that he would choose to assert it be v on the supposition of its being true, and w on the supposition of its being false. What, *after*

---

[1] The answer is:
$$\frac{a\,[1 - m(1 - b)]}{1 - am(1 - b)}$$

his assertion, is the probability that it really happened? The answer is

$$\frac{pv}{pv + (1 - p)\, w}$$

We see that however small p may be, the value of this fraction may approach indefinitely near to unity—that is, the probability that the event happened may approach certainty—provided w be much less than v: that is, provided the fact of the assertion may be much more easily accounted for by the hypothesis of its truth than of its falsehood. We must not let ourselves be influenced unduly by the *antecedent* improbability of an event but must think out the consequences of the contrary hypothesis, which may be more improbable still.

Statistics

One of the most important applications of the theory of probability is to questions regarding *statistics*, which have to be dealt with specially by actuaries, astronomers, and social workers. The connection between probability and statistics is indicated by a theorem established in 1713 by James Bernoulli, which may be thus stated: let p be the probability of the happening of an event in a single trial, and let s be the number of times the event is observed to happen in n trials, so $\frac{s}{n}$ may be called the *statistical frequency; then as* n *increases indefinitely, the probability approaches certainty that the statistical frequency will approach p.*

This law suggests that we should study what happens when the number of trials is limited, though great, and should calculate the probability of the deviations of the statistical frequency from p which then occur. The calculation is not difficult, and leads to definite *laws of frequency of error*. These are the basis of the methods used e.g. in astronomy for combining observations so as to find the most probable value of a set of quantities from a number of discordant observations of them.

If an event happens only rarely, the formula for the probability of *s* occurrences in *n* trials is different. It has been verified by comparison with the statistical frequency in such different cases as the number of deaths from the kicks of horses in the Prussian Army, and the number of alpha-particles falling on a screen in unit time in certain experiments with radioactive substances.

The theory of statistics is much concerned with what is called *correlation*, which may be explained thus. Consider a definite group containing a large number of men and let *x* be some measurable attribute of a man, say his height, while *y* is another measurable attribute, say his weight. Let the values of these attributes for a man be indicated by a dot whose co-ordinates are *x* and *y* in a diagram. The dots corresponding to all the men will cluster round a certain point O which represents the mean height and weight. Now take axes O_x, O_y, through O. We know that in general a tall man will also be a heavy man, and therefore a positive deviation of *x* from the mean will most often be associated with a positive deviation of *y*, and similarly a negative deviation of *x* will generally be associated with a negative deviation of *y*.

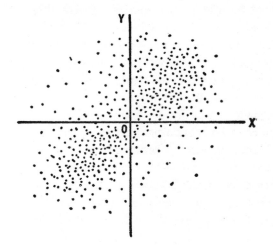

That is to say, the dots will lie chiefly in the first and third quadrants of the diagram. In such a case we say that there is *correlation* between the two attributes *x* and *y*. It can be measured by a *coefficient of correlation*, whose value can be calculated by forming the sums of the values of x^2, y^2, and *xy*, for all the points in the diagram.

Stochastic Systems

The *principle of causality* is expressed by the assertion that whatever has begun to be, must have had an antecedent or cause which accounts for it. This principle is not violated by events of the kind that has usually been studied in works on probability. Consider for instance the tossing of a coin: we do not know on which side the coin will come down, but that is because we do not know all the circumstances of its projection—the mass and shape of the coin, the force applied by the thumb of the operator, etc. We do not doubt that if all these data were available to us, it would be theoretically possible to calculate completely the behavior of the coin, and to predict the side on which it would come down; and, therefore, our lack of ability to make this prediction is due only to our ignorance and not to any failure of determinism in nature. Systems whose working is really governed by strict law, but whose performance we cannot foretell for want of knowledge, are said to have *hidden parameters:* if we knew all about the hidden parameters, we should be able to predict everything.

In the newer physics, we have phenomena like the spontaneous breakup of a radium atom, in which an alpha-particle is given off and the atom is transformed into an atom of radium emanation. It is not possible to foretell the instant when any particular radium atom will disintegrate; and, it was formerly supposed that this is because a radium atom contains hidden parameters—perhaps the positions and velocities of the neutrons and protons inside the nucleus—which are not known to us and which determine the time of the explosion. For reasons which belong to physics and therefore would not be in place here, it is now generally recognized that these hidden parameters do not exist. The disintegrations do not occur in a deterministic fashion, and the only knowledge which is even theoretically possible regarding the time of disintegration is the *probability* that it will happen within (say) the next year. A system in which events such as disintegrations take place according to a law of probability, but are not individually determined in accordance with the principle of causality, is said to be a *stochastic* system. The fact that the systems considered in microphysics are largely stochastic systems make the theory of probability of fundamental importance in the application of mathematics to the study of nature.

Conclusion: The Philosophy of Mathematics and the Philosophy of Science

This talk on mathematics may end with an attempt to answer the question, how is progress in mathematics related to progress in the other sciences?

We have seen that a very high standard was attained in mathematics as early as the fourth and third centuries before Christ; the *Elements* of Euclid are sufficient to carry the modern student of geometry to the point where university courses begin. No comparable development was reached in any other branch of science for 2000 years. Why was this?

In the generation immediately before Euclid, as we have seen, the philosopher Aristotle, whose scientific interests were in biology rather than in mathematics, tried to find a general method of adding to knowledge, by creating the science of logic, which he brought to the form in which it remained with little change until the present age. In showing how logic might be used to advance discovery, Aristotle relied chiefly on the syllogistic type of reasoning that had been so successful in geometry. But syllogisms must start from certain basic truths which are accepted as premises; and it was in the methods of finding these basic truths that Aristotle's scheme was weakest. He collected a great number of observations but does not seem to have taken care to reject those that could not be verified, and he never designed an experiment for the purpose of testing a hypothesis. Syllogisms are as a rule comparatively unimportant in the nonmathematical sciences, and the great place given to them in logic led the later Aristotelians to attach undue importance to mere words.

In the thirteenth century, the influence of Aristotle was greatly increased by the work of St. Thomas Aquinas; but, so far as science was concerned, Aristotelianism developed in a completely sterile form and a violent reaction against it set in, the leaders of which were

Galileo (1564-1642) and Bacon (1561-1626). Bacon emphasized the importance of induction from observation and the necessity for experiment, though even in Bacon we do not find any recognition of the necessity for framing hypotheses and then designing experiments to test them. This indeed can hardly be said to have figured as a doctrine of philosophers until it had become the practice of the great men of science of the seventeenth century, particularly of Isaac Newton (1642-1727). The outstanding characteristic of the Newtonian philosophy was its focusing of interest on the changes that occur in the objects considered. The Greek philosophers had marked the distinction between mathematics and physics by assigning to the mathematician the study of entities which are conserved unchanged in time, and to the physicist the study of those entities which undergo variations; but Newton created a type of mathematics in which the calculation of rates of change was fundamental. The rate of change of position of a body moving in a straight line, which is called its *velocity*, and the rate of change of the velocity, which is called its *acceleration*, were now studied. Newton regarded a curve as generated by the motion of a point, a surface by the motion of a curve, and so on. The quantity generated was called the *fluent*, and the motion was defined by what he called the *fluxion*; and he showed that when a relation was given between two fluents, the relation between their fluxions could be found, and conversely. This theory of fluxions, known later as the *infinitesimal calculus*, became the major occupation of the mathematicians of the eighteenth and nineteenth centuries, and led to wonderful advances in the study of nature.

ASTRONOMY AND
COSMOLOGY

HERMANN BONDI

about

Hermann Bondi

Hermann Bondi was born in Vienna in 1919. He lived there until 1937, attending school and showing great interest in mathematics and physics. In 1937 he went to Trinity College, Cambridge, to study mathematics. As an Austrian subject he was interned in 1940, just as he obtained his B.A. degree. After his release he returned to Cambridge for a short period as research student and spent the remainder of the war in the admiralty, doing research on radar. During this period of more than three years he was in constant contact with Fred Hoyle, whose keen interest in problems of astronomy and astrophysics did much to change Bondi's main line of work from classical applied mathematics (waves and hydrodynamics) to theoretical astronomy. Hoyle and Bondi were joined shortly afterward by Thomas Gold, and together the three men discussed astrophysical questions "during every free hour of the day and late into the night." The work done during these years led to Bondi's election to a fellowship at Trinity College in 1943. After the war Bondi, Gold and Hoyle returned to Cambridge and joined R. A. Lyttleton who had been working on similar problems at Princeton and in Cambridge before the war.

In collaboration with one or two members of this group, Bondi published numerous papers on astronomical and geophysical questions, notably the effect of interstellar gas clouds on stars. He is especially well known for the steady-state theory of the expanding universe, *proposed jointly by him and Gold in 1948, and since then widely discussed. The theory is described in the following essay. In 1952 he published a book on cosmology which, while quite difficult in spots, can be recommended to the thoughtful reader as the clearest summary of its kind.*

After many years in Cambridge as university lecturer in mathematics and as Fellow of Trinity College, Bondi moved to King's College, London, in 1954 as professor of mathematics.

Bondi is married and has three children. His wife, herself a mathematics graduate interested in astronomy and particularly in the constitution of the stars, has published papers in this field, individually and jointly with her husband. The Bondis have paid several visits to the United States. In 1951 they were for three months at Cornell University, where he was a research associate of the Laboratory of Nuclear Studies. More recently they spent the fall of 1953 at Harvard College Observatory and Bondi also gave a course of Lowell Lectures in Boston.

In addition to his professional interest in theoretical science, Bondi is, in his own words, "very keen on the application of physics and engineering to the amenities of everyday life. The subjects of domestic heating (sadly neglected in England), transport, well-designed toys all interest me greatly." He is now designing a house in the country, but within convenient reach of his new teaching post in London.

ASTRONOMY AND COSMOLOGY

HERMANN BONDI

1. Probably the most intriguing feature of astronomy is the total inaccessibility of its objects of study, the celestial bodies. All astronomical information is derived from the examination of visible light and similar radiation (ultraviolet light, radio waves). It is a remarkable testimony to the efficiency of the scientific methods employed that a large amount of knowledge rests on apparently so scanty a source of information.

The subject matter of astronomy may conveniently be divided into four fields in increasing order of the scales of size and distance:

a. The solar system (the planets, satellites and smaller bodies) and its arrangement and origin.
b. The "fixed" stars, their individual properties and close associations.
c. The organization of the stars and of other matter into distinct separate galaxies, each of them containing between a billion and a hundred billion stars.
d. The arrangement, past, present and future, of the galaxies in the universe. This subject is known as cosmology.

In a brief survey such as this it would seem most desirable to pick out a particular development in each field and to discuss the significance of the questions raised and arguments used.

2.   The growth of our knowledge of the motion of the planets raises several interesting considerations. The peculiar behavior of the planets in moving across the background of other stars attracted attention in very early times. First came the observation and description of the motions of the objects; then attempts were made to construct models which, though based on simple geometrical concepts, exhibited the complex observed behavior. The model of Copernicus, which put the sun at the center and supposed the planets to go in circles around it, was simpler and hence superior to the model of Ptolemy, in which the earth occupied the central position. Kepler refined and elaborated the Copernican model by showing that the planets moved in ellipses rather than in circles and by establishing the rules applicable to their orbital speeds. The next great step was taken by Newton.

It is well known that Newton, on observing an apple fall, speculated on whether the same force that pulled the apple down to earth also kept the moon in its orbit round the earth, and the earth in its orbit round the sun. By assuming that it did, he was eminently successful in describing all motions taking place within the solar system. Although this story is familiar, an analysis brings out a number of the characteristic lines of thought of modern astronomy.

The observation that an apple falls to the ground is a *terrestrial* observation. It describes an experiment that we can carry out at will in our surroundings, an experiment the result of which is described by Galileo's laws governing the free fall of bodies. It is a bold step to suggest that these laws of terrestrial physics apply also to distant bodies such as the moon. The underlying assumption is that our locally established laws of physics are of universal validity. It is typical of scientific activity that assumptions are made, where necessary, of such a kind that they are useful in extending the field of scientific endeavor, and are liable to observational disproof. The sole purpose of scientific theories is to bring existing observational results under one head and to forecast the results of future observations. If a theory does not attempt to do this it cannot be disproved. Accordingly it is scientifically valueless and hence is not a scientific theory. To the question "But how do you know that the law of gravitation *really* applies out there?" the scientist can only answer, "I do not *know*, but I have found it useful to assume that it does. When I assume it to apply, I am able to correlate old, and to forecast new, observations. Should my forecasts fail, the assumption would be disproved. This may happen any day, but until it is disproved I shall stick to the assumption as the most useful position I can take."

Belief in the universal validity of terrestrial physics is related to Copernicus' model. For if the earth were a *special* sort of place, with the sun, the planets, and the stars turning round it, we could not expect it to be also a *typical* place. It is only because, following Copernicus, we suppose the earth to be typical rather than special, that we can assume terrestrial knowledge to be valid everywhere.

Another highly significant feature of Newton's work is that he divided the whole set of questions relating to the solar system into two classes. The question "Given Jupiter's present position and velocity, where will it be six months from now?" does not appear intrinsically any simpler than the question "Why is Jupiter further from the sun, and why is it bigger, than Mars?" Newton's theory of gravitation, while supplying a complete answer to questions of the first kind, does not even attempt to answer questions of the second kind. It is by no means obvious that this sort of splitting-up of a set of natural phenomena is at all possible. In many problems of physics one is faced with the necessity of deciding, before one starts to form a theory, whether some aspects of the phenomenon can be explained in isolation, without having to discuss other aspects of the same phenomenon. Thus Newton had to suppose that the gravitational attraction of the earth could be described independently of any knowledge of the chemical composition of the earth's interior. The flow of air round the wing of an airplane can similarly be discussed without examining the composition of the material of the wing, the sag of a bridge under a load of given weight and location without knowledge of the nature of the load. On the other hand the resolving power of a microscope or telescope cannot be discussed without taking account of the wave nature of light, nor can the time lag in the lighting of a fluorescent bulb be discussed without considering the existence of cosmic radiation.

Newton's work on the solar system showed that such divisions, so extremely useful to the investigator, were indeed possible. He was able to show, at least in principle, how all future motions in the solar system could be found, once the position, velocity, and mass of each member were known at one instant of time. However, the question of why just these masses, positions, and velocities exist in the solar system was not examined at all, but was assimilated to the broader, much discussed, but largely unsolved problem of the origin of the solar system. Thus, while the motion of the moon can be predicted for centuries, we regard it as purely accidental (i.e., due to causes too remote and insignificant to examine) that the apparent sizes of the moon and sun are so nearly equal that both total and annular eclipses can occur, i.e., those in which the moon wholly obscures the sun, and those in which the angular diameter of the moon is a little smaller and the entire rim of the sun is visible when the center is blotted out.

3. The utility of the law of gravitation is not confined to the solar system. In looking far afield, at the stars proper (the nearest star is a quarter of a million times as far from us as the sun) one observes pairs of stars moving around each other very slowly (in periods of a century or so); and also cases in which the spectroscopic analysis of the light of a star shows that it comes from two sources alternately approaching and receding, in periods of a day or so. Ascribing the motions of these so-called binary stars to mutual gravitation is a big jump from the theories which fit Newton's apple, but the results obtained by doing so are self-consistent and lead to the general notion of stellar masses of the same order of magnitude as the sun. In this way a number of stellar masses have been determined.

The applications of terrestrial physics to distant regions are not limited to the law of gravitation. A successful theory of the constitution of the stars has been developed. This is especially remarkable when it is considered that while we have some, though only limited, direct knowledge of the surface of the stars, a theory of their interior must necessarily be wholly inferential.

Before discussing this remarkable theory itself, its setting and purpose must be made clear. What observational evidence does the theory of stellar constitution seek to correlate with ordinary physics? A somewhat lengthy description of this is required before the analysis of the methods of the theory can be resumed.

Through powerful telescopes enormous numbers of stars can be seen, but relatively few can be examined in sufficient detail to supply evidence useful for the theory. We must proceed by inferred evidence. Owing to the earth's motion round the sun, the nearest stars appear to describe in the course of a year a small circle against the background of more distant stars (Fig. 1). If this circle is

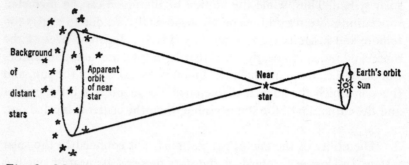

Fig. 1—Measurement of the distance of a near star by observing its apparent annual motion.

large enough, its angular radius can be measured and then the distance of the star is known in terms of the radius of the earth's orbit. For the nearest star the angular radius of the circle is less than 1 second of arc (1 inch at a distance of 4 miles), and angles down to about $\frac{1}{20}$ of this are measurable. In this manner the distances of several hundred stars have been established. The measurement of the intensity of the light received from the star, combined with the knowledge of its distance, allows the rate at which the star sends out light, its so-called intrinsic luminosity, to be determined.

Many stars provide enough light for a spectroscopic analysis. This furnishes a great deal of valuable information, including data from which the line-of-sight velocity of the stars can be inferred [1] and a rough estimate made of the relative abundance of elements (and sometimes even isotopes) in the surface of the star. For our purposes

[1] The spectrum of the light received from a receding source is shifted to the red by an amount proportional to the velocity of recession, and conversely the spectrum of an approaching source is shifted to the violet. This effect, the so-called Doppler shift, can be measured owing to the existence of well-defined dark lines of known position in the spectra of the stars. The shift is of great importance in cosmology.

the most important information afforded by the spectroscope covers the surface temperature of the star. The surface temperature determines not only the color (red-hot, white-hot, etc.), from which, indeed, the temperature is inferred, but also the rate of emission of light per unit area. Here we make use of a firmly established law of terrestrial physics. If the intrinsic luminosity of a star is known, as well as the luminosity per unit area, the surface area of the star may be deduced. Making the plausible assumption that stars are at least approximately spherical in shape, the radius of the star can now be found.

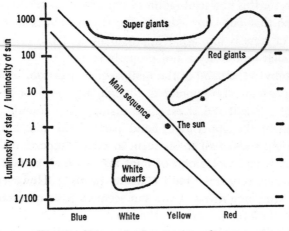

Fig. 2—The color-luminosity diagram.

The stars for which these data of surface temperature and intrinsic luminosity are known may be represented by points in the so-called luminosity-temperature or Hertzsprung-Russell diagram (Fig. 2). In this diagram brightness is represented by the height of the point above the base line; while the coolest (that is reddest) stars are plotted on the right, with the medium-hot (yellow to white) stars in the middle and the hottest (white to blue) on the left.

It turns out that the representative points of the stars follow a very definite pattern. The large majority (95%) of the points fall into a narrow band stretching from the bottom right corner (faint red stars) to the top left (bright blue stars). This band is known as the main sequence and stars belonging to it may be referred to as normal stars. The implication of this pattern of the diagram is that for these stars the radius is a definite function of the luminosity. The main sequence is much more heavily populated in the lower fainter part than in the upper brighter part. Our own sun is in the middle part of the main sequence. Most stars are fainter (down to, say, $\frac{1}{100}$th of the brightness of the sun) and though relatively few are brighter, there are a very few extremely bright stars (up to possibly 50,000 times the luminosity of the sun).[2]

It should be remembered that it is very difficult to see faint stars and relatively easy to see bright ones, even if they are far away. Full corrections for this powerful factor of observational selection are hard to make, so that our knowledge of the relative abundance of different types of stars is somewhat approximate and the lower limit (if any) of stellar luminosity is not properly known.

In addition to the band of the main sequence certain other regions of the diagram are also populated, though large parts of the plot are quite empty. Bright red stars ("red giants") are found, which are represented in the upper right-hand part of the diagram, and extremely bright stars of all colors seem to exist ("supergiants"). There is also a fairly compact group of faint stars of high surface temperature and hence very small radii ("white dwarfs"). However, stars of about the same brightness as the sun seem to have necessarily about the same surface temperature as the sun.

Brief mention must now be made of another diagram that can be drawn to represent observational results. This is the mass-luminosity diagram (Fig. 3). It has been explained how the masses of some stars can be found. If the luminosities of these stars are plotted against their masses it is found that there is a high degree of correlation between these two quantities. Though the observations are poorer in

---

[2] None of these tremendous stars are near us and their distance must be inferred by indirect means rather than by the method described above. These means generally depend on the association in a group or cluster of the big star with a star of spectroscopically known type and hence of known intrinsic luminosity. The distance of this star can then be inferred from the known law of weakening of light with distance. Since the stars are associated, the big star will be at about the same distance. Alternatively, a favorable binary system may permit the masses and radii of its components to be measured with such accuracy that the type of star can be identified and its intrinsic luminosity inferred.

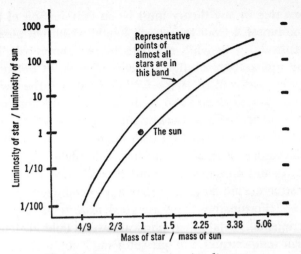

Fig. 3—The mass-luminosity diagram.

number and accuracy than those represented in the color-luminosity diagram, it emerges that the luminosity of a star is closely related to its mass and increases rapidly with it. If one star has twice the mass of another star then the first star will be about 20 times as bright as the second. The range of stellar masses is accordingly very much smaller than the range in luminosity. Very few, if any, stars differ in mass from the sun by a factor of more than ten.

4.   These results have been described in some detail because they raise a series of interesting questions for the invesigator. If he wishes to develop a scientific theory of the internal constitution of the stars he must be clear about his aim. What are the observations and experiments that it should be the prime purpose of the theory to correlate? What evidence is he to regard as confirmatory and what will he be prepared to accept as an empirical disproof of his theory? What is he to regard as a satisfactory starting point for his theory?

   It should be pointed out here that the aim of science is generally held to be to correlate phenomena and not to explain them. A personal judgment is required on whether an explanation is satisfactory, whereas the establishment of a correlation is an objective achievement.

The first step in any theory must be an examination of the guidance to be expected from terrestrial physics, which has already been used extensively in deriving the data to be interpreted. Thus the rectilinear propagation of light, the weakening of intensity with distance, the validity of spectroscopic inferences and the law of gravitation have all been assumed to apply. The best justification for this is the construction of a self-consistent theory in satisfactory agreement with observation based on such inferences and on other physical considerations. But what guidance can physics give since the temperatures and pressures that must be encountered in any theory of stellar structure are far greater than any encountered in laboratory experiments? Fortunately there are good reasons for expecting certain experimentally established physical laws to hold in stellar conditions. High temperatures and pressures imply only an assembly of fast atoms. Though it is impossible to experiment with dense *assemblies* of atoms with speeds corresponding to stellar conditions, tenuous beams of such fast atoms can easily be produced in the laboratory. In fact the electrons in the beam of a television tube have about the same energy as the particles have, on an average, in the centers of the stars. The beam is, however, so tenuous that the pressure it exerts on the glass face of the screen is wholly negligible. While beams of much higher energies (and containing protons and ions as well as electrons) can be produced in specialized equipment, the number of particles in the beam is always too small to produce appreciable pressures. Nevertheless, such experiments allow us to infer the properties of hot dense assemblies. Also, gravitational fields are believed to be fully described by our theories up to intensities well in excess of stellar ones. Since conditions in stellar interiors differ greatly from laboratory conditions, it is possible that processes insignificant (and undiscovered) in the laboratory are important in stars. However, as has been shown, this does not seem likely. The extrapolation of laboratory results to stellar conditions does not lead to any inconsistencies or internal contradictions such as might occur in the mathematical extension of physical rules beyond the range in which they have been established.

The dual aim of the theory of stellar structure is to correlate astronomical measurements among themselves and also, more ambitiously, with physics. If terrestrial physics applied to the astronomical scale leads to significant results (i.e., of relevance to observations) then such a correlation has been achieved. Of course this may turn out to be impossible, but unless we start with the assumption that such a correlation is indeed possible we have no hope of finding it.

5. The next step is to make a hypothetical examination of the properties of the matter composing the stars. In other words, assuming the law of gravitation applies, as well as other laws pertaining to terrestrial matter, what is the simplest model we can construct which will account for the observed properties of stellar bodies? Among the problems and questions which have to be considered are these:

a. Is the nature of the constituent material in fact significant for our purposes? If the answer is yes, we must try to discover what stars are made of and whether a given star is composed of the same material throughout or varies in content from place to place in its interior.

b. Are stars in a steady state or are they changing? Even a star that to us appears quite steady may be undergoing slow changes that profoundly affect its present observable properties.

c. What other factors, besides observed properties, bear upon the validity of the model? Obviously if deductions from a given theory should deny the existence of stars possessing properties such as are actually observed, the theory is false. But if, according to the theory, the range of possible stellar properties is wider than what is in fact observed, it may be that the theory is incomplete rather than false. For it may be that, although such stars can exist, they cannot be born. That is to say the limitation might lie in the process of formation rather than in the state of existence. To give an example from another subject, the strength of rocks would make the existence of mountains 100,000 feet high perfectly possible; however, the conditions permitting of their formation did not occur. We can see therefore at the outset that the theory of stellar constitution is closely linked with the problems of star formation and evolution.

The simplest theoretical model satisfying our requirements incorporates the following assumptions:

(i) The material is the same throughout a star and consists mainly of the most abundant of all elements, hydrogen.

(ii) Stellar bodies are in a steady state.

(iii) Bodies so constituted, possessing such properties and ranging over all masses found in stars, are capable of being formed.

These assumptions are specific enough to permit of a mathematical analysis of the problem. The solution is gratifying; for it turns out that the hypothetical bodies of the model have properties identical (within the limits of observational accuracy) with those of main sequence stars, both as regards dependence of color on luminosity and of luminosity on mass.

It is most fortunate and encouraging that the simplest theoretical model reproduces the observable properties of the large majority of stars. There was a priori little reason for supposing this would be the case but the supporting evidence is most convincing.

6. The method of constructing a theoretical stellar model is straightforward in principle, though the details are mathematically and physically highly complex. The gravitational forces in a star are very large but matter is kept from falling in by a steep pressure gradient, high at the center and diminishing outward. This is analogous to the earth's atmosphere, where the higher pressure at the bottom and the lower pressure on top keep the air static in spite of gravity. The pressure, density, and temperature of stellar matter are related in the same way as in a terrestrial gas[3] although the density (at the huge pressures) may be 100 times as great as that of water. The applicability of the gas law to this range of densities and pressures is a remarkable extrapolation from laboratory experiments on gases, but as explained earlier is well established thanks to the understanding of the behavior of fast particles gained by other laboratory methods.

The temperature follows the pressure in decreasing outward from the center. In a star, as elsewhere, heat flows from the hotter to the

[3] The pressure is the product of temperature and density multiplied by a constant depending only on the masses of the particles composing the gas.

colder region. This stream of heat keeps the surface of the star hot, although the glowing surface constantly radiates into space. The internal temperature gradient leads to a flow of energy from the interior to the surface. The light radiated by the star is the external continuation of the internal energy flow. The magnitude of the temperature gradient just below the surface is hence essentially determined by the rate of radiation per unit surface area and so by the surface temperature, while the pressure gradient affords support against gravity and accordingly depends on the mass and radius of the star. The properties of the internal heat flow, together with the gas laws and the pressure support against gravity, imply that there must be a certain relation between the mass, luminosity and radius of any simple homogeneous star, a relation that can be shown to hold for observed stars of the main sequence.

How is the heat flow maintained, i.e., where does the energy come from? Consideration of the period for which the heat flow has been maintained helps to answer this question.

Geological evidence indicates that the sun's luminosity has not changed appreciably for several hundreds of millions of years, and less direct arguments indicate that the sun, as well as many other stars, are several billion years old. No chemical or gravitational source of energy could sustain the required rate of burning for so long a period. Nuclear energies alone can account for the phenomenon. Nuclear energy is released in two processes, spontaneous radioactivity and induced transmutation. In the first, a suitable nucleus emits a particle and turns into a different nucleus owing to the play of internal forces. Spontaneous radioactivity cannot be the source of stellar energy because radioactive materials are rare and because they liberate relatively little energy. Induced transmutations occur when a nucleus is hit by another particle, the collision being so hard that a nuclear reaction results. Some of these reactions consume part of the energy of the incident particle; others release energy. There are two chief methods for producing sufficiently hard collisions. In the laboratory, fast beams of particles are produced and directed at suitable substances. It seems most unlikely that anything corresponding to an apparatus for producing fast beams can be found inside the stars. In the second method, material is heated to a high temperature so that the constituent particles move at high speed. Nuclei may then collide sufficiently fast to lead to nuclear transmutations. A reaction of this type is called thermonuclear and is evidently a possible energy source for the stars, if the heat produced in the nuclear reactions keeps the material so hot that the reaction continues.

To arrive at more definite conclusions, numerical values have to be considered. The temperature at the centers of the stars can be inferred from heat flow arguments and observed characteristics of the stars to be around fifteen million degrees centigrade. The average velocity of nuclei at such temperatures is very low by laboratory standards. The velocity of nuclei in beams required to produce a measurable rate of nuclear transmutations is considerably higher. But this discrepancy is only apparent. The rate of energy production per unit mass in stars is exceedingly low by terrestrial standards. Thus 200 pounds of material at the center of the sun produce merely one watt; whereas, for example, the average heat output of a human being is around 100 watts. The enormous luminosity of the stars is therefore due only to their tremendous masses. To put it more precisely, consider a thin cone with its vertex at the center of the sun and its base an area of one square inch of solar surface. Though energy is produced only at the exceedingly low rate mentioned above along the part of the cone near the vertex, the enormous size of this region (say 70,000 miles long) and the high density of the matter (several times as dense as lead) imply that the total output of energy is quite large. All this energy has to flow out through one square inch of surface area, since, by symmetry, there is no net outflow to neighboring cones. Hence the surface is kept hot and the whole star is bright.

Due account being taken of this factor, laboratory experiments can be performed in nuclear physics to determine the central temperature at which suitable thermonuclear reactions (in fact the conversion of hydrogen into helium), proceeding at a sufficient rate, produce the total heat output of stars. Knowledge of the central temperature in turn affords understanding of a relation between mass, radius and luminosity in addition to the one referred to above, and, like it, in excellent agreement with the observed characteristics of main sequence stars. Thus we have arrived at the conclusion that a homogeneous mass (of stellar magnitude) consisting principally of hydrogen can be inferred from ordinary physics to be in equilibrium when its surface temperature and luminosity have certain values, and these are the observed values for a normal star of the same mass.

This is an impressive vindication of the scientist's method of not ascribing processes in unfamiliar settings to "mysterious forces unknown to science," of not meekly saying "I do not know," but of resolutely applying the known and extending it to cover the unknown.

7. Since the homogeneous models consisting of matter behaving as a gas and composed chiefly of hydrogen reproduce the observable properties of main sequence stars, we are encouraged to devise models to match the other, rarer, types of stars.

It has been pointed out that the high temperatures of normal stellar interiors justify the astrophysicist in regarding matter existing there as being in a gaseous state despite its high density. At considerably higher densities than are met in main sequence stars new factors come into play. The famous exclusion principle of atomic physics formulated by the Nobel-prize winning Swiss scientist, Wolfgang Pauli, states that no two electrons can be close to each other both in position and in velocity. In highly compressed matter numerous electrons are close to each other in position. Accordingly numerous sufficiently different velocities must occur. This implies that many electrons must have a high speed. At ordinary densities, the velocity of particles depends only on the temperature, but the exclusion principle implies that in highly compressed matter the velocity of many particles must be high whatever the temperature.

The impact of fast particles is the pressure; accordingly highly compressed matter exerts considerable pressure irrespective of the temperature. This type of pressure therefore follows different laws from the usual gas pressure. Models can be examined in which this peculiar pressure affords the main support against gravitation. It turns out that the radius is a definite function of the mass, that the mass must be below a certain limit, but that the luminosity is indeterminate. Though points of comparison with observation are far fewer than in the case of main sequence stars, the model seems to be in excellent agreement with all that is known of white dwarf stars.

According to the model that corresponds to the main sequence stars, their energy is provided by the thermonuclear conversion of hydrogen into helium in the central regions. After a sufficient lapse of time such a star will have produced a great deal of helium, and hydrogen will no longer be the principal constituent. If the helium stays near the center where it has been generated, the inner regions will have a different composition (large proportion of helium) from the outer ones (almost pure hydrogen). The star will cease to be homogeneous. The time needed to bring about such changes can easily be computed. The rate of transmutation which will account for the star's luminosity follows from the known amount of energy liberated in each nuclear reaction. The mass of hydrogen turned into helium in, say, a billion years is simply proportional to the star's luminosity. As this in turn is such a steeply increasing function of the star's mass, it follows that a far larger fraction of the mass of a massive (and hence bright) star will be helium after a billion years than in the case of a light (and hence faint) star. The hydrogen store of the sun would last for about one hundred billion years, so that significant changes in appearance might be expected after about ten billion years. For fainter stars this period is much longer, for brighter ones much shorter. Since no star in our galaxy is believed to be more than 5–10 billion years old, no star fainter than the sun can have accumulated much helium, but stars brighter than the sun may well have done so. Though many uncertainties are involved, it seems clear that a star with large amounts of helium in the inner regions is likely to be greatly expanded and hence to look much redder than a normal star. Thus we seem to have found, in principle at least, satisfactory models for red giant and supergiant stars.

A particularly successful feature of this theory is the fact that it implies that stars fainter than the sun should be confined to the main sequence while brighter stars may be found to the right of it. This agrees perfectly with the Hertzsprung-Russell diagram.

Nevertheless it must not be supposed that we are within striking distance of having theoretical models for all stars. The luminosity of some stars varies periodically, a fact which may indicate that they oscillate. The magnetic field of stars can sometimes be found by its effect on the spectrum. It turns out that certain stars have high, and some variable, magnetic fields. Also some stars have a rather lower luminosity than main sequence stars of the same color. These so-called sub-dwarfs do not fit in too well with the interpretation of the Hertzsprung-Russell diagram given above. Though we are slowly gaining in understanding of these stars, no wholly satisfactory theory of their behavior exists. The success of the theory in describing normal stars gives one, however, great confidence that it will eventually also be able to describe the rarer types without having to rely on other than known properties of matter.

8. So far the discussion has been largely confined to stars in our astronomical neighborhood. Are they representative of stars everywhere? This question leads directly to the organization of stars into galaxies.

The Milky Way is a familiar phenomenon of the night sky. It is an arrangement of vast numbers of stars in a flattened disk-shaped portion of space. The solar system is close to the plane of the disk, though fairly distant from its center (about 25,000 light years, while the radius of the disk is about 40,000 light years). If we look around us in the plane of the disk we see large numbers of stars, while in any other direction we look out of the disk and hence see far fewer stars. This explains the luminous arc of the Milky Way.

Our galaxy is not embedded in empty space, but is surrounded, though at great distances, by innumerable similar galaxies. The best known of these is the great Andromeda nebula, visible to the naked eye. A great many more galaxies are accessible to a large telescope. Many prominent galaxies show a spiral structure, i.e., the bright stars are arranged in spiral arms, with less luminous regions between them (Fig. 4). Intricate detailed investigations have shown that the stellar population in the spiral arms resembles that of the solar neighborhood but differs from stellar populations elsewhere. In particular it is important to point out that while stars redder than main sequence stars are found outside the spiral arms, they are not as red as the spiral arm "red giants," and also that hot blue stars are confined to the spiral arms.

Fig. 4a—*A spiral galaxy—a nebula in Ursa Major (from a Mt. Palomar photo).*

Fig. 4b—*A spiral galaxy seen edge on—a nebula in Coma Berenices (from a Mt. Palomar photo).*

Because of our location we are unable to see our own galaxy from the outside; but various observational data, including star counts in different directions, measurements of stellar velocities and of occurrence of bright stars and star clusters, show convincingly that ours is a spiral galaxy, and that we are situated in a spiral arm.

Why do different types of stars exist in different parts of a spiral galaxy? The appearance of the Milky Way is distinctly patchy, and there are some very black regions, among them the well-known "Coal Sack." In view of the inherent improbability of a long vacant corridor amidst millions of stars, it has long been thought that this blackness is not due to paucity of stars, but to the presence of obscuring matter, i.e., of material tenuous by terrestrial standards, yet as opaque as smoke or fog owing to its disposition in the form of huge clouds. By examining the light of stars not wholly blacked out, but partially dimmed, the properties of the intervening medium can to some extent be established. It consists of small, solid particles of ice, carbon, calcium compounds, and the like, and so is referred to as dust. The discovery of the existence of this nonluminous matter caused a revolution in astronomy, which until then had been concerned exclusively with the shining stars, supposedly the only inhabitants of space. However, even more startling discoveries were to come. Certain arguments, partly dynamical and partly spectroscopic, indicated that besides the dust, there was also cold gas (mainly hydrogen) in the space between the stars, in quantity greatly exceeding the dust, and probably not less than the stellar matter. The interstellar gas is so tenuous that there are at most a thousand of its atoms in a cubic centimeter; a volume of this gas equal to that of the earth would have a mass of only one ton. However, the regions filled with interstellar gas are so large that huge masses exist and have a strong influence on the evolution of the stars.

Because the atoms of the gas move at the relatively low velocity of one kilometer per second it is said to be cold. It is optically inactive in that it neither shines nor absorbs light from stars behind it. However, collisions between the gas atoms are sufficient to result indirectly in the production of radio waves and they have been detected in quite recent investigations. Not only have these radio observations confirmed the inference that the gas exists, but they are also helping to establish the distribution of the gas clouds and so render more accurate our knowledge of the spiral structure of our galaxy.

The gas clouds and particularly the dust clouds seem to be concentrated in the spiral arms. The special character of the stars in the spiral arms is therefore supposed to be due to their interaction with the local accumulation of gas and dust. What is the nature of this interaction? This is one of the most absorbing fields of present-day research. It is partly concerned with the problem of the origin of the stars, of their supposed birth in such clouds. Another aspect of the problem is the increase in the mass of a star which results if it strongly attracts the material of a cloud and causes the gas to fall into the star. Thirdly, there is the opposite process, in which some stars (probably very few, but possibly many) replenish the dust clouds by sloughing matter from their surfaces.

The subject is too involved to be discussed in detail, but it will be seen that there are fascinating problems: the relation between the character of a star and its position in the galaxy, the origin of the stars, the maintenance of the very bright stars that so quickly exhaust their hydrogen, and kindred matters.

9.   To the nonscientist it must seem strange that, while the history of science appears to be a brilliant success story, from a logical point of view the stress is always on disproof and hence on the failure rather than on the confirmation of theories. There are many contributory reasons for this apparent discrepancy between the workshop procedure and the nature of the finished product. The most obvious of these reasons is that in describing the present state of any more or less complete subject one refers only to the theory that has survived and not to those that have been disproved.

The less complete a science, the more evident is the ruling part played by empirical disproof in its development. Cosmology is a case in point; and the essentially primitive state of this science facilitates the examination of its methods of inference and analysis.

The subject matter of cosmology is the structure of the universe as a whole. For a long time it was believed (and some persons still cling to this view) that, because of its subject matter, cosmology belonged to philosophy rather than to science. It was only 130 years ago that a pioneer investigation by the German astronomer Heinrich Olbers demonstrated the scientific character of cosmology. This investigation remains one of the most important arguments in cosmology and so it will now be considered in some detail.

Near stars, which appear on the average to be bright, are few in number. Medium-bright stars are more common, faint ones commoner still. It is known that there are stars too faint to be individually visible. The question is: are they so numerous that the diffuse background light received from them is significant? It is evident that in order to calculate effects emanating from distant regions of unresolvable stars, assumptions have to be made about the nature of these regions. One may then attempt to infer the intensity of the background light of the sky and compare this with observational experience.

The investigation proceeds in three stages:

a. A set of assumptions is formulated whose fruitfulness and plausibility is tested in stages (b) and (c). These assumptions need not (and generally will not) be susceptible to direct observational check.

b. Observable consequences are deduced from the assumptions.

c. The empirical connection is established by comparing the consequences of the assumptions with the actual observations. If there is disagreement, then (a) has been disproved. If there is no disagreement, then (a) remains tenable pending the exploration of further observable consequences. A set of assumptions that does not lend itself to (c) and hence cannot be disproved is empty and scientifically futile.

Olbers made the following four assumptions about the nature of distant regions:

(i) Viewed on a sufficiently large scale, the universe is the same everywhere, i.e., it is uniform in space.

(ii) Similarly, it is unchanging in time.[4]

(iii) There are no major systematic motions.

(iv) The laws of physics, as we know them, apply everywhere throughout the universe.

Some comments on these assumptions may be appropriate. As for (i), it will be required that for sufficiently large regions the amount of light emitted by stars per unit volume shall be the same for each region. The known aggregation of stars into widely separated galaxies does not upset this assumption; it merely compels the fixing of

---

[4] Assumption (i) is known as the cosmological principle, assumptions (i) and (ii) together as the perfect cosmological principle.

boundaries large enough so that each region will include many galaxies.

Assumption (iii) means that while individual stars or galaxies may have randomly distributed velocities, small compared with the velocity of light, they are not correlated with position. In particular the assumption denies the possibility that distant galaxies recede from us systematically. The main consequence of the assumption is that all effects of velocities are held to be negligible.

Assumption (iv) is almost indispensable, at least as a starting point, for without it we should have to discard all the knowledge discovered in our neighborhood and would scarcely be able to proceed.

Consider now a set of spheres, each centered on us, the difference between the radii of successive spheres being a constant length which will be taken to be large. Any two adjacent spheres enclose a spherical shell between them, and if the radii of the spheres are very large compared with their difference in length, the ratio of the distances from us of any two points inside a shell must be close to unity (Fig. 5). It will now be assumed that the volume of each of the shells

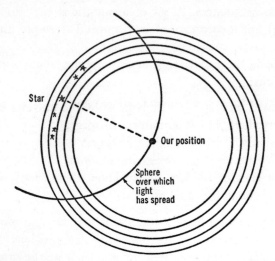

Star

Our position

Sphere
over which
light
has spread

Fig. 5—Olbers' paradox. Four of the evenly spaced concentric shells are shown. Observe that all stars in any one shell are approximately equidistant from us, and also that the light from a star in a shell has spread, when it reaches us, over a sphere of about the same size as the boundary spheres of the star's shell.

to be considered is so large that assumption (i) applies. The number of stars in any shell, and hence their total rate of emission of light, is accordingly proportional to the volume of the shell. Since the thickness of each shell is the same, its volume is, with fair precision, proportional to the surface area of the inner (or equally the outer) boundary sphere of the shell.

What of the light sent out by a star in the shell? By the time the light reaches earth it will have spread over a sphere whose radius is the distance from the star to us. If the thickness of the shell is disregarded—a permissible procedure, as has been indicated—it follows that this distance is in effect equal to the radius of either boundary sphere. The intensity of light received from any one star is therefore inversely proportional to the surface area of (either) boundary sphere of the shell in which the star is situated. Since the number of stars is directly proportional to this quantity, the total intensity of light received from *all* the stars in a shell is independent of the radius of the shell and hence the same for all shells. In other words the amount of light contributed by distant shells is the same as the amount due to near shells because the increase in the number of stars offsets the diminution in the brightness of each star.

Since each shell contributes the same amount of light, and by virtue of Olbers' assumptions the shells continue without end, it is hard to understand why we are not drowned in an infinite flood of light emanating mainly from extremely distant, very faint, but immensely numerous stars. The fallacy in this reasoning is that no allowance has been made for the fact that each star not only sends out light, but also intercepts (owing to its finite size) light from yet more distant stars. Because of the relatively small size of stars, this shadowing effect becomes important only at very large distances. When allowance is made for it, the intensity of light turns out to be finite, but as great as on the surface of an average star. This is equal to about 40,000 times the intensity of sunlight on the earth when the sun is in the zenith. It is worth remarking that this result, which may be called Olbers' paradox, can also be reached by another train of reasoning. According to the assumptions we have adopted, if one looks into the sky in any direction the line of sight will eventually intercept a stellar surface. Since this means that we are in a sense entirely surrounded by stellar surfaces, the identical paradox follows.

But this conclusion is so completely refuted by the fact that it is dark at night, that the assumptions must obviously be incorrect.[5] This is a most important result, for a set of assumptions about the nature of the universe has been disproved empirically. We know as a result of *observation* that whatever the depths of the universe may be like, they do not conform to the model based on Olbers' assumptions. With this step the relevance and supremacy of observational disproof has been established in cosmology and it has become a science.

The next step is to tinker with the set of assumptions, to see what can be saved, what must be substituted or mended. We have agreed that it is unwise to tamper with assumption (iv) (laws of physics) unless there are compelling reasons to do so. Also there is strong observational evidence in support of assumption (i) (uniformity of the universe), as will be shown below. Can Olbers' paradox be avoided if either (ii) (unchanging nature of the universe) or (iii) (no motion) is dropped?

In the case of (ii), it is easy to see that if the stars began to shine not too long ago, the paradox does not arise. For since light has a finite velocity, the light from the remote shells must have been emitted in the very distant past to arrive here now. If at that time no light was in fact emitted, then shells beyond a certain distance will not contribute to the present intensity of the background light of the sky, and so agreement with observation may be reached.

In the case of (iii) a certain amount of mathematical work has

---

[5] It is useless to suggest, as Olbers did, that dust clouds absorb the light from distant regions. For in doing so the clouds would get hotter until they glowed strongly enough to emit as much as they received. By assumption (ii) there has been ample time for this state to be reached, in which there is no resultant shielding by absorbing matter. It should also be noticed that Olbers' paradox is unaffected by the much discussed possibility that the geometry of large-scale regions differs from local (Euclidean) geometry in such a way that the universe is finite. By assumption (i) a finite universe would be unbounded, so that light could travel around it arbitrarily often, just as one can circle the globe arbitrarily often. Accordingly we would not only receive light from a star directly but also light it has emitted that has circled the globe once, twice, and so on. Therefore in this model a finite number of stars produces an infinite number of star images; thus the paradox remains unresolved.

to be done to see what types of motion are at all compatible with (i). It turns out that the only systematic motions compatible with uniformity are those in which relative to any particular member (galaxy) every other member is moving, in the line of sight, with a velocity proportional (roughly speaking) to its distance. Either the whole system is expanding or it is contracting. Now it is known from ordinary physics that light from a receding source appears dimmer than light from a similar stationary source, that this effect becomes very pronounced when the velocity of the source is close to the velocity of light, and that the opposite holds (increased brightness) if the source is approaching. Accordingly, in an expanding system the distant regions contribute less than in a stationary system to the background light of the sky, and hence Olbers' paradox does not arise in such an "expanding universe" provided the increase of recession velocity with distance is sufficiently rapid. In a contracting system the paradox would correspondingly be enhanced.

There are thus two ways of resolving Olbers' paradox while maintaining assumptions (i) and (iv). Either the system is young in that the stars only began to shine a finite time ago, or any two galaxies recede from each other with a velocity proportional to their distance apart.

There are several important cross links between theory and observation at this stage. The light from faint and hence presumably distant galaxies shows precisely the observable characteristics associated with light emitted by receding sources. The velocities inferred from these characteristics turn out to be proportional to the distance, which in turn is inferred from the apparent faintness. The greatest velocity so inferred is almost 40,000 miles per second, a fifth of the velocity of light, and the faintest galaxies visible in the biggest telescope are presumably considerably faster.

These facts lend support to one of the suggestions above for avoiding Olbers' paradox. Second, the fact that the observed motion is identical with the only pattern (velocity proportional to distance) compatible with the assumption of uniformity confers even greater plausibility on this assumption than does the observed degree of uniformity in the distribution of galaxies. Finally, a more recondite remark may be permitted. It could be argued that the observations of uniformity and motion refer to a negligibly small part of the entire universe, and therefore assumption (i) is inadequately corroborated. This argument, however, rests upon an incorrect notion of the meaning of the word "universe." Cosmology is a science and as such only concerned with observables. The validity of Olbers' assumptions for regions beyond the limit of observability is wholly irrelevant, even if such regions can be said to exist. The question deserving attention is whether the *observed* region forms a sufficiently large fraction of the *observable* region to allow inferences to be drawn in a plausible manner.

A shadowy and pragmatic boundary of the observable universe is suggested by the dimming associated with the velocity of recession. For this dimming proceeds so rapidly with increasing distance that regions beyond a certain range are effectively unobservable. In fact the latest doubling of telescope aperture has not doubled the accessible distance, but increased it only by a markedly smaller fraction. At still greater distances the law of diminishing returns would operate more strongly so that a doubling of telescope aperture would only increase the observable distance by a few per cent or even less. Although there may not be an absolute bar to seeing arbitrarily far, an elastic but nevertheless effective limit is imposed by the recession velocity. The highest recession velocity measured is about a fifth of the velocity of light and some faint galaxies observed may have a velocity of recession close to one-third of the velocity of light. There is every reason to believe (by virtue of the theory of relativity) that if an object recedes so fast as to be almost invisible, all other types of interaction will also be insignificant. Though no exact definition of effective observability has yet been given, we must nevertheless conclude that our observations cover an appreciable part of the effectively observable region. Accordingly they can be said to give substantial support to the validity of assumption (i) (uniformity) with respect to the regions that are scientifically relevant.

10. To make a further advance, one must construct a comprehensive theory of cosmology that attempts to connect observations with each other and with the rest of physics. In view of the scarcity of

available data it is not surprising that there are several theories which can be fitted to present observations. Among these theories there are two that seem to be most promising and have attracted most attention. They alone will be discussed in this essay.

Before entering upon a detailed description of these two theories and their differences it may be helpful to summarize the points common to them. These are:

a. The assumption of the spatial uniformity of the universe (Olbers' assumption (i)) known as the cosmological principle. It is agreed that this assumption can only apply on a very large scale, since on any moderate or small scale the universe is far from uniform as shown by the existence of galaxies and stars. The evidence for the cosmological principle has been discussed above.

b. The recession of the galaxies, also known as "the expansion of the universe." The evidence for this is the so-called red shift of the spectra of the galaxies referred to before. The only known interpretation of such an observational effect is a velocity of recession. Though the notion of the expanding universe seems to have caused some difficulty of understanding, few scientists are willing to postulate a special hypothetical effect to account for the red shift. The two theories to be discussed both accept the obvious interpretation of the red shift as due to a velocity of recession and hence as clear-cut and sufficient evidence for the expansion of the universe.

The difference between the two theories arises from the attitude they adopt towards Olbers' assumption (ii). The so-called steady-state theory accepts this assumption of the unchanging appearance of the universe and considers the pair of assumptions (i) and (ii) (also known as the perfect cosmological principle) as fundamental. Even assumption (iv) (the applicability of the laws of physics) is regarded as secondary compared with the perfect cosmological principle. In the other theory assumption (ii) is dropped, assumption (iv) being considered as the basis of the theory. Since the formulation which has been adopted of the behavior of matter in the large is general relativity, this cosmological theory is known as relativistic cosmology.

Taking first the steady-state theory, the chief argument in favor of maintaining both assumptions (i) and (ii) (the perfect cosmological principle) is one of necessity, based on the circumstance that our knowledge of physics has been gathered here on earth and in our astronomical neighborhood. In other words our experience is based on the exploration of regions minute on the cosmic scale, in a period of time similarly minute. There is, to be sure, no immediate reason to believe that the laws of physics so acquired are of universal validity. On the contrary it can be argued forcefully that the quantities entering in our laws of physics that are known as physical constants (the constant of gravitation, the ratio of electric to gravitational forces in an atom, etc.) are not true constants but depend on the structure of the universe. If the universe varies from place to place or from time to time, these "constants" must vary too, but in a way unknown to us. It is only because our local region and the period of physical measurements are so small that these quantities are apparently constant. Any contemplation of a changing universe precludes therefore the extrapolation of local physical laws, unless a (largely arbitrary) assumption is made as to how they vary with this change. The only way to avoid this additional complexity is to assume that the universe does not change (on the large scale) in space or time, which is to adopt the perfect cosmological principle.

Of course this step does not imply that the perfect cosmological principle is correct; but its fruitfulness is self-evident, since the principle leads without further assumptions to predictions susceptible of observational disproof. On the strength of this feature some, but by no means all, scientists working in the field accept the perfect cosmological principle. The main argument for rejecting it is that it leads to a modification of the laws of physics that many find unpalatable. The need for this modification follows directly from the discussion of the preceding section. It was shown that the only plausible resolutions of Olbers' paradox are either to substitute for (ii) the assumption that the universe is young or for (iii) the assumption that it is expanding.[6] Either choice has drastic implications. The first contradicts the perfect cosmological principle. The second, which leaves the principle intact, can be fitted into the framework of the steady-state theory, expansion being inferred from the darkness of the night sky and other more direct observations. But if this course is followed a fundamental law of physics must be revised. For the expansion seems to imply, in the light of the law of conservation of mass, a diminishing average density of matter. As this flatly contradicts assumption (ii) of the unchanging character of the universe, the only way to preserve the perfect cosmological principle is to modify the law of conservation by permitting a *continual creation of matter*.[7] The rate of creation must be such as to cancel the diminution in density due to the expansion of the system. It can further be shown that, in order to maintain the unchanging character of the universe, creation must proceed at a fairly uniform rate, that is to say, the rate per unit volume per unit time must be constant regardless of the presence or absence of matter or radiation. The matter created must be cold diffuse hydrogen or its equivalent.

The process rate comes to about one atom of hydrogen per cubic foot every few billion years. It is evident that this yield is much too small to be detected. But it is also important to realize that the experiments on which the law of conservation of matter are based are too crude by factors of hundreds of billions to exclude the possibility that matter is being created at this slow rate. Thus no contradiction confronts us between the continual creation theory and observational fact, though the theory certainly does not jibe with current mathematical formulations. It is this formal disagreement which leads many scientists to prefer a different theory.

The view favored by many is based on the theory of relativity,

---

[6] If assumption (i) is eliminated the difficulty of the background light can be quite simply resolved by assuming that beyond a certain distance there are no stars. However, the arguments in favor of assumption (i) are so strong that it cannot be dropped.

[7] The chain of arguments used is: perfect cosmological principle plus dark night sky implies expansion; perfect cosmological principle plus expansion implies continual creation.

whose formulation of the laws of the behavior of matter in our neighborhood agrees most closely with observation Relativity incorporates the law of conservation of mass and is therefore, in its usual interpretation, incompatible with the perfect cosmological principle owing to the expansion of the universe. Assumption (i) (uniformity) is compatible with general relativity. The expansion of the universe is not only directly inferred from observation but is to some extent implied by the theory. The combination of uniformity, expansion and general relativity leads to a homogeneous, changing, and evolving universe. At any instant there is large-scale uniformity and changes are taking place everywhere in such a manner that all regions keep in step and so maintain the uniformity of the system. The assumption is made that in spite of the changing character of the universe the laws of general relativity apply at all times.

Of the several different models compatible with this set of ideas, cosmologists studied most the model invented by the noted Belgian physicist, the Abbé Lemaître, and elaborated by the American, George Gamow. Its main features are the following: at the beginning the universe was in an exceedingly hot and dense state; there ensued a nuclear type of explosion in which the heavy elements were formed. In the early phase of rapid expansion following the explosion, matter was uniformly distributed without local agglomerations such as stars and galaxies. Under the influence of gravitation the expansion slowed down almost to a standstill. During this nearly static period the condensation of galaxies took place. After a time a repulsive force—the concept fits naturally into relativity—began to counterbalance gravity and expansion resumed. At present the universe is in an advanced stage of the second period of expansion, which continues at an increasing pace. The resulting diminution of density has made impossible the condensation of new galaxies.

Lemaître's universe is therefore evolving, starting with a violent birth and continuing through distinctive periods of aging. His model, like that based on the perfect cosmological principle, leads to a coherent description of the universe in agreement with what is known. However a number of observations that can be made now or in the very near future will furnish results which are forecast differently by the two theories and will therefore invalidate one or the other. Thus each is susceptible of disproof and both qualify as proper scientific theories.

One of the crucial results turns on the basic characteristics of the two theories. In the steady-state model based on the perfect cosmological principle the unchanging character of the entire universe is maintained, in spite of the aging of each individual galaxy (mainly due to the conversion of hydrogen into helium in the stars), by the continual formation of new galaxies from newly created matter in the constantly increasing spaces between the old ones. On the other hand as a galaxy grows old it drifts away into less and less observable regions through the process of expansion. In this way a population equilibrium is maintained just as in a stationary human population, where deaths are balanced by births and, though each member ages, the average of the population is constant. This model therefore exhibits galaxies of widely different ages everywhere and at all times, but in any region containing large numbers of galaxies the average age is always the same.

A different age distribution characterizes the relativistic model. The underlying theory provides for periods in the evolution of the universe favorable to the formation of galaxies, and other periods (including the present) with conditions unfavorable to the process. Accordingly all galaxies are more or less of the same age.

The observational testing of these antithetical conclusions might be accomplished in two distinct ways. One involves looking at galaxies reasonably close to ours, estimating their age distribution and seeing whether it conforms to either of the theoretical forecasts. This method, though attractive, cannot yet be applied because present knowledge does not permit of an estimate of the age of a galaxy from its appearance; but it seems likely that this obstacle will be overcome during the next ten years or so. Galaxies fall into different classes based on their appearance. It should be possible, with the aid of the theories of stellar structure and evolution discussed earlier in this essay, to discover whether the stellar content of one type of galaxy gradually changes to the stellar content of some other type. This should make it feasible to change the present purely morphological classification of galaxies into an evolutionary scheme and so to correlate the appearance of a galaxy with its age.

The second method, for which the necessary observations can be made now, is a little harder to explain. It involves the consideration that, owing to the finite velocity of light, the images of distant galaxies seen today portray their appearance a long time ago. According to the perfect cosmological principle, which implies changelessness, the time lapse does not matter. On the average the various observable properties (color, shape, size) of galaxies were the same in the remote past as they are now, so that the properties should be the same for distant as for near galaxies. But if one goes by the relativistic model, one must conclude that the distant galaxies are seen today in an early stage of their evolution and their characteristics therefore differ from near ones.

This test consists then in observing whether there is a systematic variation with distance of the average color, size, and shape of galaxies. If the variation exists, the perfect cosmological principle is untenable; the absence of variation would support the principle. Observational work along these lines is feasible with existing equipment and is about to be carried out.

This brief and compressed description of work in various fields of astronomy cannot claim to be comprehensive. It does however try to show how the whole of scientific endeavor is directed solely to obtaining, correlating, and forecasting observational results. Theories must not only agree with the facts; they must be so constructed as to facilitate attempts at empirical disproof. The data so obtained and the standard of internal consistency are the only legitimate criteria for science. Intuitive reactions, such as the difficulty of imagining various strange and remarkable features of a theory (in astronomy and cosmology, these include temperatures of millions of degrees, creation of matter, enormous velocities, etc.) are of secondary importance. The methods touched upon in this essay have proved themselves repeatedly in many branches of science; they have focused issues and organized congeries of facts and conjectures into statements capable of being tested, questions capable of being answered. Cosmology, though an infant discipline, confronted with prodigious exercises, has made progress only by availing itself of these methods. It will continue to do so.

PHYSICS

EDWARD U. CONDON

about

Edward U. Condon

Edward U. Condon was born in 1902 in Alamogordo, New Mex ico. His father was a western civil engineer who specialized in building railroads (he put the Western Pacific through the Feather River Can yon) and Condon's boyhood was, therefore, spent in nearly all of the states west of Denver. He went to high school in Oakland, California and worked as a newspaper reporter from 1918 to 1921 before enter ing the University of California. In 1926 he received his Ph.D. there and went to Germany for a year's study. This was just at the time when the new quantum mechanics of Heisenberg, Born, Schrödinger and Dirac was being developed. On his return Condon spent a year at Columbia University and at the Bell Telephone Laboratories and in 1928 joined the faculty of Princeton University. He remained there until 1937, except for one year spent as professor of theoretical physics at the University of Minnesota. During this period he developed the theory of radioactive decay with the late Ronald Gurney and wrote a definitive treatise on the theory of atomic spectra with George H. Shortley. These researches established his reputation as a foremost theoretical physicist.

In 1937 he was appointed Associate Director of Research for the Westinghouse Electric Corporation; in this post he developed a pro gram of nuclear research before the discovery of uranium fission. One of the important advances achieved in these studies was the discovery by Condon's associates of the phenomenon of photo-fission, the production of uranium fission by means of gamma radiation. In 1940 Condon turned the major part of his energy to defense work, starting with research on microwave radar at Westinghouse and at the government-sponsored project at the Massachusetts Institute of Technology. The next year he was appointed a member of the then-secret S-1 Committee set up by President Roosevelt to plan the atomic bomb project. He was closely associated with the government's atomic bomb research for the rest of the war.

Immediately after the war, beginning in the fall of 1945, he took a leading part in the campaign of the atomic scientists to acquaint the American public with the social and political problems raised by atomic energy and atomic bombs. He is responsible in no small measure for the success of this program, which enlightened the thoughtful segment of American opinion and gained administration support for the legislation that placed atomic energy under civilian rather than military control. For almost a year Condon gave valuable service as scientific adviser to the U.S. Senate Special Committee on Atomic Energy, which, in the Seventy-ninth Congress, held extensive hearings, and voted out the bill which became the Atomic Energy Act of 1946. The deliberations of the Special Committee were conducted in a tense atmosphere and no one who participated in them escaped the aftermath of recriminations when international conditions had deteriorated. Condon became a target for those who proposed legislation which would have placed atomic energy under military control. From this conflict arose the accusations directed against Condon by the House Committee on Un-American Activities under the chairmanship of Congressman J. Parnell Thomas. Thomas charged that Condon was one of the "weakest links in our atomic security." This charge has since become a journalistic refrain, almost invariably repeated when Condon's name is mentioned in the newspapers, but no evidence has been adduced to support it, nor was Condon ever afforded an opportunity to refute the charge in public before the Committee, despite his many requests to be heard.

In November 1945 he was appointed director of the National Bureau of Standards by President Truman, an appointment confirmed by the Senate without dissenting vote. He remained as director until October 1951, during which period the scientific strength and stature *of this important government agency were greatly enhanced.* Condon discharged his duties with admirable energy and imagination in the face of incessant attacks made upon him by members of Congress, political pundits and professional patriots. Fortunately he enjoyed the full confidence of the military departments and of the Atomic Energy Commission, the proof being the enormous increase in highly classified research and development entrusted to the Bureau while he was director. This work included the development of new test equipment for measuring the properties of atomic bomb explosions, improvement of proximity fuses for use in the Korean war, establishment of a new laboratory in Corona, California, for Navy guided missiles and the setting up of two laboratories in Boulder, Colorado, one for research on thermonuclear weapons, the other for special studies of radio propagation effects vital to the planning and operation of the American radar defense network in northern Canada.

In October 1951 Dr. Condon left the service of the government to become Director of Research and Development of Corning Glass Works. He held this position until his resignation in December 1954, when he returned to Berkeley, California to enter private practice as a consulting physicist and private research worker. Even during his private employment the attacks on him continued. In April 1952 his security clearance was suspended by Navy security officers. This cloud hung over him until April 1954, when a hearing of the entire Condon record was held in New York before the Eastern Industrial Personnel Security Board, under procedures established by President Eisenhower. On July 12, 1954, the Board decreed that Dr. Condon's clearance was "clearly consistent with the interests of national security." News of this verdict first became public on October 19; two days later the Secretary of the Navy ordered suspension of the clearance and "reconsideration" of the verdict by the Board. A Defense Department spokesman inadvertently admitted to the press that Condon's clearance had been revoked because the newspapers had given it publicity.

Condon was president of the American Physical Society in 1946 and president of the largest American scientific body, the American Association for the Advancement of Science, in 1953. His election to the presidency of the AAAS was in part a tribute to Condon's scientific stature, in part an affirmation by the entire scientific community of confidence in his integrity.

I have gone out of my way to set before the reader a few of the main facts involved in Condon's ordeal. I have done this for two reasons: first, because he has been my friend since we served together on the Senate Special Committee, he as scientific adviser and I as its counsel; second, because it is important to make known at every opportunity how well he has served the community and how well he has been repaid for his efforts.

PHYSICS

EDWARD U. CONDON

In 1926, when the principles of quantum mechanics were being discovered, the great Göttingen mathematician, David Hilbert, remarked that "physics is becoming too difficult for the physicists." The particular mathematical difficulties that prompted this witticism have been largely cleared up in the quarter century since then, but little progress has been made in interpreting the fundamental problems of atomic theory; meanwhile, experimentation has opened vast new areas of complexity. On balance, Hilbert's judgment is at least as true today as it was when he made it.

If physics is too difficult for the physicists, the nonphysicist may wonder whether he should try at all to grasp its complexities and ambiguities. It is undeniably an effort, but probably one worth making, for the basic questions are important and the new experimental results are often fascinating. And if the layman runs into serious perplexities, he can be consoled with the thought that the points which baffle him are more than likely the ones for which the professionals have not found satisfactory answers.

The subdivisions of science are somewhat arbitrary. Physics concerns itself with matter and energy in all their general manifestations. It started to develop in a systematic way with the study, by Galileo, Kepler and Newton, of mechanical motions of large bodies. This was only about three centuries ago. Later it became interested in electric and magnetic forces and in the nature of light, including the invisible infrared and ultraviolet radiations and the more recently discovered X rays. It deals with heat and the thermal properties of matter. Up to 1900, most of the study was carried on without regard to specific theories about the atomic constitution of matter. The work of our century has centered upon the development of a highly detailed and quantitative theory of atomic structure, the reworking of all of the older physics in terms of atomic concepts, and the exploration of new fields, particularly the phenomena of nuclear physics, under the guidance and stimulation of the fundamental theoretical ideas.

Physics is closely linked with all other sciences. Astronomy interprets its results according to physical principles and so does geology. Chemistry makes increasing use of the results of modern physics. Whether or not life is ultimately explainable in terms of physical principles alone, living things are made of matter and the biologist must therefore take physical knowledge into account.

Our era is witnessing an unprecedented activity in physics. The number of skilled investigators and the amount of elaborate and refined apparatus at their disposal is greater today than at any other time in the world's history. But despite the vast amount that has been learned there is no indication man is approaching the limits of physical knowledge. The possibilities for investigation are numberless and that is what makes the subject so thrilling to research physicists.

The major discoveries made in the first half of the century suggest the present scope of this science: the quantum character of light energy (Max Planck and Einstein), the theory of relativity (Einstein), the nuclear structure of the atom (Lord Rutherford and Niels Bohr), interpretation of the light-emitting properties of atoms (Bohr), discovery of the wave and probability properties of matter (Prince Louis de Broglie, Erwin Schrödinger and Max Born), of heavy hydrogen (Harold Urey), of the neutron (Sir James Chadwick) and of means of producing artificial transmutations of the elements (Sir John Cockroft and Ernest Walton, Frédéric Curie-Joliot, Enrico Fermi and others). And the discovery of a whole family of new kinds of subatomic things which, unlike "normal" matter, can be created and destroyed (Carl Anderson, Hideki Yukawa, C. F. Powell and others).

The purpose of this essay, then, is to try to take stock of the methods and problems of modern physics. And it must emphasize at the start that, however abstract the ideas may seem, physics at all times endeavors to arrive at a set of principles and concepts which can be used in turn to describe the directly observable events of the material world. We are discussing things which can be made to happen, and which have been seen or otherwise observed to happen, by persons who have built and operated the necessary apparatus with the necessary skill. Since all observations of crucial importance have been repeated and confirmed by different investigators, the possibility of the data being seriously in error because of subjective distortions is extremely small.

Physics is, however, much more than a description of apparatus—how it was built and operated—and of the raw data of observation thus obtained. The interpretive side of the science seeks to relate direct observations to a logical framework of concepts. This framework is periodically revised and extended to bring wider classes of data within its scope. Interpretation is important because it economizes the mental effort needed to provide an accurate and embracing description of the facts, and because it suggests the making of observations in areas never previously studied and devises "crucial" experiments—that is, tests for the validity of alternative conceptual schemes which seem in advance to provide equally good explanations of what is known. In short, theories underly the program of experiments and experiments are used to judge the merit of theories.

The physics of this century has set itself the task of interpreting all observed phenomena in terms of the behavior of atoms and molecules, and the electrical particles—electrons, protons, etc.—of which they are composed. It was characteristic of the older physics that not only were phenomena observed on a scale comparable to the size of our own bodies, but mostly they were discussed according to a conceptual scheme of very much the same scale. It is characteristic of the new physics that, while the observations must necessarily continue to be made with apparatus big enough for our hands to manipulate and our eyes to see, the purpose of the experiments is to supply details about a conceptual scheme disposed on such a fine scale as to be incapable of direct visual observation. It is a scheme which can be pictured only in the mind's eye, using linear magnifications in thought which range from one hundred million to one on up to about one million million to one.

The modern physicist and anyone who would understand what he is up to, must therefore learn to work in two worlds. One is a world of brass and glass and wax and mercury and coils and lenses and vacuum pumps—above all a world of electronic amplifiers and photo-multiplier tubes. The other is a world of visualization and creative imagination, dealing with concepts and constructs appropriate to atomic dimensions (or, in cosmology, to a domain too vast to be encompassed by direct human perception). In this second world the atomic nucleus is a little hard ball, about 10^{-12} cm in diameter;[1] it carries an electric charge and is made up of a number of smaller particles, some having electric charges (protons) and some without electric charge (neutrons). Negatively charged particles (electrons) revolve around their nuclei at distances ten thousand times greater (10^{-8} cm) than the nuclear diameter. The detailed behavior of these electrons accounts for the chemical behavior of the atom, for its light and X-ray emitting and absorbing properties, for its magnetic properties and many other distinguishing qualities.

The first goal of the beginning student is to keep both these worlds in mind at once. He has to learn how the world of direct observation serves as the means of indirect observation and controls his pictures of the atomic world. This problem is particularly difficult for the general reader who merely wishes a reasonably accurate and honest guide to what physicists are thinking. Popular writers, who cannot be sure that their hold on the reader's attention is either firm or lasting, are tempted to offer merely a pictorial account of how things look in the world of nuclei, electrons and quantum jumps. They do not try to give the reader any idea of our methods of direct observation into the world of atomic dimensions. To cover this side as well would double the length of the story and require that the reader be introduced to some highly complicated apparatus.

[1] Throughout this essay negative exponents are used. Thus $10^{-3} = 00.001$; $10^{-7} = 00.0000001$; $10^{-12} = 00.000000000001$.

Physics, perhaps more than any other science, expresses its observations in numerical terms. Measurements and techniques of measurement are never far behind the purely descriptive phase when any new branch of physics is opened up. A specialty within the science, mathematical physics, formulates the laws of physics mathematically and deduces from such general laws special consequences which can be put to the test of experiment. Mathematical analysis is one more stumbling block for the person who would achieve a general understanding of modern physics without going deeply into the subject. Many of the concepts of physics are so closely bound up with the mathematical way of describing them that it is hard to give them any other kind of description. A good example is electron spin. In many respects an electron behaves like a top spinning on its axis, yet the exact spin behavior is very different from that of the tops children play with.

The nineteenth-century physicist sought to interpret the forces acting between electric charges, and between magnets, by postulating a space-filling stuff, the ether, which was imponderable, since solid bodies could move through it freely, but which, nevertheless, could exert forces by the action of tensions along the lines of force and pressures at right angles thereto.[2] The model was like an elastic solid, the behavior of which had already been fully described by mathematical physics, and the plan was to relate electromagnetic phenomena to the already understood behavior of elastic solids.

At first this analogy was taken quite literally, but after a time physicists began to regard it more as a symbol than as a statement of fact. They came to see that the essential thing was the construction of a logical, self-consistent theory of the electromagnetic field, one whose predictions could be checked by detailed quantitative experiments. Such a theory might be aided in its initial stages by reference

[2] The seventeenth-century physicist Christian Huygens, who developed the wave theory of light, was one of the first to postulate the existence of an all-pervasive ether, building on earlier ideas of René Descartes and Robert Hooke. By the end of the nineteenth century all kinds of marvelous properties were attributed to it. This stuff, said Sir Oliver Lodge, can vibrate light, can be "sheared" into positive and negative electricity, forms the matter of the universe by arranging itself in whirls, and "transmits by continuity and not by impact every action and reaction of which matter is capable."

to an elastic solid. But the fact that the two distinct sets of physical phenomena are governed by mathematical equations of nearly the same structure does not justify the conclusion that one of them is the ultimate reality in terms of which the other is to be explained.

Thus, because electromagnetic forces are in many ways analogous to the forces transmitted by stressing special types of elastic solid, it does not follow that electromagnetic forces are "really" transmitted through the agency of such stresses in an all-pervading space-filling solid "ether." Once it is realized that the mental picture of a solid ether is scaffolding rather than the real edifice, a considerable change in outlook occurs. The constructor of theories is no longer bound by the details of the original model. He may depart from it and consider more general viewpoints. He is not merely free to do so, he must do so if he is to be productive.

How then is the theorist to be limited and guided? May he just write down any kind of mathematical relation? No, for he must recognize certain broad principles by which all physics is believed to be governed.

For example, it is generally assumed that, given the same set of circumstances, physical phenomena will happen in the same way tomorrow as they happened today or yesterday. This means that mathematical statements about the laws of physics must not contain any reference to an absolute value of time, such as the total time elapsed since the creation or some other event of basic importance.

Time itself cannot occur as a mathematical variable in the equations, but only differences of time between events related to the phenomena under consideration. The basis for this conclusion is experimental: phenomena do recur in the same way under similar circumstances when the experiments are made on different dates on the calendar.

A little reflection will show that the actual experimental basis for this conclusion is rather slim. Science is so new that most of the matters to which we would like to apply the principle have been under observation for less than a century. How then can we be sure that the laws derived from today's studies have been exactly the same at all times in the past, and will remain so in the indefinite future?

Thus, we estimate the age of rocks by their helium content, supposing this to have accumulated from radioactive disintegrations which occurred over the past billion years at the same rate as today. We cannot prove that the rate has been steady, but, since we know of no reason to assume that it has changed or will change, it is a convenient working hypothesis to assume that it has not and will not.

Similar remarks may be made about the necessity for stating the laws of physics without reference to the absolute position in space, or the orientation in space of the apparatus with which observations are made. These principles of the homogeneity and isotropy[3] of space further limit the kind of mathematical relations that can occur in quantitative descriptions of physical phenomena. They also have some limited, direct empirical validity. But mostly they are assumed to be true because no observations contradict them.

The kind of thinking that gave conscious recognition to such principles was gradually gaining ground before 1905. In that year it received a great impetus from Einstein, who applied it boldly and radically to a new field in his first paper on what is now known as the theory of relativity. The laws of electromagnetic phenomena, as we have just noted, were formulated in terms of the model of an ether somewhat like an elastic solid filling all space. If such a solid had a real existence, then there would be meaning to the question of absolute rest or motion: a body would be said to be absolutely at rest if it were not moving with respect to the ether and its absolute motion would be the direction and speed of its motion relative to the ether.

Lacking some such absolute standard, one may speak only of the relative motion of one body with respect to another, and the idea of absolute rest or motion is devoid of observational content. In the latter part of the nineteenth century, light was regarded as a wave motion propagated in the space-filling solid ether. It was natural on this view to suppose that the content of an optical phenomenon would depend on whether the light-source and the observer of the light were at rest with respect to the ether or moving through it.

A most sensitive experiment designed to test this point is known

[3] A space is isotropic if it possesses the same properties in every direction.

as the Michelson-Morley experiment,[4] first carried out in 1883 and repeated many times thereafter. The apparatus used, an interferometer, is shown schematically in Figure 1. It is rigidly built of steel bars on a stone foundation, but it is floated in a large tank of mercury and can thus be turned easily without suffering distortions or vibration. On this floating platform is mounted a source of light, part of whose ray is made into a parallel beam by the lens D. The parellel beam strikes a thinly silvered mirror at A, and is there split into a reflected beam going to B and a transmitted beam going to C. At B and C these two partial beams are reflected back on themselves by mirrors. They then return through A and are combined in a single beam which strikes the lens E which brings it to a focus for observation. One adjusts the apparatus so that B and C are at the same distance from the mirror A. Suppose now that the apparatus is oriented so that AC is parallel to the direction of motion of the earth through the ether; AB must then be perpendicular to that direction.

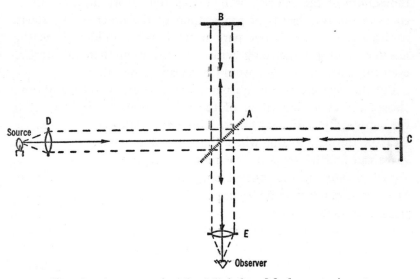

Fig. 1—*Apparatus for the Michelson-Morley experiment.*

[4] Named after its designers, the famous American physicist Albert Abraham Michelson (1852-1931) and the American chemist Edward Williams Morley (1838-1923).

Then according to the theory of wave propagation the travel-time of the beams over the two equal paths should be slightly different, just as if two swimmers were required to swim an equal distance in a swiftly flowing river, one across and back, the other, downstream and back. The cross-river swim would not take as long as the up and downstream journey (because what the swimmer gains in time going downstream is more than offset by what he loses coming back) and, similarly, it was supposed that the two beams of light, one traveling with the earth's motion through the ether, and the other at right angles to its motion relative to the earth, would not arrive at the same time at the end of their journey. Since it was not known which was the direction of the earth's motion through the ether, the observations in the actual experiment were made with the apparatus turned in various directions in the laboratory; besides, the laboratory itself was turning in space with the rotation and annual orbital motion of the earth. The expected effect would of course be small because the speed of the earth in its orbit is only one ten-thousandth of the velocity of light and the theory indicates differences in the two speeds of propagation of the order of the square of this quantity or only one part in one hundred million. Nevertheless the apparatus was built with such precision that an effect of even this small magnitude would be clearly observable.[5]

But the experiment, though many times repeated and many times checked, gives no indication of the earth's motion with respect to the supposedly stationary ether. This result flatly contradicted the ideas of the period. But when the concept of absolute motion in space can find no support in careful and repeated observations designed to detect it, the concept not only becomes of doubtful value to physics, but may even be responsible for wrong conclusions and the frustration of progress.

Einstein was bold enough to recognize that all the contradictions could be removed by postulating as a basic law of nature that the velocity of light must appear the same to all observers irrespective of the state of motion of one observer relative to another. This was

---

[5] In the difference in position of the so-called interference fringes, alternate bright and dark bands, produced by the rejoining of light waves.

certainly a clear-cut statement of the experimental evidence. But it was a statement which defied the mathematics of electromagnetism as then developed and, certainly again, that mathematics had a good deal of truth in it, for it was being used successfully to design electrical equipment.

Einstein showed that the difficulties were related to uncritical assumptions in the basic technique of space and time measurements. Length measurements in the simplest instance are made by laying a rigid measuring rod alongside the space interval to be measured. Time measurements are made by noting the readings of a clock at the beginning and end of the time interval in question. The crux of the problem revolves about the exact way in which two observers, A and B, who are in uniform relative motion with respect to each other, are to compare space and time measurements which they make of the same set of natural phenomena. In particular, they must have some way of comparing their clocks and their measuring rods.

The most direct way of comparing the measuring rods would be for B to send his to A's laboratory and have it laid along A's measuring rod to see if the distance markings correspond. But after this process has been carried out, B's measuring rod has to be accelerated from its state of rest in A's laboratory in order to get it up to the right speed to return it to B's laboratory. We know that forces must be applied to the solid material to speed it up and we have no right to assume that these do not introduce a change in the length of the rod we have just checked. In fact, the Dublin physicist George Francis Fitzgerald and the Dutch physicist H. A. Lorentz independently made the bold assumption that a moving rod contracts in length in the direction of its motion. Although this contraction could be inferred from Clerk Maxwell's theory of electromagnetism and the electrical structure of matter, the concept was regarded as no less fantastic than the Michelson-Morley result, and physicists were reluctant to accept one bizarre notion as explanation of another.

Similar critical remarks might be made about any procedure for comparing B's clock with A's clock, which involved delivering B's clock to A's laboratory in order to compare the rates at which they are running. When after being checked in A's laboratory B's clock is accelerated for the purpose of delivery to B, we have no right to assume that it continues to run at the same rate as it did when it was being checked.

To avoid these critical difficulties, Einstein proposed a way whereby A and B could compare their clocks and measuring rods without actually bringing them together.[6] His method involves the sending of light signals back and forth between the laboratories of A and B while they are in relative motion. In this case the very process of comparing measurements reproduces the arrangements of the Michelson-Morley light-transmission experiments.

But the fact that Einstein's proposal afforded no escape from the dilemma we have been considering was in itself a discovery of the greatest importance. For it supported the conclusion—which was one of Einstein's most striking insights—that *it is inherent in the nature of the measuring process* that the phenomena of propagation of light appear the same to all observers no matter what their state of uniform relative motion. In other words the Michelson-Morley result follows inevitably from the method of the experiment, and even the Lorentz-Fitzgerald concept turns out to be true though the contraction has nothing to do with the ether.

In terms of mathematical relations this can be summed up as follows: A will have done basic experiments and will have deduced from them a set of rules for calculating electromagnetic and optical effects in terms of the space and time intervals which he measures in his laboratory with his equipment. Then B will do the same thing with regard to quantities measured by him in his laboratory and he will find that the mathematical laws describing his observations have the same form in terms of his observed space and time intervals as A found in terms of his.

We describe this property by saying that the laws have an invariance of form with regard to the space and time data of the two relatively moving observers.

These ideas seemed radical and revolutionary at the time. They showed the physicists that they had been guilty of a superficiality in

---

[6] The reader will understand, of course, that we are discussing conceptual, not actual, experiments, and that Einstein's was a theoretical solution of a theoretical problem.

analyzing the process of comparing measurements in two different laboratories in uniform relative motion. This had hitherto been regarded as a matter too obvious for careful procedure.

There was another reason why these ideas were revolutionary. The laws of mechanics, formulated by Isaac Newton in 1660, were regarded as one of the most firmly established parts of physics. The laws of electromagnetism were discovered some two centuries later. Naturally men did not feel as confident of their correctness as they did about Newton's teachings. But the new ideas of Einstein demanded the change and modification, not only of the later laws, but also of Newton's hitherto unchallengeable writ.

The necessary corrections were so small that under ordinary circumstances they had no observable consequences. It was as if men, long believing that certain lines were absolutely straight, were told that they really contained a curvature too slight to be noticed. Still, it is understandable that the situation caused emotional disturbances among physicists; there is a tremendous gap between our ideal of the Perfect and of the Very Slightly Imperfect.

The velocity of propagation of light signals which, according to the experimental evidence, is the same to all observers, is about 186,000 miles a second. That is an extraordinarily great velocity compared with any of the speeds of normal experience, even of the motion of the earth and other planets in their orbits. It turns out that the changes in the old mechanical laws of Newton which were a consequence of Einstein's theory of relativity involved corrections of the order of $(v/c)^2$ where v is the speed of motion of the body being studied and c is the speed of light. For all ordinary experience the difference in the predictions of the two distinct theories was less than one part in a billion, a much smaller quantity than the accuracy or sensitivity with which even the most precise measurements of this kind can be actually carried out. Therefore the difference was of no practical consequence in regular applied mechanics. But the revision of ideas involved was so basic that it became of the utmost importance to devise experiments in which the Newtonian and Einsteinian theories could be submitted to observational test. Because the differences become appreciable only when particles are moving with speeds comparable to that of light (even when a particle is going a tenth the speed of light the difference between the theories is only about one per cent) this required study of the behavior of focused beams of electrons moving in a high-vacuum tube and deflected by electric and magnetic forces. Many such observations supported the Einstein-modified equations of particle mechanics rather than the original laws stemming from Newton.[7]

One consequence of the Einstein equations of motion was the new principle that no body can move faster than the speed of light. The rate of increase of speed of a body when acted on by a constant force is the quotient of the force divided by the mass of the body, which is a measure of its inertia. On Newtonian views the mass is the same at all speeds. On the Einstein view the mass increases with the speed, with the result that the ability of a constant force to increase the speed becomes steadily weaker as the speed increases. At first this effect is very small, but it rapidly becomes a major factor as the particle's speed rises and it completely frustrates the accelerating force when the speed of light is finally attained. Einstein also observed that the increase in inertia of the body was exactly proportional to the increase in its energy of motion; he was thus led to the more general deduction that energy of all forms has inertia and that any system has more inertia when its energy content is increased.

This result had hitherto escaped discovery because, for example, in the most energetic chemical reactions, the decrease in total mass or inertia due to the energy released amounts to only about a billionth part of the whole. But many years later, with the advent of the study of nuclear transformations, the deduction was brilliantly confirmed; for in these drastic processes the energy changes are some million times greater per unit weight of reacting substance, and the

[7] This discussion of Einstein's postulates differs somewhat from the usual popularizations. In more familiar terms and very briefly the two essential assumptions of his special theory are: (1) The velocity of light in a vacuum is constant and independent of the motion of the source, and therefore independent of relative velocity of source and observer; (2) If two systems are in uniform motion with respect to each other, then all phenomena in one system run their course with respect to the other system according to the same laws as with respect to the first; which is to say that all measurements within a system are unaffected by its (unaccelerated) motion, or to put it yet another way, that no measurements conducted entirely within a system will disclose whether or not it is moving.

accompanying changes in mass, of the order a few tenths per cent, are easily observed and of dominating importance to complete understanding.

The energy that is given to an electron in an X-ray tube operating at 500,000 volts is enough to double its inertia. Therefore X rays that are now in daily use in many hospitals are produced by electrons whose behavior is strongly affected by the consequences of the famous $E=mc^2$ formula relating the energy, E, to its equivalent mass m, where c is the velocity of light. Even in the picture tubes of millions of home television receivers, the electrons have about five per cent extra mass due to the energy of motion with which they strike the fluorescent picture screen.

Einstein's successful challenge of Newtonian physics is a sharp reminder that we must keep clearly in mind the actual range of verification of our known physical laws and be prepared to modify our initial formulations when these are proved no longer adequate to describe a wider range of phenomena.

Common sense is prepared for the idea of small and distinct particles moving in ways described by laws of motion such as Newton's or perhaps even Einstein's modification of them. Moving balls, planets and missiles are familiar objects in daily life. Likewise common sense will agree that effects may be propagated from one place to another by an oscillatory train of waves such as those which spread out on the surface of a still pond when a stone is dropped into it. Thus a physical effect may go from one place to another by the flight of a steady stream of projectiles, or it may travel from one place to another by the propagation of waves.

Three centuries ago, when men speculated about the nature of the influence we call light, that which proceeds from a candle to the eye, some believed that the candle projects outward a stream of minute corpuscles of light which fly through space and even through dense transparent materials such as glass. This is the corpuscular theory of light.

Others thought that the influence called light was a wave motion. These waves were supposed to travel in a space-filling material called the luminiferous ether, which was later identified with the space-filling ether presumed to be the means of propagating electric and magnetic effects. This was the wave theory of light.

Newton favored the corpuscular theory, and Christian Huygens, a great Dutch contemporary of his, favored the wave theory.

The shadow of an object in light from a small source is quite sharp (Fig. 2). There is an abrupt break between the surrounding brightness and the cast shadow. This is the pattern to be expected if light consists of a stream of particles moving out from the source in straight lines.

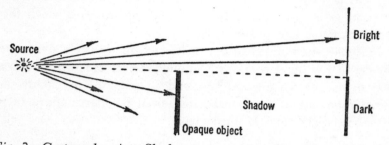

Fig. 2—Corpuscular view: Shadow cast on screen by opaque object has sharp edge if light source is small or very distant.

How waves behave when they encounter an obstacle is familiar to us from observing the ripples on a pond. Water waves are not cut sharply by an obstacle; instead, they bend partially around it and then continue, so that the wave motion can be seen on the side of the obstacle away from the wave source. Thus if light were propagated by wave motion, we should expect the shadows cast by objects to have soft, diffused edges. The observed sharpness of shadow edges seems, therefore, to support the theory that light consists of a stream of particles. This course of reasoning was decisive in leading Newton to reject the wave theory (Fig. 3).

But the problem is not so simple. Experiments performed many years after Newton revealed that the bending of waves into the region behind an obstacle is only noticeable when the obstacle is small compared with the length (distance from crest to crest measured in the direction of travel) of the waves; in the opposite case, where the wave length is small compared to the obstacle, the wave motion is inappreciable and apt to escape detection. In other words if the

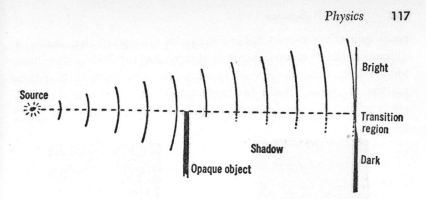

*Fig. 3—Wave view: The shadow does not have a sharp edge, but some
light penetrates into the transition region.*

wave length is small compared to the object casting the shadow—
the most common occurrence—only the most delicate tests will help
clarify the issue between the corpuscular and the wave theory of
light.

When experimental techniques and instruments had been sufficiently refined, a higher level of understanding was attained. Physicists were able to show that light really does bend somewhat into
the shadowed region. The phenomenon is called diffraction. To be
sure, a person who was determined to hold on to his belief in the
corpuscular theory might start speculating that the material of the
opaque screen exerts attractive forces on the light corpuscles that fly
past near the edge of the screen and bends their trajectories into
the region that otherwise would be the dark shadow. But exact and
detailed studies of how much the light is bent into the shadow when
passing objects of various shapes and sizes gave results that could not
be accounted for in this way. On the other hand, they could be
beautifully described according to the theory of wave propagation on
the supposition that light of a particular color consists of waves of a
particular wave length. Blue light on this view has a wave length
of close to 4×10^{-5} cm; red light, at the other end of the visible
spectrum, moves in waves about twice as long. The invisible ultraviolet radiations have a wave length shorter than the violet and
the invisible infrared radiations have wave lengths longer than the
red.

It is the smallness of these wave lengths compared with the million times greater wave lengths for the ripples on a pond that made the diffraction effects more difficult to observe and resulted in their being hidden from the eyes of man so long. Nevertheless, now that these matters are more thoroughly understood, optical effects which directly exhibit the wave nature of light may be easily observed.

Indicating the evenly spaced threads of the weave of silk cloth.

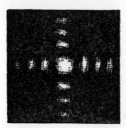

Showing the pattern of light of a distant small source, like a streetlight, observed through such a closely woven cloth. The central image is round and white. The others are elongated and show rainbow colors with the red end away from the central image.

Look at a distant street light through a silk umbrella or a tightly stretched silk handkerchief held several feet in front of the eyes. Instead of seeing only the ordinary direct image of the street light, perhaps a little blurred by scattering in the fabric, you will see two additional series of images extending away from the central direct image in two perpendicular directions. The directions in which these images extend will be easily found to be along the directions of the threads of the fabric.

These additional images are quantitatively explainable on the wave theory of light. The essential thing here is that a wave motion spreads out from the distant street light and impinges on different parts of the fabric so that parts of the wave motion get through to the other side by going through the different regularly spaced openings on the fabric. The ideas involved may be more simply considered if we suppose that the light from the distant source goes through a screen having two very narrow and closely spaced slitlike openings in it as indicated in Figure 4. If one wants to go to the trouble he can make such an opaque screen from a densely-exposed photographic plate, using a razor blade to rule two very narrow slits on it quite close together. The razor blade cuts away a narrow strip of the

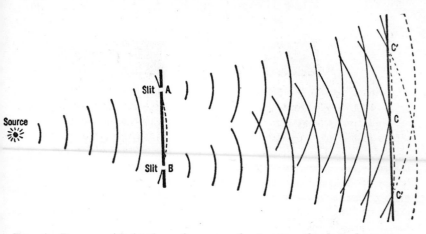

Fig. 4—Passage of light through a screen having two slit-shaped openings.

darkened film and allows the light to get through. When such a plate is used to view a distant light source it will be found that the direct image is also accompanied on each side by several weaker side images in directions at right angles to the direction of the rulings on the plate. Careful observation of the side images either as seen through the silk umbrella or as seen through the two-slit plate will show that the central image is white, but that the side images are colored like the rainbow, with the red end of the spectrum at the end farthest away from the central image.

Now we can return to the consideration of Figure 4. Suppose the screen is set up in such a way that slit A and slit B are at the same distance from source S. This is not essential but simplifies the discussion. Then the crests of waves from S will reach A and B at the same time. On the other side of the screen two new sets of waves will spread out from A and B as new centers and these will be synchronized because they are the result of feeding the new sources A and B with light coming from the source S. Next we have to recognize that what affects any light-detecting device such as the

The central part of the picture shows how a very distant and small source of light appears when viewed through a small rectangular opening held at arm's length from the eyes, the rectangular opening being the shape shown in the lower right-hand corner. Note that there are a whole series of images extending in each direction, and that they are more closely spaced in the direction corresponding to the long dimension of the rectangle. If the picture were reproduced in color it would be seen that the more or less overlapping images of the separate blobs of light away from the central image are colored with the rainbow colors, the red end being farthest away from the central image. Such extra images and dozens of other similar experiments with light going through openings of other shapes are interpreted as indicating that light is propagated as a wave motion.

eye is the resultant amplitude of all the different waves which reach it. Suppose C is a point equidistant from A and B. Then crests of waves from A will arrive at C at the same time as crests from B and will reinforce each other to make bigger waves. Thus we may expect the brightest illumination at C even though it lies within the shadow of the screen between A and B and therefore on the corpuscular view should be dark. Consider now what will be observed at a point C', a little above or below C. In moving from C to C' the distance from B is increased and the distance from A decreased. Suppose, in particular, that C' is so located that the difference between AC' and BC' is exactly half a wave length. Then at C' the crests of waves from A will fall on troughs of waves from B, and the waves will just cancel each other; in other words, assuming light is a wave motion, C' will be dark. Now move C' further up so that the difference between the distances from A and from B is equal to a whole wave length. In this case, again, the crest of each wave from A falls on the crest from B, intensifying the light. As we continue moving up C', it will alternately be light and dark as the differences between the paths is an integral multiple and an integral-and-a-half multiple of a wave length. This special property of waves of reinforcing each other or destroying each other according as crest falls on crest or crest on trough is called interference. It accounts quantitatively for the light images seen through the silk umbrella. For example the reason the red end of the spectrum is farther out than the blue is because the red wave length is greater than the blue; so it is necessary to go farther out to get a half wave length path difference with red light than it is with blue light.

During the nineteenth century a great many special cases of the behavior of light in going through obstacles having one or several holes of different shapes were analyzed carefully both theoretically and experimentally. The results were found to be quantitatively describable in terms of the mathematical theory of wave propagation. Thus the wave theory of light became firmly established: students were taught that light *is* a wave motion and received good marks on examination papers for repeating this back to their professors.

However, new phenomena began to be studied which pointed once more toward the corpuscular theory. Effects which I shall describe pointed strongly to the conclusion that a beam of light consists of a stream of particles of definite size, possessing energy and momentum content. Physicists were thus confronted with two independent sets of evidence. One set gave convincing "proof" that light is a wave motion and the other gave equally convincing "proof" that a beam of light is a stream of corpuscles. Light is emitted and absorbed as if it were a stream of particles but it moves from place to place past obstacles as if it were a wave motion. Clearly there is truth in both models, and a synthesis of the two views into a unified picture is urgently needed. This wave-particle duality is an unsolved dilemma of modern physics.

Before considering detailed effects, let it be observed that on the wave view the intensity of light is connected with the amplitude of swing of the waves; to be specific, it is proportional to the square of the wave amplitude. As a wave spreads out this becomes continuously smaller with consequent reduction in the intensity of the light. On the corpuscular view the energy in the light beam is the total energy of a large number of independently moving corpuscles, called light quanta in modern terminology. The energy carried

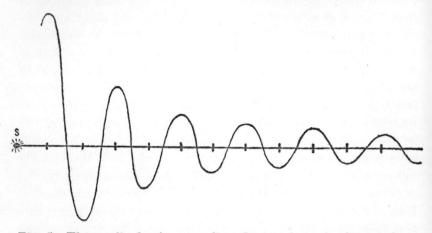

Fig. 5—The amplitude of a wave dies off inversely to the distance from the source as the wave spreads out in all directions. The intensity or brightness of the light is proportional to the square of the amplitude and so falls off with the inverse square of the distance from the source.

by each quantum is always the same—the decrease in intensity of the beam is a consequence only of the decrease in the number of particles crossing unit area in unit time. On one view the energy is continuously spread out over all the space occupied by the light beam; on the other it is localized in small bundles occupying a part of the total space, just as the molecules of a gas at ordinary pressure occupy only about one billionth of the total space which is filled by the gas.

The photoelectric effect gave the first clue to the corpuscular nature of light emission and absorption. If a piece of metal, insulated from the ground, is charged with negative electricity, the charge will leak off through the air when light, especially violet and ultraviolet light, shines on it. In this simple version of the experiment the effects are complicated by the action of the air layers which are absorbed on the metal.[8] Consequently, physicists who wish to study the photoelectric effect enclose the metal in a high-vacuum tube from which the gas can be removed to an extremely low pressure.

The amount of charge which is set free from a metal surface is proportional to the intensity of the light falling on it. This fact is explainable either on wave or corpuscular views. But it is found that the leakage of negative charge from the metal comes about through the ejection by the light of negatively charged electrons. Measurements of the speed of ejection of these electrons show that the energy with which they are ejected is approximately inversely proportional to the wave length of the light used. Actually the energy of motion of the liberated electrons is a little less than such a rule would imply. Einstein in 1905 pointed out that this experimental result could be most simply understood if one supposed that the light energy was absorbed in definite quanta of energy, the energy of one quantum going to the individual act of liberating one electron. The energy of one quantum was taken to be hc/λ, where h is a coefficient known as Planck's constant, c is the velocity of light and λ is the wave length of the light. The observed energy of motion of the freed electron is less than this by an approximately constant amount because a part of the energy supplied by the light quantum is used up in releasing the electron from the attractive forces which normally bind it within the metal.

Similar effects are observed when X rays are used instead of light to cause the ejection of electrons. The quantum effects are even more pronounced because the X-ray wave lengths are approximately ten thousand times smaller than those of visible light and therefore the energy in an X-ray quantum is some ten thousand times greater than in a visible light quantum. But because the wave lengths are so

[8] Although qualitative effects are easily demonstrated with the experiment done in air, exact measurements of the motion of the electrons ejected by the light require that the metal be enclosed in a vacuum tube, both because of chemical actions of the gas of the air, especially moisture, on the metal which strongly change its ability to emit electrons, and also because if gas is present the electrons very quickly become scattered and attached to gas molecules, making it difficult to observe the speed with which they are thrown out.

much smaller, it was for a long time impossible to observe, in the case of X rays, the diffraction and interference effects which give us our most decisive criterion for the wave nature of visible light.

It happens, however, that the wave length of X rays is just about the same as the distance between the layers of atoms in layers in the regular arrangements that occur in crystals such as those of quartz or rocksalt. This means that interference effects such as those described for light going through the silk umbrella are observed when a beam of X rays is scattered by falling on a crystal. Instead of the scattered radiations going out from the crystal more or less equally in all directions, they are scattered only in certain specific directions. These directions are determined by relations between the X-ray wave length and the spacing of atoms in the crystal. Thus the effect can be used with a known crystal to determine the wave length of X rays from a variety of sources. Or it can be used the other way round—to discover with X rays of known wave lengths exact information about the arrangement of atoms in crystals whose geometry is not known. This diffraction of X rays by the orderly arrangement of atoms in crystals was discovered in 1912 by Max Von Laue. In such work the scattering is effected by electrons that are relatively securely bound to the atoms of which the crystal is made.

In 1922 Arthur H. Compton discovered another characteristic of the scattering of X rays by matter. He noticed, particularly when high energy X rays are scattered by lighter elements such as carbon, that the wave length of the deflected X ray is somewhat longer than that of the X ray before deflection, and that the amount of this Compton-shift toward longer wave length increases steadily from zero as the angle of deflection increases. Compton showed that this behavior was exactly what is to be expected from the quantum or corpuscular theory. If the X rays are tied up in quanta of energy, it is natural to suppose that these quanta also carry definite amounts of momentum. When they strike an almost free or loosely bound electron and are scattered, they rebound from it, Compton supposed, according to the same mechanical laws as those governing the collisions of billiard balls. At a very glancing blow the X ray is only slightly deflected in direction and gives up very little energy to the electron with which it collided. When the blow is more central it is deflected through a wider angle and gives up more energy to the struck electron, losing thereby more of its own energy and thus having its wave length increased.

This completed the duality. X rays which—in respect of their being scattered by the tightly bound electrons in the regularly spaced atoms of a crystal—behave like a train of waves of a definite wave length, also behave—in respect of their scattering by loosely bound electrons —as if they were little bundles of energy and momentum rather than continuously spread out waves, these little bundles or quanta obeying the ordinary laws of collision mechanics when they collide with an electron. In order to describe all of the phenomena it is necessary to talk some of the time as if the X rays are a wave motion and some of the time as if they are a stream of particles.

There used to be a joke current among physicists that X rays were to be regarded as waves on Mondays, Wednesdays and Fridays and as quanta on the other days. In point of fact, however, the two aspects are so closely intertwined that no such neat separation of viewpoints can be effected; in Compton's experiments, for example, the scattering in carbon which is described by quantum or corpuscular language is followed by another scattering of the same X rays by a crystal for the purpose of demonstrating that their wave length was altered in the first scattering.

In the first decade of this century it had become clear that the atoms of matter contained small negatively charged particles called electrons. A great deal of attention was being given to the study of the naturally occurring radioactive elements, of which radium is the best known. Radium gives off spontaneously three kinds of radiations: gamma rays, which are a kind of high energy X rays of extremely short wave length; beta rays, which are high speed electrons, and alpha particles, which are now known to be charged particles about 8000 times as massive as the electron.

In 1912 Ernest Rutherford in England performed experiments in which he allowed a beam of alpha particles from radium to fall on a thin gold foil. He wanted to learn something of the forces by which gold atoms deflect the high-energy alpha particles from straight motion through the foil. He found that the alpha particles were sometimes scattered through more than a right angle, occasionally rebounding almost straight back on striking the gold foil. From this he was able to calculate the amount of the force exerted by a gold atom on an alpha particle. The most natural thing was to assume that the force was electrostatic since the ordinary effects of collision could not account for the phenomenon. The gold atom, being neutral, must contain positive electricity as well as the negative electrons which other evidence had shown it to contain; the positive electricity would repel the positively charged particles. Before these experiments were performed there had been a tendency to suppose that the positive electricity was distributed uniformly over a sphere of about the same size as the whole atom. Rutherford's work proved that this was impossible, for if the positive charge were thus spread out it could not exert a strong enough force on the alpha particle to reverse its direction of motion. In brief, the experiments taught that the positive charge must be confined in a tiny particle, about one ten-thousandth the radius of the atom, which Rutherford called the nucleus of the atom.

Thus originated the nuclear atom model which is the basis of all subsequent work in physics. Each atom consists of a central nucleus about 10^{-12} cm in diameter and carrying a positive electric charge, surrounded by enough electrons occupying a sphere roughly 10^{-8} cm in diameter to make the whole entity electrically neutral. The charge of the electron is accepted as 4.80×10^{-10} absolute electrostatic unit; the proton, the charged particle of the nucleus, has a positive charge equivalent to the negative charge of the electron but possesses a mass approximately 1,845 times as great. Different kinds of atoms are characterized by the magnitude of the electric charge on the central nucleus and, correspondingly, by the number of electrons surrounding the nucleus. This is called the atomic number, Z, and ranges from one, for hydrogen, the simplest atom, up to 92 for uranium, and even higher for some of the atoms resulting from artificial transmutations.

Niels Bohr of Copenhagen, then a young research student working with Rutherford, took up the idea of the nuclear atom. He combined it with the idea of emission and absorption of light in quanta, which had come out of photoelectric effect studies, and showed how the characteristic spectrum of colors of light emitted by atoms in electric arcs and sparks could be given detailed and exact interpretation.

To do this he had to make some radical assumptions about the motion of electrons in atoms. These constituted a much more severe break with Newtonian mechanics than the small corrections implied in Einstein's relativity theory of 1905. He assumed that mechanical systems could exist only in certain states of discrete energy values. That is, the atom could have certain "allowed" values of its total energy: contrary to classical mechanics, it was supposed incapable of having a stable existence at other values of the total energy. He supposed that light emission occurred by the giving off of one light quantum when the atom passed in a transition from one stable energy state to another one of lower energy. Thus the wave lengths of the characteristic light, as observed in a spectroscope, were a direct indication of the intervals between the allowed levels.

These ideas were enormously fruitful in interpreting the spectrum of light emitted by atoms. It was soon found that they could be extended to the analysis of X-ray spectra and also to the much more complicated spectra emitted by molecules. From 1912 to 1924 physicists were mainly occupied with working out the implications of Bohr's model. In the course of doing so, they added many exciting new details to the rapidly developing theory. In particular, they discovered electron spin—that electrons behave like little magnets and spinning tops in addition to exerting force by virtue of their negative electric charge.

Nevertheless, as Bohr repeatedly emphasized, the foundations of the development were far from definite, because he had not been able to give rules general enough to determine the allowed energy levels in all cases. Even the calculations on the next simplest atom after hydrogen, that of helium, having two electrons, went wrong.

In 1924, Louis de Broglie made a suggestion in his doctor's thesis in Paris that opened the way for the next great advance. He asked whether the wave-particle duality of light might extend also to the fundamental particles of matter, whether there might be a wave aspect to the energy of electrons, just as there was a by then well-recognized quantum aspect to the wave motion of light. He was not explicit about how an electron is accompanied by or associated with a wave motion. But he did suggest as a tentative hypothesis that the relation between the wave length of these waves and the momentum of the electron was the same as had been established for light and X rays.

The way such a wave motion would limit the atom to particular energies was then to be regarded as similar to the way a violin string of definite length and tension can vibrate only in the particular frequencies known as its fundamental and overtones. The vibrations of the string must be such that an integral number of half wave lengths must be contained in the length of the string. Two years later Erwin

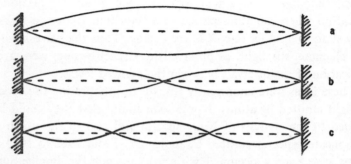

Fig. 6—Forms assumed by a vibrating string vibrating at its fundamental frequency (a) and its first two overtones (b) and (c). In (a) the frequency is such that the string's length equals exactly one half wave length; in (b) and (c) the length is equal to two and three half wave lengths respectively. For a uniform string the frequency of (b) is exactly twice that of (a), so musically it is one octave higher. Other relations hold if the string is nonuniform.

Schrödinger, then of Zürich and now of Dublin, gave a more specific and precise mathematical formulation of De Broglie's wave ideas. This summary went beyond Bohr's original formulation and was quickly found to accord with experiments in situations where Bohr's earlier formulations had gone astray.

Soon thereafter C. J. Davisson and L. H. Germer in New York and G. P. Thomson in England independently performed crucial experiments on the scattering of high-energy beams of electrons by crystals which directly confirmed the wave nature of the electron by showing that the electrons are scattered in only certain definite directions and that these are the ones to be expected from the scattering of the De Broglie waves from a crystal. And again a short time later, experiments performed by Otto Stern in Hamburg proved that protons, the positive nucleus of the hydrogen atom, were also scattered like waves from crystals. Thus the wave character of atomic particle behavior was firmly established.

Another mathematical consequence of the difference between the behavior of particles and waves proved to be the key to understanding the radioactive disintegration of natural radioactive materials such as radium, uranium and thorium. In classical particle mechanics the actions of forces on the particle may be described by giving its potential energy at each position in space. To this must be added the particle's kinetic energy to find its total energy, which remains constant throughout the motion of the particle. The kinetic energy is proportional to the square of the particle's velocity and is therefore essentially positive. It follows classically that a particle cannot move to a place where its potential energy is greater than its total energy, for this would require the kinetic energy to be negative. However the mathematics of wave propagation introduces departures from this rule. The rule is still approximately true in that the wave does not get very far into the classically forbidden region, the potential barrier, but the essential point is that it can do so.

This gives rise to a characteristic feature of atomic or quantum mechanics which was applied in 1928 independently by E. U. Condon and R. W. Gurney in Princeton and George Gamow in Göttingen to a quantitative interpretation of the way in which alpha particles are ejected from the nuclei of radioactive materials such as radium. This interpretation clinched the wave theory for nuclear particles and provided the first detailed theoretical interpretation of any dynamic feature of the behavior of atomic nuclei.

Figure 7 is a graph relating the energy of interaction of an alpha particle with the rest of the nucleus to the particle's distance from the rest of the nucleus. The scale of ordinates (vertical scale) is in MEV units, that is, million electron volts, where one million electron volts is the energy acquired by an electron in falling freely through a potential drop of one million volts; the scale of distance, on the abscissas (horizontal scale), is in units of 10^{-12} cm.

At distances greater than about one of these units the entire en-

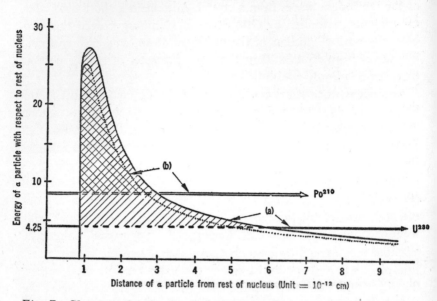

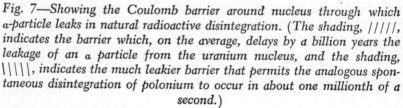

Fig. 7—*Showing the Coulomb barrier around nucleus through which α-particle leaks in natural radioactive disintegration. (The shading, /////, indicates the barrier which, on the average, delays by a billion years the leakage of an α particle from the uranium nucleus, and the shading, \\\\\, indicates the much leakier barrier that permits the analogous spontaneous disintegration of polonium to occur in about one millionth of a second.)*

ergy of interaction consists of the electrostatic repulsion between the alpha particle and the rest of the nucleus, both of which are positively charged. Curve (a) portrays the interaction with uranium, curve (b) with polonium; the latter curve is lower because the rest of the nucleus of polonium has 82 charge units after emitting n alpha particle, against 90 in the case of uranium.

At distances less than one unit, strongly attractive forces come into play. These counteract the electric repulsion and cause a sharp diminution in the energy of interaction as shown by the almost vertical descent of the two curves. The over-all energy barrier is sometimes called the Coulomb barrier because it is mainly the result of electrostatic repulsions of the kind first quantitatively studied by the French physicist Charles A. Coulomb late in the eighteenth century.

The energy of emission of an alpha particle from uranium 238 is known to be 4.25 MEV, indicated in the figure by a straight line at this level. According to classical mechanics a particle possessing this energy could either exist inside the nucleus, or outside at distances greater than 6.2 units, where the total energy exceeds the barrier height, but could not exist in the region between (where the line is dashed), where the total energy is less than the barrier height. Classically a particle situated inside would simply oscillate back and forth making about 10^{21} collisions a second with the inside surface of the nucleus.

But according to wave mechanics, such a particle has an extremely small, but nevertheless quantitatively calculable probability of escaping—about one chance out of 10^{36} at each collision with the wall. Another way of saying this is that the particle will have to make 10^{36} tries to have a probable single success of slipping through; and since there are 10^{21} collisions per second, it will take 10^{36-21} or 10^{15} seconds of oscillations, on the average, for the liberating event to happen.[9]

It is as if the alpha particles were patrons of a gambling house in Las Vegas, each playing the slot machine 10^{21} times a second. Imagine the machines, which are aptly dubbed one-armed bandits, so rigged that the jackpot comes up on the average only once in 10^{36} times of play. Then any one player can look forward to pulling the handle 10^{15} seconds (on the average)—about a billion years—before hitting the jackpot. Of course the jackpot pay-off for an alpha particle patron is to be thrown out of the gambling house at a terrific speed.

In the case of polonium 208, the energy of the alpha particle is more than twice as great (8.95 MEV) and the barrier is lower, so the chance of penetration is about 10^{23} times larger. In consequence atoms of this kind have an average life before disintegrating of only one ten-millionth of a *second* instead of the billion *years* of geologic time represented in the average life of an atom of uranium 238.

These researches were the basis of a new system of mathematical principles. It was called wave mechanics by some and quantum mechanics by others, the latter term being more commonly used now-

[9] Here the argument rests on very roughly stated numbers, but actually it can be carried out to give quite accurate agreement with experiment.

adays. Either term refers to the mathematical apparatus that describes the structure and behavior of atoms, molecules and nuclei, and which has arisen from the strange combination of wave and particle ideas whose development has just been sketched in outline. Many persons contributed to the full mathematical development, most prominent among them, perhaps, being P. A. M. Dirac of Cambridge, England and John Von Neumann of Princeton.

Physicists now had a set of rules by which they could compute marvelously correct answers to definite questions, yet none of them felt very comfortable about the real meaning and significance of the rules he was using. I remember one day in 1928 when Professor Bergen Davis of Columbia said to me, "I don't think you young fellows understand it any better than I do. You just all stick together and say the same thing!"

The deeper meaning of the wave-particle duality remained as much a puzzle as ever. In 1927 Max Born, then of Göttingen, supplied the interpretation which has been in use ever since—although some physicists believe that it is no more than a makeshift which must eventually be supplanted by a more basic truth. This was Einstein's position.

On Born's view, we may picture light and electrons and other such entities as "really" particles, but particles whose behavior is entirely different from those considered in classical mechanics such as tennis balls or the moon. Born sees the behavior of a particular particle as indeterminate. We are unable to follow its motion in detail. The most we can do is to calculate the numerical values of certain relative probabilities. These probabilities are to prefigure the possible ways of behavior, under observation, of a large number of particles; in other words the arithmetic is to tell us what we can expect to see. Thus, the wave motion aspect of the theory is interpreted as a device for predicting the relative likelihood of different things happening: where the wave motion is intense, the particles are more likely to be found.[10]

[10] In atomic experiments the observations are always made on the behavior of large groups of particles. The results are therefore statistical, which is to say large numbers of the more probable events are seen, fewer of the less probable. The pattern resembles that of observations of a human population; for example, if there is a greater probability of death from heart disease than tuberculosis, the annual sta-

This interpretation joins on smoothly with classical mechanics in the following way. When wave or quantum mechanics is applied to large particles the characteristic diffraction and potential barrier penetration effects of quantum mechanics become negligibly small and the probability rules predict that the particles will almost certainly behave as they do in classical mechanics.

Soon after Born put forward the probability interpretation, Niels Bohr and Werner Heisenberg provided an analysis of how one might attempt the study of an atomic particle's motion with the same thoroughness as can be applied to the observations of the moon. The analysis led to a startling conclusion. Classical mechanics requires that we know at the outset the initial position and velocity of each particle present, if we are to calculate the subsequent motion of each of them. Now to find the position of an electron one must shine light on it and try to see where it is by observing where the light is scattered. Owing to the wave nature of the light this procedure is capable of localizing the electron only to a degree determined by the wave length of the light used. To get greater accuracy one would then tend to use light of shorter wave length. But when short wave lengths are scattered by an electron they cause it to recoil irregularly, as we noted in connection with the Compton effect. This recoil introduces an uncontrollable inaccuracy in our measurement of the electron's initial velocity. In other words, the very act of observation of the electron's position destroys in some degree the accuracy of our knowledge of its velocity.

This analysis explains why a statistical interpretation, characterized by uncertainty, is forced upon us; it is an inescapable consequence of the fact that the thing observed reacts to the means we use to observe it. To avoid the reaction one must refrain from observation; then one remains ignorant of what happened. Statistical uncertainty

---

tistics of cause of death will show that more persons have in fact succumbed to heart disease than tuberculosis. But an important distinction must be noted between the statistics of human and particle populations. In mortality tables, the probabilities of death from various causes are in the first instance based upon observed frequencies; but in the probability estimates of quantum mechanics, the probabilities are initially inferred from fundamental theory, and later interpreted (and confirmed) as relative frequencies of occurrence in a large ensemble of observations.

seems to be the price that must be paid for gaining any knowledge at all.

For a quarter century physicists have been warding off this conclusion; it is both so important and so unsatisfying that they are reluctant to accept it until every possible alternative has been refuted. No way out has yet been found. As of today we simply do not know whether the statistical interpretation of the wave-particle duality is inescapable because basic, or whether it will be discarded in some future theory which is fully deterministic.

Many physicists in the past quarter century have been busy working out the consequences of the ideas we have been discussing.

First, the detailed analysis of visible and X-ray light-emitting properties of atoms was almost completed. Immense amounts of precise experimental data have been closely correlated with exact theoretical predictions.

Second, the same ideas were applied to the more complex task of interpreting light-emitting properties of molecules. This too is in satisfactory shape and continues to be studied in detail because it yields precise information applicable to chemistry.

Third, the ways in which atoms are bound together to form solids came to be better understood. This is particularly true of the electrical properties of solids, of why metals conduct electricity easily and why materials like paraffin and quartz do not, and why some metals, notably iron, are easily magnetized. Physics has discovered and coped with the properties of solids called semi-conductors (silicon and germanium are good examples) which on contact with metals pass electricity easily in one direction but not in the other.

The barrier leakage interpretation of natural radioactivity has proved an important innovation. It pointed the way to obtaining artificial nuclear transmutations with electrical machines limited to several hundred thousand volts, whereas earlier it was thought that machines of a capacity of several million volts would be required. The experiment was tried in 1932 by Cockroft and Walton in Cambridge, England. When they directed a beam of protons which had been accelerated with a voltage of 500,000 volts against a target of metallic lithium, they detected what seemed to be high-energy alpha particles like those from radium coming out of the target. Alpha particles were known to be the high-speed nuclei of helium atoms, and the simplest explanation of the observation was that a hydrogen atom had reacted with a lithium atom to produce two helium atoms: in other words, a real transmutation of the elements such as had been for centuries the goal of medieval alchemists.

Nuclear physics received two other great boosts that year. One was the discovery of the neutron by James Chadwick in England. The other was the discovery of the heavy isotopic form of hydrogen, now called deuterium, by Harold Urey of the University of Chicago, then at Columbia University.

The neutron is a particle (possessing wave characteristics as do, apparently, all particles) whose mass is almost equal to that of the proton, or nucleus, of the simple hydrogen atom, but differs from it in having no electric charge. Discovery of the neutron made it clear that atomic nuclei are compounds of tightly bound protons and neutrons. The word nucleon is now used as a generic term for either protons or neutrons, the constituent particles of every atomic nucleus. Thus the complete picture of the atom emerged, along lines already indicated (see page 126): a central nucleus which is a tight core of protons and neutrons is surrounded by electrons in a larger space. The chemical nature of the atom is determined by its atomic number, Z, which is both the number of protons in the nucleus and the number of electrons outside the nucleus; the weight of the atom is given approximately by the number, called A, which represents the sum of the protons and neutrons in each nucleus. (The electrons are not counted in A because their weight is negligible.)

The number of neutrons in the nucleus contributes to the over-all weight of the atom but has hardly any effect on the chemical properties. So different kinds of atoms which have the same atomic number but different atomic weights are said to be *isotopes* of the same element. The simplest example is that of hydrogen. Ordinary abundant hydrogen has $Z = 1$ and $A = 1$, that is, its nucleus is simply a proton. The heavy kind, which Urey discovered in 1932, is nearly identical chemically with ordinary hydrogen because its $Z = 1$; but for this isotope $A = 2$, indicating that its nucleus consists of a binary compound of one neutron and one proton. In still another kind of hydrogen, called tritium, $Z = 1$, but $A = 3$, because its nucleus is a compound containing one proton and two neutrons.

Chemists are accustomed to designate the different elements by symbols. Thus they write Li to represent one atom of lithium and Na to denote one atom of sodium. Physicists interested in nuclear work use the same symbol to designate an atom or a nucleus, usually attaching the Z value as a subscript and the A value as a superscript. Thus they write Li_3^7 for one atom of the particular isotope of Lithium $(Z = 3)$ whose A is equal to 7. Such a nucleus has three protons and four $(7-3)$ neutrons.

In terms of this notation the reaction studied by Cockroft and Walton in their pioneer researches in 1932 would be written:

$$H_1^1 + Li_3^7 = He_2^4 + He_2^4$$

This means that some at least of the high speed protons on striking a lithium atom on the target in the proper way penetrate the nucleus, momentarily creating an unstable melange of four protons and four neutrons, which is just the stuff necessary to make two helium nuclei. These in turn group together and promptly fly apart. In such a violent process the electrons get knocked off, but later when the atoms produced come to rest they will manage to pick up some stray electrons and become normal neutral atoms again.

Concurrently with these advances in nuclear physics, experimental means were developed for making precise measurements of the masses of the different kinds of atoms, using an instrument known as a mass spectrograph. This made possible the full quantitative verification of Einstein's 1905 prediction that mass and energy were equivalent.

The operation of this instrument is rather neat. There are many kinds of mass spectrographs but all have in common a highly evacuated tube which can be placed partly between the poles of a magnet producing a uniform magnetic field. Figure 8 shows a schematic drawing of the type spectrograph developed by A. J. Dempster of the University of Chicago. An electric discharge in the ion source con-

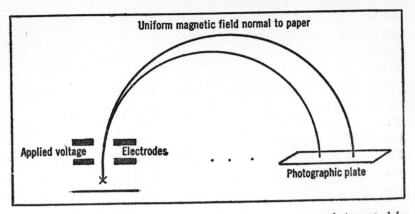

Fig. 8—Schematic diagram of one type of mass spectograph invented by Arthur J. Dempster of the University of Chicago.

verts gas atoms into ions[11] which are then accelerated by applying a proper electric voltage between the two electrodes, each containing a slit, just above the ion source. The ions which have been thus accelerated then move in the main part of the vacuum tube in a magnetic field which, in the diagram, is at right angles to the plane of the page. The action of the magnetic field causes the ions to travel in semi-circular paths, ions of larger mass moving in larger circles. By careful measurement of the radii of curvature of the paths, the applied voltage, and the magnetic field strength, a precise determination can be made of the mass of the different ions.

In the experiment in which pairs of helium nuclei are produced when hydrogen ions (protons) bombard lithium, the measured energies of motion of the two helium ions are much greater than the 0.5 million electron volts of energy of motion of the accelerated hydrogen ions. In fact their energy measured 17.06 MEV (million electron volts). But it was also known from mass spectrograph work that the mass of two helium atoms is less than the sum of the mass of a hydrogen atom and of a lithium-7 atom. Here are the figures, expressed in units such that the abundant isotope of oxygen is arbitrarily set exactly equal to 16:

[11] An ion is an atom either deficient in electrons or possessing more than its normal share; in this state the atom is not electrically neutral, being either positively or negatively charged, depending on the defect or excess of electrons.

Mass of		H_1^1	1.00812
Mass of		Li_3^7	7.01822
	Sum		8.02634
Mass of two		He_2^4	8.00780
Mass loss in reaction			0.01854

According to Einstein's rule, one such unit of mass is equivalent to 931 MEV and therefore this mass decrease must correspond to the release of 17.26 MEV, which checks with the observed energy of the helium ions (within the range of experimental uncertainty of measurement).

In the early nineteen-thirties many atomic masses were very accurately measured and the energy of products of many nuclear reactions became known. Thanks to this work detailed and exact verification of Einstein's idea became commonplace. One of my most vivid memories is of a seminar at Princeton when a graduate student was reporting on researches of this kind and Einstein was in the audience. Einstein had been so preoccupied with other studies that he had not realized that such confirmation of his early theories had become an everyday affair in the physical laboratory. He grinned like a small boy and kept saying over and over, "Ist dass wirklich so?" Is it really true? as more and more specific evidence of his $E = mc^2$ relation was being presented.

Now that literally hundreds of nuclear reactions have been examined in great detail, a wealth of remarkable facts has been uncovered. It has been learned, for example, that some of the reactions go well only if the particles hit each other at the right relative speed. In general, the yield of such reactions goes up as the bombarding energy is increased, but in these cases a small increase in bombarding energy above the key value will greatly decrease the yield. This phenomenon is known as resonance and finds its theoretical explanation in the wave nature of the nuclear particles, according to ideas developed by Gregory Breit of Yale University and Eugene Wigner of Princeton.

Although reactions with lighter elements can be made to go with machines producing voltages of less than a million, more powerful equipment is needed for study of analogous reactions in the heavier elements. That is because the greater electrical charges on their nuclei produce stronger forces of repulsion. The discoveries about the lighter elements acted as a compelling stimulus to the building of such machines. The cyclotron, invented by Ernest Lawrence, of the University of California, is the best known.

An important by-product of this work was the discovery that many nuclear reactions produce unstable isotopes whose instability manifests itself in radioactivity. In this way it is possible to produce small quantities of a radioactive isotope of nearly every chemical element and these have become important tools for study of chemistry.

In the Cockroft-Walton bombardment of lithium by hydrogen, more energy is given off in the resulting helium, as we have noted, than was in the original proton, but this source of energy has no practical significance: no way is known to aim the accelerated protons so that every one of them makes a direct hit on a lithium nucleus. The vast majority of the nuclear bullets fail to score and therefore there is no over-all gain in energy in such an apparatus, even though there is a large gain in the case of the particular protons that make the right kind of hit.

But in 1938 in Berlin Otto Hahn and Lise Meitner made a fateful discovery of a new kind of nuclear reaction which releases enormous quantities of energy. When they allowed a beam of neutrons to fall on a uranium compound, they found in the resulting material a large variety of radioactive isotopes of chemical elements having about half the atomic weight of the original uranium. From this they inferred that the uranium atoms captured some of the incident neutrons and became highly unstable, splitting apart into roughly equal fragments. Uranium consists principally of two isotopes, $A = 238$ and $A = 235$, so the fragments would be atoms in the general range $A = 100$ to 130. From the known masses it was at once evident that the fragments would have a great deal more energy than the original uranium atom and the neutron which struck it. Later experiments showed that the energy release was about 200 MEV for each uranium atom split.

The process was called fission. It began to be intensively studied for its fundamental interest in several laboratories and soon it was discovered that, besides the larger fragments, several neutrons were released for each uranium atom split. These in turn could split more uranium atoms, releasing more neutrons, and so on, giving the possibility of a violent explosion. The result is the atomic bomb, now part of the armament of several nations. When such reactions are suitably controlled they will also release energy in forms that can be used to generate electric power.

Other developments in the theory of light elements showed that reactions which build elements like carbon and oxygen from hydrogen are the primary source of the energy given off by the sun and other stars. Details of this grand synthesis were worked out by Hans Bethe of Cornell. Recently some of the same ideas have been used to produce military weapons of much greater power (equivalent to more than ten million tons of TNT) than the atomic bombs based on uranium fission.

The program which today occupies nuclear physicists consists in part of filling in gaps of knowledge in familiar areas, in part of coming to grips with new fundamental problems. A major task is to determine exactly all the properties of atomic nuclei—not merely their masses but also their magnetic strength and their behavior in regard to emission of gamma rays and in various transmutation reactions. Another question of the first importance centers on the nature of the forces which hold nucleons together in a complex nucleus. It is recognized that these forces are not like any previously known. They are not electromagnetic or gravitational, but of a specifically new kind.

Nucleons, as I have indicated, consist of protons—positively charged particles—and neutrons—possessing no electric charge. The protons repel each other because they have like charges, and the neutrons are unaffected by electrical forces. Yet despite this electrical arrangement which should result in disintegration of the nucleus, the particles are in fact very tightly bound together. One infers, therefore, that there are strong cohesive forces at work in a nucleus, which are not electrical in character, at least not in the ordinary sense. That is, while they may be related to electromagnetic effects, they do not manifest themselves as do the usual repulsions and attractions between charges, varying as the inverse square of the distance between them. It has been observed that these forces are especially strong in binding together a pair of protons and a pair of neutrons to make the very stable alpha particle or nucleus of the helium atom. And it is known also that the forces are "short-range" in effect: although they are very strong when the interacting particles are within a distance of 10^{-12} cm (or less) of each other, they become negligibly weak outside this range, so that the nucleons in a large nucleus exert strong forces on their nearest neighbors but do not appreciably affect the nucleons on the other side of the nucleus. The exact mathematical law of the dependence of the forces on the distance between the interacting particles is not known. These are among the matters being studied energetically in laboratories all over the world.

Besides the electrons, protons and neutrons of ordinary matter, other kinds of particles have been discovered which have transient existences in our laboratory apparatus.

First there is the "neutrino," an affectionately diminutive Italian word which means little neutron. The evidence for its existence is far from being as complete or convincing as one would like.

Some radioactive atoms are called beta-emitters. They emit a high speed electron from the nucleus when they undergo transformation into the next higher element. As we do not think there are any electrons in the nucleus, we must suppose that a neutron changes itself into a proton and an electron in this process.

Both before and after transformation the atoms involved seem to be all alike, in respect of their mass which is a measure of their total energy content. Now according to the principle of conservation of energy the difference in energy of the initial atom minus that of the final atom ought to be the energy observed to be carried off by the emitted particle. But the remarkable thing is that the emitted electrons do not all come out with this same definite amount of energy, but show a wide statistical spread in their energies of motion. One supposes therefore that there were really two particles emitted in each spontaneous disintegration of this type and that the total available energy is divided between them in different ways in different specific instances of disintegration. One of these particles is the observed electron and the other is the hypothetical unobserved neutrino. It is postulated that the neutrino has the necessary properties to account for the strange fact that it is able to penetrate the walls of the apparatus and escape detection: that is, that it has no electric charge and no mass. Thus the neutrino, if it can be said to exist, reveals itself by the absence elsewhere (in the electron) of the energy it is supposed to have appropriated rather than by any direct evidence of its presence. We know it exists in the same way that we know of the existence of burglars who are successful but not caught.

Second, there is the positron. This particle is like the electron, but positively charged. It has only a transient existence, for when a positron collides squarely with an electron they mutually annihilate each other, the total energy which is inherent in their mass being transformed into two quanta of high energy X rays. Alternatively, if the positron collides with an electron that is attached to an atomic nucleus, the electron and positron may annihilate each other with the emission of only one gamma ray quantum, the momentum of recoil being taken up by the atomic nucleus.

The energy needed to bring a positron into existence is about 500 kev. (One kev. is the energy gained by an electron on falling freely through a potential difference of one kilovolt.) There is no evidence that electric charge can be made from nothing, so when a positron is created, an electron must be created at the same time; thus the total charge involved in the created electron-positron pair is zero.[12] The total energy needed to generate such a pair is about one million electron volts or 1,000 kev.

[12] Perhaps an additional word of clarification is needed on this point. Electric charges of opposite tendency are by convention called either positive or negative. This convention is then elaborated in mathematical treatment. The advantage of representing opposite charges by numbers of opposite algebraic sign is easily understood. For with this method the force between two charged bodies can in all cases be written as proportional to the product of the individual charges. Thus the fact that like charges, whether positive or negative, repel each other with a force proportional to their product, is conveniently expressed in the algebraic rule that the product of two numbers of like sign is positive. No processes have ever been observed in which there is a change in the total algebraic amount of electric charge present. This is to say that electric charge can neither be created nor destroyed. If an electron is created by some physical action, it is always accompanied by a counterbalancing positron, of equal and opposite charge, so that the net result is to leave unchanged the algebraic balance sheet, or, in physical terms, the net amount of electric charge in the world.

Positron and electron pairs are generated as one of the processes which occur when X rays having quantum energies in excess of one million electron volts go through matter. Likewise, when high energy electrons go through matter they may interact with nuclei in such a way that positron-electron pairs are created by materialization of some of the incident electrons' energy of motion.

Positrons were discovered in cosmic rays by Carl Anderson at Pasadena in 1932. Since then a great deal has been learned experimentally and theoretically about the details of their generation and annihilation. These processes afford the first direct experimental evidence that the total number of particles of each kind in the universe is not constant—except in the case of light quanta, which are believed to be created and destroyed in the light-emitting and absorbing process.

Third, there are mesons. Several kinds of these particles are found, some positive, some negative and some neutral, and having various masses of the order of two hundred times the mass of the electron and therefore about one-tenth the mass of the proton. The name meson was chosen to indicate their intermediate character with regard to mass between electrons and protons.

Mesons occur in cosmic rays, being produced in the upper atmosphere by high-energy particles from interstellar space which make up the primary beam of cosmic ray particles. Mesons transform spontaneously into each other with emission of gamma rays in a complicated series of processes which is not yet fully worked out.

With the construction of high-energy particle accelerators giving particle energies in excess of 300 million electron volts, it has been possible to produce mesons in the laboratory in far larger quantities than occur in cosmic rays, so that knowledge of their properties is now being accumulated at a rapid rate.

The existence of mesons was first postulated on theoretical grounds by H. Yukawa in Japan in 1935, before their discovery in cosmic rays. Yukawa suggested their existence to explain certain features of the forces between protons and neutrons, and they are today believed to play an important role in that way. But our knowledge of the relation between free mesons, and those which may play such a role inside stable nuclei is still quite meager.

I have devoted a large part of this essay to nuclear research because in recent years it has been the major field of interest in fundamental physics. But it would be wrong to suppose that all progress in that science has been confined to one branch. On every front work has been done to improve our understanding and control over the properties of matter. The fascinating phenomenon known as superconductivity has been intensively studied. Superconductivity is a property of certain metals whereby they lose all their electrical resistance at very low temperatures, so that currents induced in them seem to flow indefinitely; at the same time the metals in this state become almost impermeable with respect to magnetic forces. Technical devices of great importance have been devised—among them the means of generating elecric waves of a few centimeters' wave length, and the electron microscope for seeing detail much finer than is possible with light.

Beyond X-ray diffraction and electron diffraction, physicists have developed the technique of using diffraction of a beam of neutrons falling on a crystal as another powerful tool for studying how atoms are arranged in crystals and in molecules. Radioactive by-products from uranium reactors have been perfected as tools of research in chemistry and biochemistry and radiations from such man-made sources are being used in cancer therapy.

A vast amount of progress has been made, and a vast amount more remains to be made. There was probably never such an exciting period in the history of the science. Physics today is lavishly supported because of the military importance of many of its findings. It has suddenly become a popular science, an object of national interest and concern. This official solicitude has created a host of difficulties, some intruding harshly into the lives of scientific workers, some affecting the very course of research. Not a few scientists, especially in the United States, are concerned lest huge government grants and contracts distort the direction and emphasis of studies in physics. At any rate it is clear that physics in the near future will run out of neither problems nor money.

Summary of the Particles of Atomic Physics

The important particles of atomic physics are summarized below for convenient reference. The mass of the particle is given in units of the electron mass which is 9.107×10^{-28} gram. The charge is given relative to the magnitude of the electron charge which is 1.602×10^{-19} coulomb.

The mass-energy relation of Einstein, $E = mc^2$, is conveniently expressed in laboratory units by expressing the energy in million electron volts (MEV), one MEV being the amount of energy acquired by an electron on falling freely across a potential drop of one million volts. The energy equivalent of the mass of one electron is then 0.511 MEV. Atomic masses are usually expressed on a scale of atomic mass units (amu) in which the mass of the ordinary oxygen atom is arbitrarily assigned the value 16. The energy equivalent of 1 amu corresponds to 931.04 MEV.

Photon or Light Quantum (Mass, 0; Charge, 0)

These names are used interchangeably to emphasize the corpuscular character of light and X rays and gamma rays. The quantum idea was first introduced by Max Planck in 1900 and extended by Albert Einstein in 1905.

The energy of a quantum is proportional to the frequency of the light or inversely proportional to its wave length. Quanta of red light correspond to two electron volts and of violet light to four electron volts. X-ray quanta as used in radiography correspond to 30,000 to 50,000 electron volts. For X-ray therapy energies up to several million electron volts find application. Gamma rays are the same physically as X rays. The term gamma ray usually connotes that the radiation was emitted in a nuclear process or in positron-electron annihilation.

Electron (Mass, 1; Charge, — 1)

Name suggested in 1891 by G. Johnstone Stoney. Ratio of charge to mass measured in 1897 by J. J. Thomson. Charge measured in 1909 by R. A. Millikan.

Electrons make up the parts of atoms outside the central nucleus.

An atom containing Z electrons is said to have an *atomic number* of Z which ranges for naturally occurring elements from $Z = 1$ for hydrogen to $Z = 92$ for uranium. The chemical properties of the atom are determined by Z so each chemical element corresponds to a different value of Z.

Positron (Mass, 1; Charge, $+1$)

Same mass as electron but positively charged. Existence was predicted theoretically by P. A. M. Dirac in 1930. Positrons were discovered experimentally by Carl Anderson in 1932. Positrons do not exist in normal matter. In certain collisions involving high-energy particles and high-energy gamma rays, pairs (that is, one electron and one positron) are created or materialized, their mass being created from the mass equivalence of part of the energy of impact. The positrons so formed have only a transient existence being later annihilated in collision with electrons, their energy and that of the annihilated electron being given off as gamma rays.

Nucleon

This is a generic term referring to either a proton or a neutron. The nucleus of an atom of atomic number Z contains Z protons together with N neutrons, where $Z + N = A$. A is the total number of particles in the nucleus, and is therefore the integer closest to the atomic weight of the atom on the usual scale. Except for hydrogen, A is always equal to or greater than 2Z.

Proton (Mass, 1836.5; Charge, $+1$)

The proton is the nucleus of the atom of ordinary hydrogen and is the electrically charged constituent of all nuclei. The proton was "discovered" gradually during the 1890s with the evolution of ideas concerning electrical conduction in gases.

Neutron (Mass, 1839; Charge, 0)

The neutron carries no charge and has a mass slightly in excess of that of the proton. Neutrons are apparently stable when bound in atomic nuclei. Free neutrons however are radioactive and transform spontaneously into protons, electrons and neutrinos, with an average life of about 13 minutes. In terms of atomic mass units,

Neutron	1.008982
Proton + electron	1.008142
Difference	0.000840

The mass difference is equivalent to an energy of 0.782 MEV which appears as energy of motion of the proton, electron and neutrino in the spontaneous disintegration of the free neutron.

The neutron was discovered by James Chadwick in 1932.

Neutrino (Mass, 0?; Charge, 0)

The neutrino is a hypothetical particle, not directly observed, which has been supposed to be emitted in radioactive processes in which electrons or positrons are also emitted. Such radioactive processes are called beta-processes, the simplest example being that of the spontaneous radioactive decay of the free neutron. First suggested by Wolfgang Pauli and developed into theory of beta-decay by Enrico Fermi in 1934.

Deuteron (Mass, 3671.2; Charge, + 1)

The deuteron is the simplest compound nucleus, consisting of a binary compound of one proton and one neutron. It is the nucleus of the heavy form of hydrogen known as deuterium which was discovered by Harold Urey in 1932. Its mass is less than the sum of the mass of the proton and the neutron by about 4.4 units. This is the mass equivalence of the energy released when one deuteron is formed by the union of one proton and one neutron. Because of the strong binding energy of the proton and the neutron, the energy of a deuterium atom is less than the sum of the energies of a proton, a neutron and an electron, separate and at relative rest, and therefore deuterium is stable with regard to radioactive decay.

Alpha Particle

This is the historic name given to the heavy particles emitted in the radioactive decay of heavy elements such as uranium, thorium, radium and others. An alpha particle is the nucleus of the helium atom and consists of a very stable compound of two protons and two neutrons. The energy released on formation of one alpha particle from two neutrons and two protons is 28 MEV.

Meson

A generic name for a class of particles originally discovered in cosmic radiation, but which have also been produced artificially by bombardment of targets with particles accelerated to several hundred million volts in modern high-energy particle accelerators. Mesons are of various types, both charged and uncharged, and have masses of the general order of several hundred electron masses. The full story on these particles is not yet known and is the subject of vigorous experimental investigation in laboratories throughout the world. Existence of mesons was first predicted theoretically in 1935 by H. Yukawa in Japan.

Pions or π mesons. (Mass, 280 ± 10; Charge, ± 1)

These mesons are of two kinds, positively and negatively charged. They were first recognized in cosmic radiation by C. M. G. Lattes in 1947, and first generated artificially in the laboratory in 1948 by E. Gardner and C. M. G. Lattes using a beam of alpha particles of 360 MEV energy from the 184-inch synchro-cyclotron at the University of California. Pions have a mean life of 0.9×10^{-8} sec. before decaying spontaneously into a charged muon and a neutral particle of uncertain nature. Those occurring in cosmic rays are produced in the upper atmosphere by collision of high speed protons and neutrons from outer space with the atoms of the atmosphere.

Muons or μ mesons. (Mass, 215 ± 2; Charge, ± 1)

These mesons were first discovered in cosmic radiation by C. D. Anderson and S. Neddermeyer and also by J. C. Street and E. C. Stevenson in 1937. Later they were recognized to be the products of decay of the pions. The muons in turn decay spontaneously into high energy electrons (maximum energy about 55 MEV) and neutral particles of uncertain nature, having a mean life before decay of

2.15 x 10⁻⁶ sec., more than two hundred times greater than that of the pion.

Neutretto

A name sometimes used to refer to hypothetical mesons without electric charge.

Hyperon

A generic designation of particles heavier in mass than the proton, which can decay spontaneously into nucleons and pions. Intensive cosmic ray research is at present revealing a vast range of complicated phenomena seemingly involving a number of additional kinds of particles of masses greater than that of the pion which undergo various kinds of spontaneous transmutations not as yet fully understood.

Anti-proton

A hypothetical particle of mass equal essentially to that of the proton but having unit negative charge instead of unit positive charge.

CHEMISTRY

JOHN READ

about

John Read

John Read was born February 17, 1884, in the English west country. He was educated in Somerset and at Finsbury Technical College, London. After completing his college course he enrolled at the University of Zurich, where he followed research in chemistry and took his doctorate under Alfred Werner, distinguished for his contributions to stereochemistry and the study of complex inorganic compounds. For eight years, beginning in 1908, Read conducted joint researches with W. J. Pope who held the chair of chemistry at Cambridge; in 1916, as a result of the reputation gained in this work, he was appointed professor of organic chemistry in the University of Sydney, Australia, where he worked extensively on the chemistry of Australian plant products. He returned to Britain in 1923 to become professor of chemistry and director of the chemistry research laboratory in the United College of St. Salvator and St. Leonard, University of St. Andrews, Scotland.

The author of many outstanding papers in the fields of organic and stereochemistry, Professor Read is equally well known for his books on alchemy and the history of chemistry. Among his best known writings addressed to a general audience are Prelude to Chemistry, *(N.Y., 1937);* Humor and Humanism in Chemistry, *(London, 1947);* The Alchemist in Life, Literature and Art, *(London and Edinburgh, 1947).*

A Direct Entry to Organic Chemistry (1948), *a popularization* of this rather difficult subject, won for Read the newly inaugurated Cortina-European prize of a million lire in 1949, as "the best book on popular physical science published in any language within the preceding five years." Since its publication Read has lectured extensively in Italy and other European countries, and in 1953 was appointed by the British government as one of the five British members of an Anglo-Italian cultural commission.

Read has long been interested in the region of his birth. He visited Thomas Hardy frequently at his home in Dorchester; he likes to walk through the Wessex countryside making friends with the farm folk, observing the local customs, recording the folk speech, stories and beliefs. He has written books and plays and given dialect broadcasts about this part of England. He has also written a history of the city of St. Andrews and its university. His numerous academic distinctions include Fellowship of the Royal Society since 1935 and the presidency of the chemical section of the British Association for the Advancement of Science in 1948. He is married and has two sons, one of whom, Arthur Hinton Read, is a mathematician and author of an attractive popular book, A Signpost to Mathematics.

CHEMISTRY

JOHN READ

Owing to its vast extent, natural science has been divided, both on practical and intellectual grounds, into the physical sciences, such as chemistry, physics and geology, and the biological sciences, such as botany, zoology and physiology. Nature, however, has an essential unity; so that the various branches of science are interdependent and possessed of no rigid boundaries.

Chemistry is a branch of science which deals with the study of matter, or in other words with the character of the "stuff" of which the material universe is composed. It is obvious to the senses that matter abounds around us in many kinds and forms. It is the task of chemistry to separate from this heterogeneous assemblage of matter, various homogeneous portions known as substances, each of which has its individual composition and properties. A vast mass of information of this kind has been accumulated as a result of patient experiments and observations. The observed characters and interrelationships have led to many consequences, notably to the classification of substances, to the preparation of one known substance from another, and to the elaboration of new substances unknown in nature. Prolonged work of this kind was necessary before any accurate idea could be formed of the proximate or ultimate nature of matter. In the modern development of chemistry, facts, accurately established by experiment, led to the formulation of generalized statements, or *laws*. Certain laws, fitted by imaginative processes of thought into a wider conception, gave birth to *hypotheses,* which when fully established took higher rank as *theories.* Theories are thus conclusions drawn from accumulated facts and capable of leading to the prediction of new facts.

In tracing the origin and development of chemical knowledge it must be emphasized that chemistry is based fundamentally upon very obscure principles, which were brought to light only after the lapse of long ages of preliminary speculation and arbitrary experiment. Although probably the most obscure, chemistry is certainly the most romantic of all the branches of science. The history of its development stretches back through a thousand years of alchemy into the misty prehistory of primitive superstitions and religions. Primitive man, in a rough and ready way, must have paid attention to the various materials around him and have adapted them to various uses; herein we discern the dawn of pure and applied chemistry.

The ancient civilizations of the Middle East, in the course of unnumbered centuries, developed a knowledge of various metals and alloys, and of methods of making and using fermented liquors, soap, glass, stoneware, leather, alum, and many other materials. They had, however, no knowledge of what we now call chemistry, although the dawn of imaginative ideas may be seen in the Chaldean association of the known planets and metals—"the bodyes sevene eek" as Chaucer called them much later—with human organs and individual destinies.

At this point, in order to get a clearer notion of early views of the cosmos, it may be mentioned that until the time of Descartes, in the seventeenth century, matter and mind were not regarded as mutually exclusive. That is a modern view. In ancient and medieval times, gross or tangible matter was supposed to shade away through increasingly subtle grades of matter, like mists, smokes, exhalations, and air, to ether, animal spirits, the soul, and spiritual beings, all forming links in an essential unity.

The earliest imaginative idea of physical science which may be dignified by the title of a "theory" was that of the four qualities and the "four elements," usually ascribed to Aristotle but traceable in Egypt and India as far back as 1500 B.C. This theory, held so widely in one form or another by many civilizations over a long period, bears out the statement that "there is a great oneness in the human mind in the matter of broad principle in crude cosmical ideas." The theory has often been represented diagrammatically in some such form as that given below (Fig. 1):

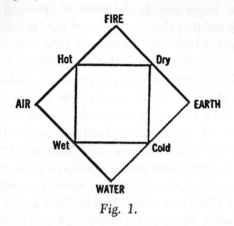

Fig. 1.

According to this theory, all matter is composed of the four so-called "elements," earth, air, fire and water. Each element, in turn, is pictured as a material embodiment of pairs of fundamental qualities: the hot, the dry, the cold, and the wet. This primitive theory is not to be scorned: the "elements" were selected with discrimination, and the scheme summarizes a great deal of observation and reflection. At an early stage in his intellectual development, man must have been led to discriminate between what we now call the three states of aggregation of matter: the solid, liquid, and gaseous, here represented by earth, water, and air. The fourth "element," fire, stood for what we now term heat or energy.

Let us look into this conception a little further. Water is cold and wet. Heat water and replace the cold quality by the hot one, and the result is a change of water into steam, that is, into a vapor or "air." One "element" has thus changed into another, or undergone transmutation, to use an alchemical term. The fundamental alchemical idea of transmutation is thus implicit in the theory. Nowadays, of course, the process is viewed simply as a change of liquid water through the absorption of heat, or energy, into the gaseous form of the same substance and there is no question of transmutation.

This ancient theory may be traced back to a still more primitive mode of thinking, known as the "Doctrine of the Two Contraries," dependent upon the recognition of a distinction between pairs of opposites, such as cold and hot, dry and wet. An apposition of primary importance in alchemy was that of the two opposed, or contrary, "elements"—fire and water.

So we come to alchemy, the immediate precursor of chemistry. Alchemy was a long-lived ancestor, for it lasted for more than a millennium, from at least early Christian times until the end of the seventeenth century. Alchemy was not merely rudimentary chemistry. It was a vast network of this incipient science, interwoven with astrology, philosophy, religion, mysticism, theosophy, magic, and many other strands. Its tenets made a great appeal to the human mind; so much so that the authoritative opinion has been expressed in recent years that alchemy is no less important in the study of psychology than in that of chemistry. But alchemy has been outmoded for more than two centuries; and so there is little realization at the present day of the extent to which alchemical conceptions and imagery permeated the thought and also the art of the Middle Ages.

No definite statement can be made concerning the origin of alchemy; but there is little doubt that alchemical knowledge and ideas were gathered from the ancient civilizations of Egypt, Babylonia, India and China. From Greece, Syria and Persia this accumulated corpus of alchemy was transmitted to Islam. Eventually the accumulated knowledge of the Moslem alchemists, drawn from these various sources and augmented in its passage through Islam, was brought into western Europe, chiefly through Spain.

The main tenets of alchemy were, first, that all forms of matter are one in origin; secondly, that these forms are produced by evolutionary processes; thirdly, that matter has a common soul which alone is permanent, the body or outward form being transitory and capable of undergoing transmutation, or change into a different outward form. Essentially, these views are very similar to those of modern physical science; for in this twentieth century "modern alchemy," as Lord Rutherford called it, has achieved many transmutations of the elements of modern science, formerly supposed to be immutable.

In the deductive philosophy of ancient Greece the idea first came to birth that imaginative thought could lead to the deduction of truths from considerations of general principles. Alchemical reasoning and ideas were derived in large measure from Greece; so it is not surprising that alchemical reasoning was mainly deductive and based to a great extent on two a priori assumptions. These were, first, the unity of matter; secondly, the existence of a potent transmuting agent, known as the philosopher's stone. From the postulate of the essential unity of all things it followed that this medicine of the metals became also the medicine of man. In this guise the philosopher's stone was known as the *elixir vitae,* or elixir of life.

Herein may be discerned the powerful incentive which actuated the strenuous, costly and often unpleasant labors of some forty generations of alchemists. "Gold," wrote Goethe, "gives power; without health there is no enjoyment, and longevity here takes the place of immortality." And, as Liebig observed: "In order to know that the philosopher's stone did not really exist, it was indispensable that every substance accessible should be observed and examined . . . in this we perceive the almost miraculous influence of the idea."

The alchemists themselves ranged from impostors and charlatans having no real claim to the title, through uninstructed "puffers" (Fig. 2) and would-be goldmakers, to skilled practicants, scholastic philosophers, adepts, and religious mystics. To the higher type of alchemist, alchemy was much more than an experimental science. It was a grandiose philosophical system. In their own eyes, the efforts made by the adepts and religious mystics to transmute metals were attempts to prove the truth of the broad philosophical system of alchemy by means of material experiments.

Now, to follow along the chemical strand of the alchemical web, the two opposed "elements," fire and water, came to light in a new form in the "sulphur-mercury theory" of the metals, which seems to have been propounded by the Moslem alchemists possibly in the eighth century A.D. The sulphur and mercury of this theory were not the tangible substances bearing these names. They were abstract "principles," sulphur being essentially a principle conferring upon combustible bodies the ability to burn; while mercury denoted the mineral spirit of metals and also the property of liquidity or fusi-

Fig. 2—A "Puffer" and his assistant. Hans Weiditz, 1520.

bility. Essentially these imagined principles constituted a new view
of the fire and water of Aristotle's four elements.

According to this conception the medieval alchemists considered
that when these two natural principles came together under planetary influences in the bowels of the earth they gave rise to the perfect
metal, gold; if they were slightly impure they gave silver; if they were
markedly impure they furnished base metals, such as tin and lead.
If, however, the two principles could be brought together in states of
superfine purity, they could yield something so much purer than
ordinary gold that a small amount of this product (the philosopher's
stone) would be able to transmute a very large quantity of a base
metal into gold of ordinary purity.

This was the idea which animated generation after generation of
alchemists throughout the medieval period, and even down to the
days of Boyle and Newton. The chief task of the alchemical adept
was to imitate, and even surpass, nature in bringing about such
changes. After all, that is a leading motive of modern chemistry. Also
in modern parlance it would be correct to call the philosopher's stone
a catalyst. Here again the alchemists are vindicated; for what more po-

tent catalyst could be imagined than the neutrons which start and propagate the explosive transmutation of uranium 235 into other elements? "Everything possible to be believ'd," wrote the English poet and mystic, William Blake, "is an image of truth. What is now proved was once only imagin'd."

Beyond chance discoveries of new substances and processes and the development of various kinds of apparatus, alchemy had little to show in the way of advance until early in the sixteenth century when Paracelsus gave a new direction to operative alchemy and greatly enlarged its scope by allying it with medicine. Paracelsus (1493-1541) was a Swiss propagandist of a new order, both in alchemy and medicine, and he lashed the physicians of his day with a merciless tongue and pen. The true goal of alchemy, he insisted, must be to prepare medicines instead of seeking gold. The ensuing period of "iatrochemistry," spagyric chemistry, or chemistry applied to medicine, lasted into the eighteenth century. Meanwhile the old alchemy persisted, but slowly declined. Paracelsus modified the ancient sulphur-mercury theory by introducing a third principle which he termed salt. In this system of the *tria prima*, or three hypostatical principles, often shown symbolically by a triangle (Fig. 3), the names sulphur, mercury, and salt had both a chemical and a mystical significance. Chemically they stood for inflammability, metallicity, and fixity; mystically, for the soul, spirit, and body of man.

In medicine, the herbalist of the ancient Galenic order now became a pharmacist, or compounder of chemical medicines. The end of the seventeenth century found iatrochemistry on the wane; but, during this period of transition the iatrochemists, despite certain excesses, had promoted the steady growth and diffusion of chemical knowledge and laboratory practice. The gradual change from alchemy to chemistry became evident in a notable succession of early textbooks of chemistry published in the seventeenth century and culminating in Lemery's celebrated *Cours de Chymie* (1675). Lemery (1645-1715) practised as an apothecary in Paris and gave some of the earliest public lectures and demonstrations in chemistry. His book, severely practical and completely devoid of the cryptic expression and mysticism of alchemy, achieved an unprecedented popularity in several languages, and did more to bring chemistry to the popular

Fig. 3—An alchemical emblem.

notice than any other work published before the birth of modern chemistry at the end of the eighteenth century. This same century produced, in the person of Glauber (1604-1670), the son of a Karlstadt barber, a true research chemist, whose discoveries and writings exerted a widespread and stimulating effect upon the incipient science. He died in poverty, leaving it on record that "by all that ever I writ I never gained one half-peny."

Attention must now be turned from these practical empiricists to contemporary thinkers and men of ideas. In so doing we are faced with the question: Why did the scientific revolution of the seventeenth century fail to reach chemistry? Looking back, we can now see that before chemistry could divest itself of the accretions of alchemy there were certain outstanding problems to be solved. Chief among them were: (1) the nature of a chemical element; (2) the nature of chemical change, especially of burning or combustion, and of the so-called "element," fire; (3) the chemical nature of the so-called "elements," air and water. It is a great tribute to the Aristotelian scheme that three of its "elements" figure in this list of obstacles that blocked a break-through from alchemy to chemistry in the eighteenth century —more than 3,000 years after the idea of the four elements was conceived in India and Egypt.

These issues could not be resolved by processes of pure thought. They called for the application of systematic experiments—logical questions put to nature—followed by accurate observation and intelligent interpretation. That is the scientific method in a nutshell.

It is sometimes held that the publication of *The Sceptical Chymist* by Boyle in 1661 heralded the end of alchemy. The Hon. Robert Boyle (1627-1691), whom a schoolboy aptly described as "The Father of Chemistry and the Uncle of the Earl of Cork," was a versatile worker in physics, "a great Lover of Chymical Experiments," and a man of singular beauty of character. It is true that in his famous book Boyle assailed vigorously the systems of the four elements and the *tria prima*, and put forward the modern idea of a chemical element as a body which cannot be resolved into simpler bodies. But the emergence of modern chemistry had to wait for more than another century.

Why was the nature of combustion so important? . . . Because it is the most spectacular and fundamental of all familiar chemical processes. Notice also that it involves all four of Aristotle's elements. A piece of wood burns: air is necessary; fire is manifest; water is an important product of the burning; earth (ash) is left. Also, we must not overlook the literally "vital" importance of combustion; for it is a slow and regulated combustion that maintains animal heat in the metabolic processes upon which life depends.

That great scientific, experimental and mechanical genius, Hooke (1635-1703), one-time assistant to Boyle, got very near to the core of the problem when he stated in his *Micrographia* (1665) that burning is due to "a substance inherent, and mixt with the Air, that is like, if not the very same, with that which is fixt in Salt-peter." His penetrating remarks on combustion occur as a kind of aside in this first major work illustrating microscopical objects, and containing plates beautifully engraved by Hooke himself. Hooke's contemporary, Mayow (1641-1679), a brilliant but short-lived English physician, confirmed and emphasized earlier observations showing that air contracts in combustion and that the residual air cannot support combustion (or respiration).

Why did the nature of burning remain unsolved for another century? . . . Because Boyle, Hooke, and Mayow knew little of methods of isolating or handling gases; consequently, they held no clues to the composition of air, fixed air (carbon dioxide), or water. And while air is "the food of fire," as the alchemists realized, fixed air and water are the products of combustion of all organic materials.

It was essentially lack of knowledge of gases and of the experimental technique of handling them that gave a wrong direction to chemical theory when Stahl (1660-1734), professor of medicine at Halle, Prussian councilor, and royal physician, attributed combustibility to the presence in the combustible body of a constituent which he called "phlogiston" (1702). Burning was thus equivalent to a loss of phlogiston, and a metal was regarded as a compound of its calx (oxide) with phlogiston. It was therefore held that loss of weight occurred in the burning of metals, just as it seemed to occur (because the gaseous products could not be collected and weighed) in the burning of a piece of wood or a candle. This view was held in spite of experimental evidence that tin and other metals increase in weight when heated in air, and that air contracts when bodies are burnt in it. It is fatal in science to close one's eyes to established facts.

All the same, here was a theory that co-ordinated many hitherto isolated observations and that stimulated scientific enquiry. Under its aegis a remarkable band of eighteenth-century investigators accumulated the evidence and worked out the experimental technique that led to its fall, late in the century. Chief among them were Black (Scotland), Priestley and Cavendish (England), and Scheele (Sweden).

Black (1728-1799) was professor of chemistry at Edinburgh from 1766 to 1799, during "the golden age of Edinburgh society." A precise and confirmed bachelor, "he sung, and performed on the flute, with great taste and feeling; and could sing a plain air at sight"—which is more than can be said of many (if any) professors of chemistry in the present age of intense specialization. Black (1755) showed that heated chalk or marble gave much less than its weight of quicklime, the loss being due to the expulsion of "fixed air" (carbon dioxide), a gas which Black collected and characterized. Black's discovery that fixed air could be differentiated from common air, that it could be held in solid combination in chalk or marble, and that it could be weighed in that state, contained the germ of Lavoisier's later theory of combustion. Besides this, Black's use of the balance in following chemical changes inaugurated another profound advance, this time in the development of quantitative chemistry. Modern chemistry owes its birth to the use of the balance and other instruments of precision in following chemical changes quantitatively. The *qualitative* observation that chalk decomposes into quicklime and carbon dioxide is only the first of two steps necessary in studying this chemical change; the next step —a vital one—is to ascertain by experimental measurement what weight of lime and what volume (and eventually weight) of carbon dioxide are yielded by a known weight of chalk. This is the *quantitative* step.

Priestley (1733-1804), the son of a humble Yorkshire cloth dresser, became a brilliant amateur of science, whose discoveries, sometimes made at random, were of profound significance. His unorthodox and advanced views, especially in politics, made him the victim of mob violence, and he emigrated to America, ending his days at Northumberland, Pennsylvania. Priestley devised methods of isolating and handling gases effectively. He introduced the pneumatic trough, and collected his gases not only over water, as Boyle, Mayow and Hales had already done, but also over mercury, thereby discovering sulphur dioxide, ammonia, hydrogen chloride, and other gases which dissolve in water. The pneumatic trough consists of a vessel in which an inverted jar filled with a liquid (usually water) is supported on a perforated shelf submerged in the same liquid; a gas rising from a tube dipping beneath the jar is thus collected in it.

Priestley seems to have regarded his various gases, or "airs," as common air associated with different amounts of phlogiston. In 1774 he made a discovery, at Calne in Wiltshire, that was destined to exert a trigger-like action on the development of chemistry. August 1 in that year is a date rarely to be found in history books, yet it is one of tremendous significance in the record of human progress; for it was on this day that Priestley discovered oxygen, by heating some red calx of mercury (mercuric oxide) with a new burning glass of a foot in diameter, the calx being put into a glass tube closed at the upper end, "filled with quicksilver, and kept inverted in a bason of the same."

This gas supported combustion with unprecedented vigor. "A piece of red-hot wood sparkled in it, exactly like paper dipped in a solution of nitre," wrote Priestley; and a mouse "remained perfectly at its ease" in the gas for twice the time it would have lived in an equal amount of common air, and was alive and kicking when taken out. Priestley therefore concluded that this gas was air completely deprived of phlogiston, and so named it "dephlogisticated air."

Oxygen was discovered independently by Scheele (1742-1786), a great pioneer of qualitative chemistry, who in his short span of life discovered oxygen, chlorine, tungstic acid, numerous organic acids, glycerol, and many other substances. This struggling pharmacist, whose memory is honored in Stockholm by a handsome statue, once wrote to a friend: "You may think perhaps that material cares are going to absorb me, and take me away from experimental chemistry. Not so! That noble science is my ideal."

From the struggling Swedish apothecary the chemical scene changes to disclose Cavendish (1731-1810), the eccentric and aloof millionaire, grandson of an English duke, with "a peevish impatience of the inconveniences of eminence," a dislike of women, of all meats save mutton, and of all towns save London. As a scientist, this enigmatic figure was richly endowed with the quantitative instinct and with superb manipulative skill. He characterized various gases ("factitious airs") by measuring their specific gravities. He analyzed common air, showing that it contained just over 20 per cent of "dephlogisticated air" (oxygen); also he found that when a mixture of two volumes of "inflammable air" (hydrogen) with one volume of "dephlogisticated air" was exploded, the sole product was water, the two gases disappearing in the process. These researches led quickly to the elucidation of the chemical nature of the ancient "elements," air and water.

Now, as so often in the history of science, a point had been reached at which the known facts enabled a tremendous step forward to be taken. The only remaining obstacle was a mental one; for one of the most difficult of all mental processes is to reassemble a series of familiar facts and relationships and to regard them from a new viewpoint.

In this ability lay the great genius of Lavoisier, who, without making a single discovery of any new body, or property, or natural phenomenon, demolished in the 1780s the barrier that had hitherto blocked progress in chemistry. By carefully planned quantitative experiments he showed that the air absorbed by heating mercury in a closed vessel was equal in volume to the "dephlogisticated air" produced by heating more strongly the resulting red calx of mercury. This simple and logical experiment sealed the fate of the phlogiston theory: it showed that the calx was a compound of mercury with "dephlogisticated air," the active atmospheric constituent which Lavoisier now called oxygen. So arose the modern "theory of combustion." Passing to the problem of the constitution of water, Lavoisier first confirmed Cavendish's synthetical experiments, and then devised the analytical method of passing steam over heated iron filings contained in a gun barrel, thereby verifying his prediction that when oxygen was abstracted from water by the iron, to form a substance akin to ordinary rust, free hydrogen would remain.

Lavoisier (1743-1794) was a lawyer, a scientist, and a prominent figure in the public life of France. His execution in 1794 was perhaps the most insensate of all the crimes of the French Revolution. "La République n'a pas besoin de savants," pronounced the egregious Coffinhal, president of the tribunal; but Lagrange gave expression to the sobered feelings of France in the words: "Il ne leur a fallu qu'un moment pour faire tomber cette tête, et cent années peut-être ne suffiront pas pour en reproduire une semblable." In conformity with this thought, Pasteur, who ranks beside Lavoisier as one of the three or four greatest men that France has produced, died almost exactly a century later (1895).

The abolition of the old theories and the accumulation of accurate quantitative data led rapidly to the formulation of that comprehensive "Atomic Theory" whose innumerable ramifications form the nervous sytem of the wonderful body of physical science as we know it today. Dalton (1766-1844) began his career as a humble Quaker schoolmaster in a Cumberland village. Unlike Cavendish, although he remained a bachelor, Dalton, "like most men of higher sensibility and intelligence, greatly enjoyed the society of ladies, provided that they were women of superior talents and mental culture." The first printed account of Dalton's theory appeared in 1807. Epicurus, as long ago as 300 B.C., held that matter was discontinuous or grained; and this conception may be traced back through Democritus to Leucippus, in the sixth century B.C. Dalton's conception of an atomic constitution of matter was derived from Newton rather than from the ancient Greeks. He converted a vague speculation into a precise theory: this was based upon laws resting in turn upon quantitative experimental data.

Newton had pictured the *atom* as a "hard, impenetrable, movable particle . . . so very hard as never to wear or break in pieces: no ordinary power being able to divide what God himself made One, in the first creation." The idea that matter is uncreatable and indestructible led to the so-called law of the conservation of matter, a conception inherent in Dalton's atomic theory. Dalton held that the multitudinous substances of the material world are built up from a limited number of kinds of atoms, corresponding to the different elements, all the atoms of a particular element being alike and having the same weight. He regarded the formation of compounds as dependent upon combination between small whole numbers of atoms of the elements concerned, the resulting "compound atoms" (now known as *molecules*) of a compound being again alike and having the same weight.

These conceptions, or postulates, led to the establishment, by experimental observations, of three main laws which formed the original foundations of Dalton's atomic theory. (1) *The law of fixed proportions* (or constant composition) states that the elements combine together in fixed proportions by weight; in other words, the same chemical compound always consists of the same elements combined together in the same proportions. For example, pure water, however obtained or prepared, always contains one-ninth of hydrogen and eight-ninths of oxygen by weight.

(2) *The law of multiple proportions* states that when two elements unite to form more than one compound, the different weights of one which combine with a constant weight of the other bear a simple ratio to each other. Thus, hydrogen and oxygen give rise to (*a*) water, and (*b*) hydrogen peroxide, containing 11.11% and 5.88% of hydrogen, respectively. The weights of oxygen combining with one part by weight of hydrogen are therefore 8 parts in water and 16 in hydrogen peroxide, these being in the simple ratio 1:2.

(3) *The law of reciprocal proportions* states that the proportions in which two elements combine separately with a third element are in a

simple ratio to those in any compound of the first two elements. For example, 1 part by weight of oxygen combines with 0.125 part of hydrogen (to form water), or with 0.875 part of nitrogen (to form nitric oxide). The proportions here are 0.125 (hydrogen) to 0.875 (nitrogen), or 1:7. The first two elements, hydrogen and nitrogen, combine together (to form ammonia) in the proportions 1 to 4.67, or 1½:7. The "simple ratio" is thus 1/7 to 1½/7, or 2:3.

A little thought will show that the conclusions summarized in these three laws are logical consequences of Dalton's original postulates.

Although excessively minute, each kind of atom has its distinctive atomic weight. The absolute weight (or mass) of the hydrogen atom is now known to be 1.66×10^{-24} gram; but since originally the absolute weights could not be determined, the *atomic* weight of the lightest element, hydrogen, was taken as unity, and the relative weights of other kinds of atoms were based upon this standard. In the early days of the atomic theory the determination of these relative atomic weights, by accurate analytical methods, owed much to the practical skill of the eminent Swedish chemist, Berzelius (1779-1848).

Dalton, following the alchemical tradition, used symbols to represent simple atoms and "compound atoms" (molecules); but Berzelius replaced these symbols by letters. The first six Daltonian symbols reproduced below (Fig. 4) represent, in order, the elements hydrogen, nitrogen, carbon, oxygen, phosphorus, and sulphur. The second line shows the "arbitrary marks or signs" for a "compound atom" (molecule) of each of the following compounds: water, ammonia, nitrous gas (nitric oxide), olefiant gas (ethylene), and carbonic oxide (carbon monoxide).

Fig. 4—Some Daltonian symbols.

In modern chemical notation the literary symbol stands for one atom of the element it represents, so that the equivalents of the above symbols would be H, N, C, O, P, S, for the elements; and HO, HN, NO, HC, OC for the compounds. Each of these last five would now be called a *molecular formula,* which is an expression of the kind and number of each atom in the molecule concerned. The correct molecular formulae for the five compounds shown above are, in fact, H_2O, NH_3, NO, C_2H_4, and CO. Often it is inconvenient to use the first letter of the name as the symbol of an elementary atom, some common examples being: Cu, copper; Au, gold; Fe, iron; Pb, lead; Hg, mercury; K, potassium; Ag, silver; Sn, tin.

With the discovery and examination of more and more elements it became possible for Newlands (1838-1898), a chemist in a London sugar refinery, to expound a so-called *law of octaves* in papers published between 1863 and 1866. He pointed out that when the elements were arranged in the order of increasing atomic weights, each element showed a family likeness to elements which were seven, or some multiple of seven, places before or after it. He was however discouraged by the cold reception of his idea, especially when a member of an audience of the Chemical Society of London asked him whether he had ever thought of looking into an alphabetical arrangement!

Other chemists pursued the idea of a systematic classification, and in 1869 the Russian chemist Mendeléeff (1834-1907), the youngest of a family of fourteen children, who became professor of chemistry in St. Petersburg, published a comprehensive arrangement known as the "periodic system," in which he showed that the elements, when arranged in the order of increasing atomic weights, fell into definite families or groups, showing a periodicity of chemical and physical properties. Without going into details, the following sequence (Fig. 5) may be taken from the current periodic table in illustration, the symbol and atomic weight of each element being given below its name:

HELIUM	LITHIUM	BERYLLIUM	BORON	CARBON	NITROGEN	OXYGEN	FLUORINE
He 4	Li 7	Be 9	B 11	C 12	N 14	O 16	F 19

NEON	SODIUM	MAGNESIUM	ALUMI-NUM	SILICON	PHOS-PHORUS	SULPHUR	CHLORINE
Ne 20	Na 23	Mg 24	Al 27	Si 28	P 31	S 32	Cl 35.5

GROUP							
O	I	II	III	IV	V	VI	VII

Fig. 5—Part of the Periodic Table of Elements.

Group O contains the rare gases of the atmosphere, helium, neon, argon, etc., which are distinguished from all other elements by their abnormal chemical stability and unreactivity. Group I is the family of the alkali metals, lithium, sodium, potassium, etc. These soft, silvery metals decompose water readily, liberating hydrogen; simultaneously they form strongly alkaline solutions of sodium hydroxide (caustic soda), etc. Group VII, known as halogens, combine with hydrogen giving rise to acids, such as hydrochloric and hydrobromic acids; these acids, in turn, react with the alkaline hydroxides of Group I to form salts: hydrochloric acid and sodium hydroxide, for example, react to yield sodium chloride (common salt, NaCl) and water.

Mendeléeff ascribed certain gaps in his classification to the existence of undiscovered elements, and soon afterward some of these were discovered and found to have the very properties predicted by Mendeléeff. Such relationships, when well established, gave rise to much speculation concerning their fundamental cause, and attention became increasingly focused upon the nature of the atom. Were the elements possibly the result of variations upon an atomic theme, dependent ultimately upon atomic structure? If so, Dalton's conception of an unbreakable particle, not possessed of any organized structure, would have to be abandoned, carrying with it a celebrated aphorism of the great Quaker man of science: "Thou knows no man can split an atom."

Meanwhile, from about 1850 onward, physicists had devoted growing attention to the study of electric discharges in high vacuums. With the refinement of experimental technique in physical science, which became increasingly apparent toward the end of the nineteenth century, researches in this field culminated, in 1897, in the discovery by J. J. Thomson (1856-1940), Cavendish professor of experimental physics at Cambridge, of a particle of matter having only 1/1840th the mass of a hydrogen atom. This lightest of all particles, obtained from various kinds of matter, was identified as a unit of negative electricity and given the name of *electron*. Thus arose the conception of the "electronic constitution of the atom" and consequently of matter. After much further experimental work of a physical nature, the atom gradually took shape according to the views of Rutherford (1871-1937), who succeeded his old master, J. J. Thomson, at Cambridge, Bohr (b. 1885), professor of physics at Copenhagen, and others, as a positively charged nucleus surrounded by revolving electrons in different numbers characteristic of the particular kind of atom. The nucleus, which accounts for practically the whole mass of the atom, is pictured as an aggregate of positive and negative electrical units, known as protons and electrons, these being present in the form of protons and neutrons (proton-electron pairs). The number of protons (apart from those of the neutrons) in the nucleus is identical with the *atomic number*, or serial number of the element in the revised periodic classification.

Some typical atomic structures are shown diagrammatically in Fig. 6: the nucleus is indicated as a circle enclosing protons (p) and neutrons (n), and the extranuclear electrons (e) are shown outside the circle; the atomic weight (A.W.) and atomic number (A. No.) are also noted.

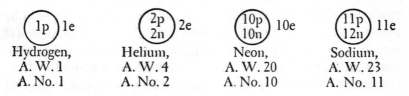

Hydrogen, A. W. 1, A. No. 1   Helium, A. W. 4, A. No. 2   Neon, A. W. 20, A. No. 10   Sodium, A. W. 23, A. No. 11

Fig. 6—Diagrammatic structures of atoms.

Protons (+) and electrons (−) have equal and opposite electrical charges. In a normal atom the positive nuclear charge is neutralized by extranuclear, or planetary, electrons, the total number of electrons and protons in the atom being equal. The gain or loss of a planetary electron destroys the electrical balance of negative and positive charges, and gives rise to a charged atom, or *ion*. The planetary electrons revolving in closed orbits about the nucleus are depicted in shells (layers or levels), these forming stable assemblages when they contain 2 (in the innermost shell), 8, 18, or 32 units. The neutral atom of sodium and the derived sodium ion (carrying 1 positive charge) are represented in Fig. 7.

The chemical character of the atom depends upon the number of electrons in its outermost shell: these, the so-called *valency electrons*,

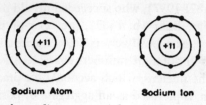

Sodium Atom   **Sodium Ion**

Fig. 7—Diagram of a sodium atom (electrically neutral) and a sodium ion (electropositive).

do not usually exceed eight. Newlands' law of octaves (1863) is thus seen to be an expression of the recurrence of chemical properties due to the building up of the valency electrons from one to eight. Each member of a natural family of elements has the same number of valency electrons.

A modern form of classification of the elements is shown in Fig. 8, which gives the atomic numbers of the elements and also summarizes their arrangement into Groups I-VII and O. (The so-called rare-earth elements (58-72) are not shown individually.) Altogether ninety-two elements have been discovered in nature, ranging from hydrogen (H, atomic number 1, atomic weight 1) to uranium (U, atomic number 92, atomic weight 238). In addition a few other purely artificial elements (93 onward) have been produced.

As stated above, the chemical nature of an atom depends upon the extranuclear electrons. The same number and arrangement of these may be associated with more than one kind of nucleus. This possibil-

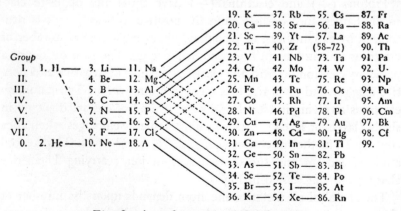

Fig. 8—A modern table of the elements.

ity accounts for the formation of *isotopes,* which are atoms with similar chemical properties and the same atomic number but different atomic weights. Most elements can exist in isotopic forms. For example, there are three known isotopic forms of hydrogen and three of uranium (Fig. 9). Ordinary hydrogen consists of about 6000 parts of protium mixed with 1 part of deuterium; tritium is a purely artificial isotope. A very small proportion of deuterium oxide ("heavy water"), D_2O, exists in natural waters.

Fig. 9—*Isotopic forms of hydrogen and uranium (diagrammatic).*

The modern theory of the ultimate constitution of the chemical elements takes us back to Aristotle's idea of a primordial matter and the derived alchemical tenet of the unity of matter. Plato, some twenty-three centuries ago, held the view that nature is based upon a mathematical plan, and that the ultimate realities must be sought in mathematics. How right he was! Going still farther back in time, the electronic theory of the constitution of matter may be regarded as the latest expression of the primitive doctrine of the two contraries: the human mind, like the electrons it has bodied forth, seems to work in closed orbits.

In all ordinary chemical processes atoms are quite stable and behave as if they were indivisible particles. However, evidence was forthcoming from 1896 onward that some of the elements of very high atomic weight, such as uranium (238) and radium (226), exhibited the phenomenon of radioactivity, which was later traced to spontaneous atomic disintegration into atoms of a different kind, energy being continuously emitted in the process. This was tantamount to natural transmutation, and in 1919 Rutherford brought about the first artificial transmutation by "bombarding" nitrogen atoms with the so-called α-particles (helium nuclei), which are projectiles of tremendous kinetic energy emitted by radium atoms. Nitrogen was thus transmuted into oxygen; and similarly beryllium gave rise to carbon. These atomic nuclear changes were accomplished only on a tiny scale, but it was noticed that the amount of energy liberated was enormous in comparison with that of the most energetic chemical reaction (in which the atoms remain unchanged). In all such examples investigated before 1938, however, the total energy supplied by the bombarding particles was much greater than the liberated energy, and the process required continuous bombardment.

By means of a laborious process, uranium 235 (Fig. 9) may be separated from natural uranium, of which it constitutes only about 0.7%. In 1938 it was discovered that upon bombarding this uranium isotope with neutrons, a self-propagating process was set up, due to the continuous release of fresh neutrons in an atomic fission or nuclear disintegration accompanied by a release of energy incomparably greater than that furnished by the most powerful organic explosive. It was a deplorable tragedy for humanity that the first application of this new and marvelous source of energy should have taken the shape of an "atomic bomb." One of the greatest problems now facing science is to achieve control of atomic power or nuclear energy, enabling it to be applied as a convenient source of heat, light, and locomotion. Perhaps the greatest of all human problems is to prevent the misuse of atomic energy: "We must indeed pray," said Mr. Winston Churchill in 1945, "that these awful agencies will be made to conduce to peace among the nations, and that instead of wreaking measureless havoc upon the entire globe they may become a perennial fountain of world prosperity."

Returning now to ordinary chemistry, atoms usually form combinations called *molecules,* instead of remaining in a state of "single blessedness," for reasons explained below. The molecule of ordinary hydrogen is formed by the mutual linkage of two atoms, and is written H_2. The water molecule, H_2O, contains two atoms of hydrogen and one of oxygen; similarly the molecule of ammonia is written NH_3 and that of methane CH_4. The molecules of a particular substance are all alike. The molecules of elements contain only one kind of atom; those of compounds contain two or more kinds of atoms. Any change which leaves the molecules intact, such as conversion from solid into liquid, or liquid into gas, is a *physical change*; any change which breaks them open, such as the decomposition of water into hydrogen and oxygen, is a *chemical change.*

A very important general property of molecules was first stated in "Avogadro's hypothesis" (1811), according to which equal volumes of all gases, under the same conditions of temperature and pressure, contain the same number of molecules. In gases we perceive a picture of the final condition of a completely democratic society: their constituent units (molecules) have the same "living space"; they display no individuality or originality, and are precisely alike in every respect.

The *molecular formula* of a substance, such as H_2, H_2O and NH_3, given above, shows the name and number of each kind of atom in the molecule; it is obtained by a simple numerical calculation from a knowledge of the relative atomic weights of the constituent elements and the percentage composition (found by chemical analysis) and molecular weight of the substance. The *molecular weight* is the weight of the molecule referred to the weight of a hydrogen atom as unity; it is most readily obtained by comparing the vapor density of the substance with the density of hydrogen gas, applying Avogadro's hypothesis, and taking into account the fact that the hydrogen molecule contains two atoms.

According to the "Theory of Valency," first advanced in 1852 by Frankland (1825–1899), professor of chemistry at Manchester, each kind of atom has a definite combining capacity or *valency* (valence), expressible as a low whole number. The univalent hydrogen atom is written H—; the bivalent oxygen atom, —O—. The strokes represent so-called valency bonds or points of attachment of one atom to another. The water molecule may thus be shown as H—O—H in a *structural formula*, showing how the atoms are linked together in the molecule. An atom often varies in its valency; for example, the

nitrogen atom is 3-valent in ammonia, H—N—H, and 5-valent in

nitric acid (HNO_3), H—O—N$\big<{}^O_O$. This last structural formula shows both single bonds and double bonds between atoms; triple bonds are also known.

The later "electronic theory of valency" depicts the nature of these bonds, of which there are two main types. As a simple example of *covalency*, the molecule of hydrogen is held together through each atom sharing its single valency electron with the other, H. + ·H → H : H, thus forming a stable (innermost) shell of two extranuclear electrons for each hydrogen atom. Or again, the covalent compound, methane or marsh gas, CH_4, may be formulated electronically as shown in Fig. 10, in which the four valency electrons of the carbon atom are represented by small open circles: the carbon atom shares its four electrons with those of four hydrogen atoms, thereby enabling each hydrogen atom to achieve its stable shell of two electrons and the carbon atom to complete its stable shell of eight electrons, a so-called octet. *Single bonds* are here concerned. A double bond is formed through the sharing of four electrons, of which each atom contributes two, as in the molecule of carbon dioxide, CO_2, in which each constituent atom has completed its stable octet:

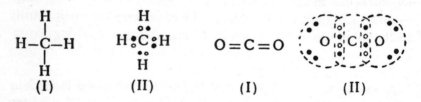

(I)   (II)   (I)   (II)

Fig. 10—Ordinary structural formulae (I) and electronic formulae (II) for methane and carbon dioxide.

The covalency, or nonpolar bond, represents one main type of interatomic combination. Another type, of equal importance, is the *electrovalency*, or polar bond. For example, in sodium chloride (common salt), NaCl, the sodium atom transfers its sole valency electron to the chlorine atom which already has seven valency electrons: thus a stable octet of eight valency electrons is built up as the outermost shell of each of the two atoms. The sodium atom is now positively charged (through losing an electron) and the chlorine atom is negatively charged (through acquiring one): the two atoms are held together by electrostatic attraction, or linked by a polar bond. Such substances, unlike those of the first type, tend to sever into oppositely charged ions, especially in solution. In the following representation, which should be compared with Fig. 7, only the outermost shells of valency electrons (each shown by a dot) are denoted:

$$Na\cdot + .\ddot{C}l: \rightarrow Na\ \ddot{C}l: \rightarrow [Na]^+ \ [:\ddot{C}l:]^-.$$

All salts of acids and bases are particularly prone to ionization owing to the occurrence of polar bonds; but covalent compounds, including notably the great majority of organic compounds, do not show this tendency. According to the theory of electrolytic dissociation, acids and bases are ionic compounds, yielding, respectively, hydrogen ions $[H]^+$ and hydroxyl ions $[OH]^-$ in aqueous solution.

The modern chemist has to think simultaneously in two ways, the qualitative and the quantitative; these two kinds of relationships, which attend all chemical change, are conveniently embodied in a concise notation, finding one of its most useful forms in the *chemical equation*. For example, the reaction between nitric acid and sodium hydroxide, giving rise to sodium nitrate and water, may be summarized in the equation: $HNO_3 + NaOH = NaNO_3 + H_2O$. Written in the ionic way this becomes:

$$[H]^+ + [NO_3]^- + [Na]^+ + [OH]^- = [Na]^+ + [NO_3]^- + H_2O$$

(water being almost non-ionized). In general, an acid reacts with a base to form a salt and water.

To pursue further the information summarized in a chemical equation, we may take the simple example: $2H_2 + O_2 = 2H_2O$. This shows that 4 parts by weight of hydrogen (atomic weight, 1) combine with 32 parts by weight of oxygen (atomic weight, 16), to form 36 parts by weight of water; also (by Avogadro's hypothesis) that, at the same temperature and pressure, 2 volumes of hydrogen and 1 of oxygen yield 2 volumes of gaseous water (steam).

A still more complete equation shows the energy-change concerned, and gives the exact amount of heat produced in this *exothermic* reaction, $2H_2 + O_2 = 2H_2O$ (liquid) $+ 136.8$ calories. The equation means that the combination of 4 grams of hydrogen and 32 grams of oxygen gives rise to 36 grams of water, in the liquid form, with the evolution of 136.8 calories of heat. Conversely, the decomposition of 36 grams of liquid water into hydrogen and oxygen requires exactly the same quantity of heat or other form of energy. Nature is a strict accountant in all such processes. In certain other chemical changes, called *endothermic*, heat is absorbed. Here we encounter an elementary aspect of "thermochemistry," which in turn forms part of a major branch of the science known as PHYSICAL CHEMISTRY, concerned with the study of physical properties in relation to chemical constitution and chemical change. Physical chemistry, like physics, has become increasingly mathematical in its development.

The elements combine together in a practically unlimited number of ways, determined by their valencies and chemical nature, to form molecules of many grades of complexity, ranging from hydrogen molecules, H_2, with two like atoms, to molecules built up of various kinds and numbers of atoms. It was realized in due course that of all these distinct forms of matter (substances, or chemical compounds) which gradually became known, some occurred in lifeless mineral matter, while others were invariably found in association with living, or "organized" matter. A distinction was thus recognized in the eighteenth century, between *inorganic* and *organic* substances. Thus arose the two great divisions of this science known as INORGANIC CHEMISTRY and ORGANIC CHEMISTRY.

Among the great variety of inorganic materials are, for example, the gases of the atmosphere, water, rocks, minerals, metals and their oxides and salts, nonmetals and their compounds, such as sulphuric and hydrochloric acids, and so forth. Natural organic materials include plant and animal fats, carbohydrates, proteins, dyestuffs, alkaloids, perfumes, alcohol, organic acids, rubber, coal, petroleum, and so on, in almost endless variety. A glance at such lists is sufficient to indicate that all the great manufacturing industries, including agriculture, the oldest industry of all, depend upon these two great branches of chemistry; it is evident also that the raw materials of the world can be applied economically to industrial purposes only by the application of systematic chemical methods. Inorganic chemistry is linked closely to geology, mineralogy, and metallurgy; organic chemistry to physiology, biochemistry, and biology in general.

Early in the nineteenth century it was realized that all the so-called natural organic compounds contain carbon as a constituent element. At the present day many of the natural organic compounds have been synthesized by artificial processes; moreover, thousands of artificial carbon compounds unknown in nature have been produced. Organic chemistry embraces all these compounds; so that now *organic chemistry is the chemistry of the carbon compounds.* Inorganic chemistry embraces all the others.

Carbon compounds outnumber those of all other elements added together, although they are composed chiefly of carbon in combination with hydrogen, oxygen, and nitrogen: C, H, O and N are the "Big Four" of organic chemistry. The cause of this prodigality first came to light when Kekulé (1829-1896), professor of chemistry at Ghent and later at Bonn, whose ideas were born in a series of visions, published his "theory of organic molecular structure" in 1858. This theory is based upon two simple postulates: (1) the 4-valency of carbon atoms, and (2) the capacity of carbon atoms to link together. Kekulé relates that he fell into a reverie upon a London omnibus, late at night, "and lo, the atoms were gamboling before my eyes! . . . I saw how, frequently, two smaller atoms united to form a pair; how a larger one embraced two smaller ones; how still larger ones kept hold of three or even four of the smaller; whilst the whole kept whirling in a giddy dance. I saw how the larger ones formed a chain, dragging the smaller ones after them . . . This was the origin of the Theory of Molecular Structure."

In the simplest organic types, known as *hydrocarbons*, the spare valencies of the carbon atoms forming these chains are taken up solely by hydrogen atoms. In a simple chain, such as $C — C — C — C$, each of the end (primary) carbon atoms needs three hydrogen atoms, and each of the intermediate (secondary) ones needs two, to take up the unsatisfied valencies of the 4-valent carbon atoms. In this specific example the structural formula of the hydrocarbon will thus be $CH_3 — CH_2 — CH_2 — CH_3$. Lengthening the carbon chain will be tantamount to introducing more bivalent $— CH_2 —$ groups. It follows that organic compounds may be arranged in so-called *homologous series*, adjacent members of which have the common molecular difference $— CH_2 —$.

Hydrocarbons occur plentifully in nature, particularly in natural petroleums, which consist almost entirely of such substances. Pennsylvanian petroleum is rich in a homologous series known as the paraffin series, the first four members of which are methane, CH_4 (compare Fig. 10); ethane, C_2H_6 (molecular formula), or $CH_3 - CH_3$ (structural formula); propane, C_3H_8, or $CH_3 - CH_2 - CH_3$; and butane, C_4H_{10}, or $CH_3 - CH_2 - CH_2 - CH_3$, which may be written more compactly as $CH_3 - (CH_2)_2 - CH_3$. This homologous series, having the general molecular formula C_nH_{2n+2}, in its natural occurrence may have up to about 70 carbon atoms in the molecule. Its simple members are gases (as in "bottled gas"); then come liquids (as in gasoline, lubricating oils, etc.), followed by solids (as in paraffin wax).

From butane onward in this series the molecular formula is no longer unequivocal, since it may be expanded structurally in more than one way. For example, there are two butanes, C_4H_{10}, namely, $CH_3 - (CH_2)_2 - CH_3$ (normal or *n*-butane), and $CH_3 - CH - CH_3$
$$|$$
$$CH_3$$
(*iso*butane). The first molecule contains an unbranched, and the second a branched, chain of 4 carbon atoms. This is a simple example of *structural isomerism*. The two compounds are called *isomers*, that is, substances which are distinctive, although having the same molecular formula, because the atoms are differently arranged within their molecules. Isomerism is very rare in inorganic chemistry, but it permeates organic chemistry in many forms. With the more complex formulae the number of possible isomers approaches astronomical dimensions; for instance, the relatively simple molecular formula, $C_{30}H_{62}$, in the paraffin series (containing only two kinds of atoms), corresponds theoretically to more than 4,000 million isomers rendered possible solely by the great diversity of ramified carbon chains.

No other element except carbon shows more than a rudimentary capacity for the self-linking of its atoms. It is this unparalleled property of the carbon atom, taken in conjunction with its 4-valency, that accounts for the practically unlimited number of carbon compounds, and hence for the existence of the vast realm of organic chemistry.

Sometimes two adjacent carbon atoms are linked by a double bond of two covalencies, like the carbon and oxygen atoms in the molecule of carbon dioxide (Fig. 10). The simplest example is seen in the hydrocarbon ethylene (or ethene), C_2H_4, which is shown structurally as $H_2C = CH_2$. Triple bonds are possible also, the simplest example being acetylene (or ethyne), C_2H_2, with the structural formula, $HC \equiv CH$. Double and triple bonds are vulnerable or reactive positions in the molecules of such substances, which are called *unsaturated*, in contradistinction to *saturated* substances, like the paraffin hydrocarbons, which have no double or triple bonds in the molecule. The reactivity of ethylene is shown, for example, by its ability to acquire two extra atoms of hydrogen per molecule, when mixed with hydrogen gas in presence of a suitable catalyst (such as finely divided nickel): thereby it undergoes catalytic hydrogenation, passing into the saturated hydrocarbon, ethane: $C_2H_4 + 2H = C_2H_6$. This is a typical example of an *addition reaction*, characteristic of unsaturated substances.

A *catalyst* is a substance of which a comparatively small amount can promote a chemical reaction without itself undergoing any permanent change or loss. It probably acts either through the formation of unstable intermediate compounds, or through the production on its surface of a high concentration of the reacting substances.

Theoretically, hydrocarbons may be regarded as the parent compounds of a great variety of other organic types, in which various hydrogen atoms are replaced by other atoms or groups of atoms. It does not follow that this pictured replacement, or substitution, may be experimentally feasible; even if it is, the process may not provide the best way of preparing the substitution product. For example, ordinary alcohol (ethyl alcohol) may be regarded as hydroxy-ethane, $C_2H_5 - OH$, in which one of the six hydrogen atoms of ethane has been replaced by the univalent hydroxyl group, $- OH$. Actually, ethyl alcohol can be prepared from ethane in two stages, summarized in the following equations: (1) $C_2H_6 + Cl_2 = HCl + C_2H_5 - Cl$ (ethyl chloride); (2) $C_2H_5 - Cl + NaOH = NaCl + C_2H_5 - OH$. Each of these equations represents a *substitution reaction*, characteristic of saturated substances. In practice however alcohol is prepared by fermenting sugars, such as glucose, $C_6H_{12}O_6$, this reaction being induced by a complex organic catalyst, or *enzyme*, called zymase, which is produced in certain living microorganisms known as yeasts: $C_6H_{12}O_6 = 2C_2H_6O + 2CO_2$.

The typical group of all alcohols is — OH, attached directly to a saturated carbon atom. This group is not ionized, like the — OH group of sodium hydroxide, since it is attached to the carbon atom by a covalent bond. Indeed, the covalency is almost invariable in organic chemistry, except in specific parts of the molecules of organic acids, bases, and salts, which like their inorganic analogues, are ionizable. With such exceptions, organic compounds do not undergo ionization. Of the great variety of other typical groups of organic

chemistry, the carboxyl group $- C \diagup^{O}_{\diagdown OH}$, of organic acids, and the

aldehyde group, $- C \diagup^{O}_{\diagdown H}$, may be mentioned. Simple examples are

found in acetic acid, $CH_3 — COOH$, and acetaldehyde, $CH_3 — CHO$.

These, and many other organic compounds, may now be synthesized, or built up in a series of chemical processes, from elementary carbon, in such forms as coke or charcoal. At a very high temperature, usually produced by hydroelectric energy in the electric furnace, carbon reacts with lime (calcium oxide, CaO) to form calcium carbide and carbon monoxide: $CaO + 3C = CaC_2 + CO$. Water acts on calcium carbide to give acetylene and calcium hydroxide (slaked lime): $CaC_2 + 2H_2O = C_2H_2 + Ca(OH)_2$. In the presence of a suitable catalyst, acetylene combines with water to form acetaldehyde: $C_2H_2 + H_2O = CH_3 — CHO$. The addition of hydrogen to acetaldehyde, by catalytic hydrogenation or in other ways, yields ethyl alcohol, identical with the substance obtained from sugar; and the addition of oxygen to it, by a catalytic process or in other ways, yields acetic acid: $CH_3 — CHO + 2H = CH_3 — CH_2OH$ (ethyl alcohol); $CH_3 — CHO + O = CH_3 — COOH$ (acetic acid). These last two processes are simple examples of very important general chemical changes, opposite in character and known as *reduction* and *oxidation*, respectively.

Among many other types, organic bases are specially noteworthy. These may be depicted as derivatives of ammonia, NH_3, simple examples being ethylamine, $C_2H_5 - NH_2$, and aniline, $C_6H_5 - NH_2$. Aniline is at the same time a derivative of the famous coal-tar hydrocarbon, benzene, C_6H_6, also found in some natural petroleums; and the mention of benzene opens out a great new vista of organic chemistry, and brings us to Kekulé's culminating vision.

Although the innumerable army of the so-called "open-chain compounds" came into line with Kekulé's original structural conception of 1858, yet benzene and its great array of associates (the so-called "aromatic compounds," because many of them had been discovered in aromatic plant products) remained in a camp apart. For several years Kekulé failed to devise a structural formula for benzene which would harmonize his fundamental postulates with the extraordinary stability of the benzene system of six carbon and six hydrogen atoms. Then, in 1865, the flash of insight came to him at Ghent. In his own words: "I was sitting, writing at my textbook; but the work did not progress; my thoughts were elsewhere. I turned my chair to the fire and dozed. Again the atoms were gamboling before my eyes. This time the smaller groups kept modestly in the background. My mental eye, rendered more acute by repeated visions of the kind, could now distinguish larger structures, of manifold conformation: long rows, sometimes more closely fitted together; all twining and twisting in snakelike motion. But look! What was that? One of the snakes had seized hold of its own tail, and the form whirled mockingly before my eyes. As if by a flash of lightning I awoke; and this time also I spent the rest of the night in working out the consequences of the hypothesis."

So arose, from this vision of the Ouroboros ("tail-eater") Serpent (Fig. 11) of ancient Egypt and Greece, a symbol "half as old as time," the conception of the "benzene ring," or closed chain, of six carbon atoms: a fundamental idea which has been hailed as the crowning achievement of the doctrine of the linking of carbon atoms (Fig. 12). It should be mentioned that the double bonds shown in Kekulé's benzene ring are much less reactive than those described above in open-chain systems; accordingly, benzene readily enters into substitution reactions.

Meanwhile, Perkin (1838-1907), a young student at the Royal College of Chemistry in London, had prepared in the Easter vacation

*Fig. 11—The Ouroboros Serpent. The enclosed words, "the all is one,"
refer to the Platonic idea of the unity of matter.*

of 1856, "in my rough laboratory at home," the first harbinger of
thousands of coal-tar dyes, which became known as mauveine, or
Perkin's Mauve. Through this discovery and the way in which he
followed it up industrially, Perkin became the founder of pure and

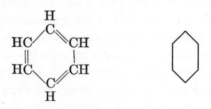

*Fig. 12—The Benzene Ring. Kekulé's original formula (left), with a
later abbreviated representation.*

applied coal-tar chemistry. Benzene and a number of other closely
related "primaries" found in coal tar, notably toluene (methyl-ben-
zene), phenol (hydroxy-benzene), naphthalene, and anthracene
(Fig. 13), gave birth to this great new field of organic chemistry.

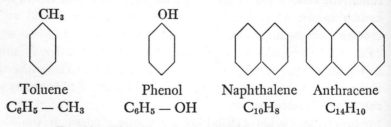

Fig. 13—Formulae of some Coal-Tar Primaries.

Kekulé's theory of the benzene ring came at the psychological moment; for it acted as the guiding principle in assiduous researches springing from Perkin's discovery and lasting even to the present day. Certain "primaries," actually present in coal tar, are converted by chemical processes into "intermediates," of which hundreds are now in common use. For example, benzene reacts with a mixture of nitric and sulphuric acids to give a monosubstitution product, nitrobenzene: $C_6H_6 + HNO_3 = H_2O + C_6H_5 - NO_2$. Treatment with iron and hydrochloric acid (generating hydrogen), reduces nitrobenzene to aniline, one of the most useful "intermediates": $C_6H_5 - NO_2 + 6H = 2H_2O + C_6H_5 - NH_2$. By the application of further chemical processes to aniline and other "intermediates" it has proved possible to synthesize thousands of purely artificial dyes, drugs, photographic chemicals, perfumes, explosives, and fine chemicals in general. These developments, of such profound economic significance, have all sprung from the test tubes and beakers in which Perkin— then little more than a schoolboy—prepared mauveine; and from Kekulé's somewhat later vision of the snake biting its tail.

At the present day, the hydrocarbons occurring so richly in natural petroleums offer a somewhat similar growing-point in synthetic organic chemistry, leading to the so-called "petro-chemicals."

In another sense the benzene ring opened the floodgates to a vast sea of other ring-systems, or cyclic molecular structures, which are no less numerous and important than open-chain structures. An almost unending variety of ring-systems is now known, containing from three to more than thirty atoms in the ring. These molecular ring-systems may be either *homocyclic*, consisting of carbon ring-atoms only, as in benzene and the structures of Fig. 13, or *heterocyclic*, containing other kinds of ring-atoms (notably nitrogen and oxygen) in association with carbon atoms, as exemplified in Fig. 14.

Monocyclic systems (Fig. 14) contain one ring only in the molecule; polycyclic systems contain more than one, as in naphthalene and anthracene (Fig. 13). The different kinds of homocyclic and heterocyclic rings, joined together in many ways and numbers, give rise to multitudinous systems, each with its own series of derivatives. Moreover, there is no practical limit to the ways in which open-chain structures also may enter into molecules containing ring-systems.

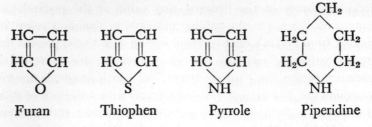

Fig. 14—Some Simple (Monocyclic) Heterocyclic Systems.

Such are the unending possibilities of the tangled molecular webs of the molecular world of organic chemistry, "built on a craftily complex plan, founded in deep simplicity." All life as we know it depends ultimately upon the startling and unique capacity of quadrivalent carbon atoms to link together in rings and chains.

Molecules of all grades of complexity are found among both natural and artificial organic compounds. Natural organic molecules (a great many of which are also susceptible to artificial synthesis) range over a wide gamut of complexity, from those containing one or two carbon atoms (with their associated atoms of different kinds) to those containing thousands. On the whole, natural organic molecules tend toward complexity, as may be illustrated, for example, by glancing at the large natural groups of the carbohydrates, the plant and animal fats and oils, and the proteins.

In the last analysis, the elaboration of all organic materials on the face of the earth depends upon the synthetic activities of the green leaves of plants, the tiny cells of which are the most efficient organic chemical laboratories in existence. It is in them that the initial synthetic operations are consummated. As the prophet Isaiah recognized long ago, "all flesh is grass." The organic chemist might follow out this thought by exclaiming of nature: "What a tangled web she weaves, Starting in the cells of leaves!"

Carbohydrates, and also proteins, function in building up the tissues of living organisms as well as in providing energy for their life processes. Carbohydrates include sugars, starches, and celluloses, and are synthesized in plants from carbon dioxide and water through so-called photosynthetic processes initiated in the leaf in the presence of the green plant pigment and catalyst, chlorophyll, and fostered by the radiant energy of sunlight. This energy enables the completely oxidized, or "burnt out," carbon and hydrogen in carbon dioxide and water to be largely deprived of their oxygen and built up into large molecules acting as storehouses of energy, such as glucose, $C_6H_{12}O_6$, sucrose, $C_{12}H_{22}O_{11}$, and starch, $(C_6H_{10}O_5)_n$. In further biochemical processes, still more oxygen is removed, and more energy stored up, in the constituents of fats and oils, such as triolein, $C_{57}H_{104}O_6$, of olive oil. When such substances are slowly oxidized in the living organism, by uptake of atmospheric oxygen, they give up their stored energy, in the form of animal heat, muscular energy, etc., and revert, ultimately, to carbon dioxide and water.

For example, the formation of 342 grams of ordinary sugar (sucrose) in the sugar cane or sugar beet, starting from atmospheric carbon dioxide and water, requires an intake of energy by the living plant equivalent to 1349.6 calories of heat; and this exact quantity of energy is released when the resulting sugar reverts completely by oxidation (whether slow or rapid) to carbon dioxide and water: $C_{12}H_{22}O_{11} + 12O_2 = 12CO_2 + 11H_2O + 1349.6$ calories.

This, in barest outline, is the natural *carbon food cycle*, shown diagrammatically in Fig. 15. There is also a *nitrogen food cycle*, in which the nitrogenous proteins, with molecular weights sometimes exceeding 100,000, are built up, and then degraded finally to carbon

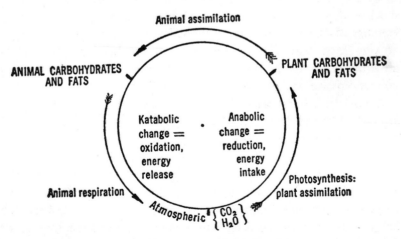

Fig. 15—*The carbon food cycle.*

dioxide, water, and ammonia, with an accompanying uptake and release of energy.

The most concentrated form of organic energy is found in hydrocarbons. These occur notably in the enormous subterranean deposits of natural petroleum, which may have been formed in the course of geological ages from vast deposits of the remains of marine and swamp life, through their subjection to decomposition by various natural agencies. When hydrocarbons are burnt in air, or vaporized and exploded with air (as in the internal combustion engine), two highly exothermic processes are concerned, namely, the oxidation of carbon and hydrogen to carbon dioxide and water, respectively. Consequently there ensues a copious liberation of energy in the form of heat. Now hydrocarbons are not assimilable, like carbohydrates, fats and proteins. Thus they cannot act as foods by delivering their stored energy to living organisms; but in such mixtures as natural gas, gasoline (petrol), kerosene, oil fuels, etc., derived from natural petroleums, they are used on a colossal scale through oxidation with atmospheric oxygen as sources of power for heating, lighting, and locomotion.

The energy-content of certain specialized types of molecules finds a spectacular expression in organic explosives, such as nitroglycerine, $C_3H_5O_9N_3$; these have molecules containing much stored energy and capable of undergoing sudden intramolecular oxidation, started by shock or detonation, with the instantaneous generation of enormous volumes of gaseous products (carbon dioxide, steam, nitrogen, etc.) at very high temperatures. Under such conditions, liquid nitroglycerine generates, in the twinkling of an eye, about 10,000 times its own volume of hot gases.

Among the almost unending series of natural organic compounds are pigments and dyes such as chlorophyll, hemoglobin, indigo, and alizarin; perfumes, occurring in the fragrant oils of plants and elsewhere; hormones (adrenaline, thyroxine, etc.); antibiotics (penicillin, etc.); alkaloids (strychnine, quinine, etc.); vitamins (ascorbic acid, etc.); and so on. The molecular constitutions of a great number of these have been determined; and as a rule this result has been followed in time by the artificial synthesis of the substance. One result of this work has been to establish the prevalence of standard molecular patterns in natural organic products. Another outcome has been the possibility in many cases of modifying these natural patterns, and preparing simpler synthetic substances retaining the valuable properties of the more complex natural ones. For example, the physiologically active fragment of the natural cocaine molecule reappears in the much simpler molecule of novocaine, a purely artificial substance which is much cheaper and in some respects even superior to natural cocaine. Work of this kind is leading to a rational system of therapeutics; but a great deal remains to be done in this direction.

From what has been said it will be seen that much is now known of the general relationships existing between molecular structure and physiological action. To refer to a different field, a still more detailed correlation has been established between molecular structure, color, and dyeing properties. Thus, artificial dyes of manifold colors and shades, which nature never knew, have been synthesized by the thousand, mainly from constituents of coal tar. About half the dyes in common use are azo dyes, built up from coal-tar "intermediates." These owe their color to an unsaturated molecular unit, $-N=N-$, called the azo group; and many other so-called *chromophores*, or color-conferring groups, are known. In general, it is hardly possible to overestimate the importance of molecular structure in organic chemistry.

A very important growing-point of organic chemistry at present lies in the artificial production of materials composed of *macromolecules*, or molecules of very high molecular weights. These include a great variety of synthetic plastics, rubbers, fibers, etc. As a simple example, the gas ethylene, $H_2C=CH_2$, readily produced from ordinary alcohol, is unsaturated, since the carbon atoms do not carry their full quota of hydrogen atoms. Under very high pressures, the ethylene molecules are rearranged into bivalent ethylene units, $-CH_2-CH_2-$, and hundreds of these units then link together, end to end, to form the long-chain molecule of polythene, $(-CH_2-CH_2-CH_2-CH_2-CH_2-CH_2-)_n$, a waxlike plastic solid, used in a great variety of ways.

The long threadlike macromolecule of natural rubber may be regarded theoretically as composed of thousands of so-called isoprene units, C_5H_8, linked together in a regular head-to-tail sequence, the dotted lines showing their points of junction in the molecular fragment of the natural rubber hydrocarbon depicted below:

$$\text{etc.} \vdots CH_2 - \underset{\underset{CH_3}{|}}{C} = CH - CH_2 \vdots CH_2 - \underset{\underset{CH_3}{|}}{C} = CH - CH_2 \vdots \text{ etc.}$$

Natural rubber has not been produced artificially; but many purely synthetic variants of the natural pattern are now manufactured extensively, for example, neoprene, in which the methyl groups ($-CH_3$) of natural rubber are replaced by chlorine atoms ($- Cl$):

$$\text{etc.} \vdots CH_2 - \underset{\underset{Cl}{|}}{C} = CH - CH_2 \vdots CH_2 - \underset{\underset{Cl}{|}}{C} = CH - CH_2 \vdots \text{ etc.}$$

Molecules of neoprene result through the ready spontaneous rearrangement (compare ethylene, above) and coalescence of molecules of chloroprene, $CH_2 = CCl - CH = CH_2$, which is readily synthesized from acetylene. Such a coalescence of a number of like molecules to form a molecule of multiple molecular weight is called *polymerization*; the simple molecule is the *monomer*, and the multiple one the *polymer*. Macromolecules are often, but not always, produced by polymerization.

Synthetic rubbers are not necessarily substitutes for natural rubber, as they show wide variations in physical properties, such as resistance to abrasion, oil, chemicals, and oxidation. They are built up in stages from simple organic substances, including acetylene, ethylene, alcohol, and benzene. It should be added that macromolecules abound in nature, profoundly different types being represented, for example, by natural rubber, cellulose, and proteins, these last in such diverse forms as egg-white and silk. The purely artificial macromolecules of nylon are modeled structurally, with important variations, upon those of proteins.

The complexity of organic chemistry is much enhanced by the fact that, as a consequence of work initiated by Pasteur in 1848, a "theory of molecular configuration" (or "space theory," for short) was advanced in 1874 by the French chemist, Le Bel (1847-1930), and the Dutch chemist, van 't Hoff (1852-1911). In a beautiful and classical research, at the very beginning of his scientific career, Pasteur showed that tartaric acid can exist in distinct right- and left-handed forms, solutions of which turn the plane of a beam of polarized light in right- and left-handed directions, respectively. This is a refined physical distinction; the chemical properties of the two forms are identical. Later researches showed that many other organic compounds can exist in forms of this kind, one of the simplest of them being lactic acid, CH_3-$CH(OH)$-$COOH$.

It is a matter of common observation that many familiar objects, such as the hand, the foot, gloves, shoes, and spiral shells, can exist in right- and left-handed forms. They are said to be asymmetric, or devoid of symmetry. Indeed, all shaped objects fall into two classes, symmetric and asymmetric. A symmetric object, such as a teapot, gives an identical image in a looking glass; an asymmetric image gives a non-identical image, that of a right hand being a left hand. Only solid, three-dimensional, objects can exist in right and left forms. Consequently asymmetric molecules (and, by implication, molecules in general) must be regarded as three-dimensional, and not flat, or two-dimensional.

The space theory, which has been amply confirmed, replaces the flat structural formulae of Kekulé by three-dimensional models, in which the four valencies of the carbon atom are directed toward the four corners of a regular tetrahedron (of which the carbon atom occupies the center), instead of toward the corners of a square. In terms of the later electronic theory of valency, the covalency is directional (incidentally, the electrovalency is nondirectional). It follows from the space theory that the "natural angle" between any two covalencies of a carbon atom is the "tetrahedral angle" of 109° 28″ (Fig. 16).

The tetrahedral model for methane is symmetric and therefore does not exist in right and left forms. If, however, the four atoms or groups attached to a carbon atom are of four different kinds the model becomes asymmetric. This condition holds for the lactic and tartaric acids, both of which exist in *optically active* forms, representing right- and left-handed molecules, related as object and non-identical image, as shown below in the space formulae, or *molecular configurations*, for the two forms of lactic acid (Fig. 17). The carbon

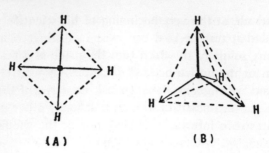

Fig. 16—*Methane, CH₄: after* (A) *Kekulé,* (B) *Le Bel and van 't Hoff.*

atom attached to four different kinds of groups, known as an *asymmetric carbon atom*, is situated at the middle of each diagram, and the arrows represent the opposed directions of rotation of polarized light.

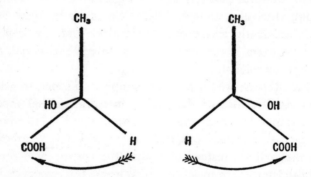

Fig. 17—*Molecular configuration of the optically active lactic acids.*

The tetrahedral angle is preserved in general, so as to minimize strain in organic molecules: for instance, in the symmetrical paraffin hydrocarbons the chains of carbon atoms take up a zigzag conformation instead of assuming Kekulé's plane rectilinear disposition. Similarly, large ring-systems undergo buckling or folding into multiplanar conformations, so as to maintain the tetrahedral angle and avoid the production of strain. Considerable strain is unavoidable, however, in double and triple bonds and three- and four-membered ring-systems.

Most of the simpler organic compounds have symmetric molecules; but asymmetry is very common in the more complex ones. In particular, the great mass of the organic material of plants and animals is asymmetric and optically active.

For ordinary purposes the flat Kekuléan formulae are still in general use; but for the finer aspects of organic chemistry, especially in the borderland with biochemistry (which itself may be regarded as an outgrowth of organic chemistry), it is becoming increasingly necessary to refer to the fuller spatial interpretation of the organic molecule, seeing that, for example, the right- and left-handed forms of the same substance often differ profoundly in their physiological action. This is a result of the asymmetry of the constituents of living matter. As Pasteur wrote in 1860: "If the mysterious influence to which the asymmetry of natural products is due should change its sense of direction, the constitutive elements of all living beings would assume the opposite asymmetry. Perhaps a new world would present itself to our view. Who could foresee the organization of living things if cellulose, right as it is, became left; if the albumin of the blood, now left, became right? These are mysteries which furnish much work for the future, and demand henceforth the most serious consideration from science."

Pasteur (1822-1895), a child of humble parents who became one of the greatest of all Frenchmen, has been described as "the most perfect man who has ever entered the kingdom of science"; he was also one of the most versatile in the range of his researches. His foundation of the subscience of STEREOCHEMISTRY, or chemistry in space, which now permeates the whole vast realm of the organic world, was but the first episode in a scientific career of unsurpassed brilliance. The space theory, arising from his first research, does not supplant Kekulé's ideas. Rather, this theory (1874) supplements that of molecular structure (1858), by extending the molecule from two dimensions into three: in Tennyson's words: "Science moves, but slowly slowly, creeping on from point to point."

During the present century, however, the advance of chemistry, as of science in general, has become increasingly rapid, in a kind of geometrical progression. Techniques have increased in number and subtlety, keeping pace with theoretical ideas which have grown constantly in refinement and complexity. The brilliant amateur, and the old-fashioned natural philosopher who took all natural knowledge for his province, have alike disappeared, to be replaced by professional scientists with highly specialized interests, knowledge, and outlook. At the same time the literature of scientific publications has become so vast as to threaten to engulf those whose work it records.

The material achievements of modern chemistry, accomplished by an ever-increasing army of workers, are astounding; but, more than this, the intimate chemical and physical knowledge that man has now acquired of his terrestrial environment represents the greatest of all his intellectual achievements; and this triumph of mind over matter is rendered even more complete by the proof that the unity of matter is universal, extending to the planets, stars, and nebulae. Science moves ever onward, and cannot "stand at gaze, like Joshua's moon in Ajalon." It rests with the moral and political leaders of man to see that science is applied in his service and not misapplied in his disservice: herein lies the greatest problem of civilization today. Man must learn to master and control himself as he has learned to master and control nature.

This brief survey of a vast subject may end aptly in some words written long ago by Lucretius, in the first century B.C.: "Practice, together with the acquired knowledge of the untiring mind, taught men by slow degrees, as they advanced on their way step by step. Thus time by degrees brings each several thing forth before men's eyes, and reason raises it up into the borders of light; for things must be brought to light one after the other, and in due order in the different arts, until these have reached their highest point of development."

The Four Elements and the Three Principles.

BIOCHEMISTRY

ERNEST BALDWIN

Ernest Baldwin

Ernest Baldwin was born at Gloucester, England, in 1909 and after attending local schools took his bachelor's degree at St. John's College, Cambridge. Further studies, with emphasis on biochemistry, gained him a Ph.D. degree from Cambridge University in 1934. From 1936 to 1943 he was a university demonstrator in biochemistry at Cambridge, and then university lecturer until 1949. His present position is professor of biochemistry, University College, London, an appointment which he has held since 1950. The main lines of Dr. Baldwin's researches have been in the fields of biochemical evolution and comparative biochemistry. Besides conducting investigations at Cambridge and the University of London, he has pursued his scientific work as a guest worker at the Marine Biological Laboratories in Plymouth, England, at several stations in France and, in 1948, at Woods Hole, Massachusetts. In addition to a large number of research papers and review articles he has written two standard works, An Introduction to Comparative Biochemistry, *an admirable little primer now in its third edition, and* Dynamic Aspects of Biochemistry, *regarded as a landmark in its field.*

Dr. Baldwin has been married for 22 years and has two children, a daughter, Nicola, age 17, and a son Nigel St. John, age 15. He writes, "I am not interested in politics except insofar as they affect income tax and similar unpleasant phenomena, but outside biochemistry I find a great deal of pleasure in music, particularly Bach and thereafter up to the period of Debussy and Ravel. I make no claim either to like or understand the majority of contemporary composers. I can't sing or paint or speak foreign languages with any fluency, but I do get a good deal of pleasure out of playing the piano with much verve and little accuracy. I am a confirmed pipe smoker of long standing and, like Dr. Johnson, I love to invigorate myself with wine but abhor drunkenness. I can think of only one other interest that might be mentioned and that is that, since my family moved recently to a new house after living for some years in a London flat, I find myself developing a keen interest in gardening."

BIOCHEMISTRY

ERNEST BALDWIN

Introduction

The use of chemical tests as an aid to the diagnosis of various diseases formed the foundations upon which the science of biochemistry came afterward to be built. The detection of "sugar" in urine and that of protein in urine are still among those used as aids to the diagnosis of diabetes and certain forms of kidney disease, but physiological chemistry, as it was formerly called, saw wider fields for the application of chemical methods to biological problems. In the course of time biochemistry, as we know it today, grew up and developed as an independent discipline of which physiological chemistry is now only a comparatively small part. Living matter of any and every kind offers a proper field for biochemical study, and of the academic and, indeed, the economic value of its discoveries there can be no doubt whatsoever.[1]

The study of living things began with the observation of objects visible to the naked eye and was later carried downward to more intimate levels by dissection and, later still, by microscopy. Eventually however further exploration of the fine details of morphological structure became restricted by the purely physical limits of resolution of the ordinary optical microscope. Even the most recent developments

[1] The reader can get some idea of the wide range and variety of subjects covered by present-day biochemistry if he will glance at the section headings of this essay.

in microscopy have pushed the limits of resolution very little further, although newer devices, especially the electron and "flying-spot" microscopes, show great promise for the future. In the meantime biochemistry has added much to the methods available for the study of biological objects and phenomena. Starting from the level of atoms and molecules it has been the biochemists' business to work upward, through large and complex molecules to progressively larger and more complicated systems, until in the end this "upward from below" line of progress meets that of "downward from above." Already, in fact, certain subcellular particles, known to microscopists as mitochondria, have become a favorite material for biochemical study.

Like other branches of biology, biochemistry can be considered as divisible into two main branches. There is first of all the problem of the chemical composition of living stuff, corresponding to the structural, morphological or "static" approach which, in the end, amounts to a very specialized kind of organic chemistry. It is the second, the physiological and essentially dynamic approach, that is most characteristic of biochemistry today; the primary question has shifted from "what is it made of?" to "how does it work?"

As a result of study along both these lines, studies embracing animals, plants, bacteria, protozoa, fungi and so on, it has been found that living organisms of every kind have a great deal in common. Among animals, for example, the over-all chemical composition and the general chemical dynamics are remarkably similar. Admittedly there are differences between different types and groups of animals, but the most striking fact of all is not that there *are* differences, but rather that there are not more of them.

More is known about the biochemistry of animals than of any other group of living things and, since in an article of this kind the material selected for discussion can necessarily be only a fragment of all that is available for consideration, the main emphasis here will be placed upon the biochemistry of animals.

Metabolism

From the structural viewpoint it can be said that living stuff is composed chiefly of water and small amounts of simple inorganic salts, and that the predominant organic constituents are proteins, lipids (fats) and carbohydrates—all relatively complex substances as judged from the point of view of classical organic chemistry. The chemical changes that go on within the structural framework of the living cell are characterized by the fact that they proceed far more rapidly in the cell itself than they do when the reactants are taken together in a test tube or a flask. The familiar sugar glucose, for example, is a very stable substance, even in aqueous solution, provided that it is kept under sterile conditions, but if living yeast cells have access to it the sugar is very rapidly decomposed with production of alcohol and carbon dioxide. Other microorganisms similarly attack glucose, rapidly and with production of other and different products.

The sum total of all the chemical reactions taking place in a living system collectively make up its *metabolism* and can be classified under two broad headings, first *katabolic* or breakdown processes, which involve the chemical degradation of complex substances into simpler materials, especially carbon dioxide and water. These katabolic changes provide the energy which is expended in muscular movement, heat production and other forms of what we may call "biological work." They also furnish energy for processes of the second, or *anabolic* kind; these are essentially energy-consuming and synthetic in character and play a part, for example, in the storage of foodstuffs in the tissues. Glucose, to take a specific example, is a fairly simple chemical substance which can be built up by an energy-consuming process into the complex polysaccharide glycogen and is stored in that form in the liver and muscles of animals. Very similar processes are involved in the production of starch, the chief storage polysaccharide of many plants. Glycogen and starch alike are extremely complicated substances and both are built up by the chemical union of large numbers of glucose molecules. Other anabolic changes are concerned in the production of new tissue material in growing organisms, and in the continued formation in the adult of numerous specialized substances such as hormones, pigments, enzymes and the like, quite apart from making good the general wear and tear of everyday life, e.g., by producing expendable materials such as hair, nails and skin.

Enzymes

Metabolic changes, anabolic and katabolic alike, can proceed as fast as they do in living cells only because they are catalyzed by the entities known to the biochemist as *enzymes*. An enzyme is a biological catalyst, i.e., an agent which accelerates some particular chemical change, and, although it participates in some way in the reaction it influences, is regenerated at the end of the reaction and so can be used over and over again. Very few metabolic reactions proceed at a detectable speed in the absence of the appropriate enzyme and yet the total number of reactions taking place in even a comparatively simple cell such as yeast is very large, from which it follows that the total number of enzymes is also exceedingly large.

A considerable number of enzymes have been isolated in the pure state and shown to be proteins. Sometimes, and notably among enzymes concerned with biological oxidation reactions, there is attached to the protein a specialized nonprotein moiety known as a prosthetic group and, in all such cases about which we have information, this prosthetic group plays a leading part in the reaction which the enzyme catalyzes. This point may become clearer if the reader is reminded of hemoglobin, the red coloring matter of blood. This consists of a protein, globin, to which is attached a prosthetic group known as heme, and it is to this prosthetic group that the oxygen is attached which the hemoglobin carries from the lungs to the tissues that require it.

These enzymic catalysts form the groundwork upon which all dynamic intracellular events are organized. These include a great variety of energy-yielding processes, such as the katabolism of fats and carbohydrates, and numerous synthetic operations which produce proteins and innumerable other important substances such as enzymes themselves, together with hormones, pigments and so on. For two decades or more research was largely concentrated upon the detailed study of individual enzymes and the particular reactions they catalyze, but more recently it has become not only possible and desirable but even fashionable to study them in groups and systems.

Many of these systems are extremely complex, and involve not only the enzymes themselves but in addition a larger or smaller number of accessory cofactors. These cofactors, or coenzymes as they are usually called, are required in some cases because they are, in effect, parts of the enzymes themselves, in others because they participate in the reaction or reactions undergoing catalysis. The nature of these cofactors varies over a wide range of chemical types; but one simple example will perhaps illustrate and clarify the point. Saliva contains a powerful starch-digesting enzyme called salivary amylase and this plays an important part in the digestion of starchy foodstuffs. If, however, saliva is freed from chlorides, which is easily enough done in the laboratory, it loses its starch-splitting properties. These properties are promptly restored however if a little common salt (sodium chloride) is added to the solution: chloride is, in fact, the cofactor of salivary amylase.

Perhaps the most characteristic features of enzymes as a whole are their susceptibility to heat and their extremely high specificity. A few minutes heating to 100°C suffices to inactivate completely the majority of enzymes. With regard to specificity, various degrees of "exclusiveness" can be recognized, but as a rule (and in this respect these biological catalysts differ markedly from such familiar laboratory catalysts as platinum black) one enzyme can catalyze one chemical reaction and one only. Practically every reaction going on in a living cell has its own particular, specific enzyme, but the reader must not picture the cell as a mere bag full of enzymes, for these catalysts are organized into teams or systems, each team carrying out some particular part or parts of the whole metabolism of the cell and being geared up to other teams. Every sort of chemical transformation going on in a cell is, in fact, more or less immediately associated with all the rest.

The chief classes of enzymes are (a) those which catalyze processes of *hydrolysis*, i.e., processes in which a given substance is split by means of water, for example.

$$\text{cane sugar} + \text{water} = \text{glucose} + \text{fructose}$$

All of the enzymes concerned with digestion belong to this group. A second group (b) catalyzes the transference of some given chemical grouping or radical from one substance to another. A particularly large and important subgroup of transferring enzymes is that involved in biological oxidations. In this case the radical transferred consists of a pair of hydrogen atoms and these are transferred from the substance undergoing oxidation to an appropriate "hydrogen acceptor." Often this hydrogen acceptor is a coenzyme and one example of this sort is catalyzed by an enzyme called lactic dehydrogenase. It can be represented thus:

$$CH_3CH(OH)COOH + coenzyme = CH_3CO.COOH + coenzyme = 2H$$
(lactic acid)   (pyruvic acid)

A third group (c) catalyzes *isomerization,* i.e., the rearrangement within a molecule of its constituent atoms.

Digestion

Normally, although enzymes can usually be separated from the tissues within which they discharge their biological functions and can be studied individually, they act in nature in an organized manner. In the processes of digestion, for example, the food material is submitted to the action of a series of hydrolytic enzymes as it passes along the alimentary canal from mouth to anus. Each of these digestive enzymes individually can catalyze one particular step or one small group of similar steps in digestive hydrolysis, but digestion does not proceed in a series of discrete steps or stages; it is, rather, an organized procession of chemical events, the products of activity of one enzyme becoming the substrate of the next enzyme in the chain. All the enzymes concerned in digestion are members of the class of "hydrolases."

The over-all result of digestion is that the complex molecules making up the food are broken down into their chemically simpler constituent materials, a necessary preliminary to their absorption by the digestive tract. For instance, the large, complex molecules of starch and glycogen are broken down into molecules of the simple sugar glucose, a process in which several enzymes are concerned, viz., salivary amylase, a similar amylase produced by the pancreas, and the intestinal enzyme maltase. The two amylases break down starch into maltose, the molecule of which is only twice the size of that of glucose. Even so, maltose cannot be absorbed as such and its formation is followed by its decomposition into glucose by the enzyme maltase.

Proteins similarly are chemically dismantled and in this case the final products of digestion are comparatively simple substances known as amino acids. This time an even larger number of enzymes are involved, including the pepsin of gastric juice, trypsin and chymotrypsin, contributed by the pancreas, and a large number of other enzymes known as peptidases which arise partly in the pancreatic juice and mainly in intestinal secretions.

It is mainly in the form, therefore, of comparatively small and chemically simple molecules that the food of an organism is actually absorbed into the body, passing through the wall of the intestine, entering the blood or the lymph and being distributed thereby to the body as a whole.

Storage of Fat and Carbohydrate

Fats and carbohydrates can be stored in the body, the former to an almost unlimited extent, as witness the professional "fat men" whose fat-storing prowess can be appraised at most fairs and side shows for a modest charge. Carbohydrate material is stored in the form of glycogen, the principal storage house for which is the liver, but the capacity of the latter is limited. Carbohydrate can also be stored, though again to a limited extent and again in the form of glycogen, in the muscles, but if more carbohydrate material is ingested than can be accommodated in the storage space available, the excess is transformed into fat and deposited in the fat depots of the body.

The nature of the fat present in these depots is, chemically speaking, exceedingly complicated, for part is derived directly from the food fat and part by the transformation into fat of excess carbohydrate, so that the nature but not the quantity of the depot fat is open to modification by the nature of the food fat. The *amount* of fat stored is influenced however by the amount of carbohydrate consumed, even if no fat at all is eaten. The acquisition of a slim figure means deprivation of starchy as well as fatty foods, and even proteins must be kept to a low level.

The reserves of carbohydrate on the other hand consist entirely of glycogen, a polysaccharide that is built up exclusively from glucose and resembles the more familiar starch in many respects. Glycogen is the hub about which the wheel of carbohydrate metabolism revolves in the animal kingdom; polysaccharides containing sugars other than glucose play important parts in the storage and metabolism of carbohydrate material in plants, but have little or nothing to do in animals. Being formed as it is entirely of glucose units, the composition of glycogen is not influenced by the nature of the carbohydrates ingested. The main product of the digestion of a carbohydrate meal is, as has already been mentioned, glucose itself, which can yield glycogen directly, but appreciable quantities of certain other sugars are also produced, absorbed and subsequently transformed into glucose and in this way also contribute to the synthesis of glycogen.

Function and Metabolism of Protein Foods

Proteins are built up entirely from amino acids. The latter are relatively simple, nitrogen-containing substances which behave both as acids and as bases at one and the same time. Proteins are built up from large numbers of these amino-acid units, the acidic group of one being united with the basic group of another. The resulting long chains of amino-acid units can assume a great variety of forms; sometimes they are exceedingly insoluble and aggregate together to form skin and hair; some have catalytic properties and are, in fact, enzymes; in others again the chain becomes coiled up to form virtually structureless, soluble molecules like those of egg white (egg albumin).

Unlike fats and carbohydrates, proteins and the products of their digestive breakdown, the amino acids, are not stored in the body to any great extent except during periods of tissue growth, e.g., during pregnancy and childhood or during convalescence after a wasting illness; in these exceptional cases, new tissue proteins are being laid down and amino acids are accordingly retained for their formation. Now proteins have a unique importance in that they are the body's principal source of nitrogen, which is of enormous importance in the animal body, entering into the composition not only of proteins but of many other substances as well. Even during periods of protein deprivation, and even indeed during total starvation, small amounts of nitrogenous substances are excreted in the urine. This nitrogen arises from metabolism of proteins and amino acids in the body, metabolism which still goes on so long as the animal is alive at all. If nitrogen thus wasted is not replaced, the nitrogen necessary for maintenance of the essential processes of keeping alive is found by breaking down some of the proteins of the tissues, especially those of the muscles, and it follows that an adequate supply of protein must always be included in the diet if loss of weight, emaciation and eventual death are not to result.

The question of adequacy has been much discussed in the past and is an important problem of rationing in times of war and famine. If too little protein is consumed the organism loses more nitrogen than it gains, and makes good the over-all deficit by breaking down its own tissues. If input is equal to output, however, a state known as nitrogenous equilibrium is attained, and much work has gone into determinations of the quantity and quality of protein food required just to maintain this condition of equilibrium. According to the classical work of the German nutritionist Rubner and his associates, something of the order of 100 gm of mixed protein is required daily, but in later experiments on himself Chittenden, an American biochemist, found that he could keep himself in equilibrium on only 30-35 gm protein daily and, moreover, his health improved during the period of the experiments. But the disparity between these estimates does not reflect differences in individual requirements but differences rather in the nutritional value of the different proteins.

The essential function of protein food is that of supplying the animal with certain particular amino acids. Altogether some 20-25 different chemical species of amino acids are known to occur in proteins and of these the animal body can synthesize some by its own resources even if its diet does not contain them, but there remain some ten or a dozen which are said to be "essential"; essential because, although they enter into its structure and metabolism, the animal cannot synthesize them for itself and has perforce to rely on

its food proteins. The list of essential amino acids includes such substances as histidine, lysine and tryptophan, some of the more complex
members of the amino-acid family (see Fig. 1). If nitrogenous equilibrium is to be maintained, therefore, the dietary protein must supply enough of each and every one of those amino acids that are essential. But proteins vary widely in chemical composition as far as
their amino-acid constituents are concerned, and it is worthy of mention that certain plant proteins are totally devoid of certain of the
essential amino acids, notably the maize protein, zein. This protein
contains no tryptophan and no lysine, both of which figure on the
list of essential amino acids, and consequently, if zein were the only
protein present in the diet, nitrogenous equilibrium could never be
attained, no matter how much might be consumed. Some classical
experiments carried out by the American biochemists Osborne and
Mendel showed that if young rats were kept on diets of which zein
formed the sole protein, they lost weight and would have died if the

NON-ESSENTIAL

$CH_2(NH_2)COOH$
glycine

$CH_3CH(NH_2)COOH$
alanine

COOH
|
CH_2
|
CH_2
|
$CH(NH_2)COOH$
glutamic acid

ESSENTIAL

$CH_2CH(NH_2)COOH$
tryptophan

NH_2
|
CH_2
|
CH_2
|
CH_2
|
CH_2
|
$CH(NH_2)COOH$
lysine

Fig. 1—*Formulae of some amino acids.*

experiment were continued. If tryptophan were added to the diet the
animals maintained their weight but failed to grow, and only when
the other missing amino acid, lysine, was also provided was there any
resumption of normal growth.

Generally speaking, animal proteins such as are present in meat,
fish, eggs, cheese and milk are much richer in essential amino acids

and are therefore of higher nutritional value than are plant proteins. Correspondingly less animal protein need therefore be consumed for the maintenance of nitrogenous equilibrium than if the food consists mainly of cereals and pulse. In Chittenden's experiments animal proteins of high nutritional value were used exclusively whereas, in the older work of the Rubner school, where a mixture of plant and animal proteins was taken, a three times larger total protein intake was required to attain the equilibrium condition.

The primary and essential function of protein foodstuffs is, then, that of providing a sufficiency of all the essential amino acids required for the maintenance of body structure and of the body machinery. Indeed, protein food can be totally replaced by mixtures of purified amino acids. This has been done in experiments on dogs and on groups of medical students, none of which experienced any untoward consequences as a result. When, however, the essential amino acids are taken in the form of protein, the essential components are invariably accompanied by relatively large quantities of non-essential amino acids, such as glycine and alanine. In any case the vast majority of human beings take considerably more protein than the minimum necessary for the maintenance of nitrogenous equilibrium, so that in either case a larger or smaller surplus of amino-acid material remains when the immediate requirements of the tissues have been satisfied. The surplus amino acids are not wasted; instead they undergo chemical manipulations which divert them into the pathways of carbohydrate and fat metabolism. Some contribute to the carbohydrate stores and are accordingly said to be glucogenic; others, which give rise to fats, are said to be ketogenic. It is thus possible to lay down fat or glycogen in an animal by feeding massive meals consisting wholly of protein.

We have already noted the inability of the animal body to store amino acids or proteins as such. Any amino acids over and above the amount required to satisfy the immediate needs of the tissues are treated as surplus material. The nitrogenous part of the molecules is removed and excreted, and it is from the residual nitrogen-free materials, known as α-keto-acids, that new fat and new carbohydrate are elaborated.

The removal of the nitrogen-containing part of the molecule is known as deamination and is catalyzed by means of a transferring enzyme. A superfluous amino-acid molecule reacts with α-ketoglutaric acid (see Fig. 2). The latter, which arises in the normal course of carbohydrate metabolism, takes over the nitrogenous part of the molecule so that the latter becomes an α-keto-acid available for conversion into fat or carbohydrate, while the α-ketoglutaric acid is converted into glutamic acid. Subsequent further reactions detach the nitrogenous radical from this glutamic acid so that α-ketoglutaric acid is regenerated and can be used all over again.

Starting with surplus amino acids, then, we arrive at two new sets of products: first the α-keto-acids which contribute to the fat and carbohydrate stores of the body, while the second product consists of the nitrogen-containing groups of glutamic acid molecules. These groups, as has been said, are removed and subsequently excreted. In some animals they are split off and excreted in the form of ammonia; in others they are put through a series of anabolic reactions leading to the formation of urea, which is excreted as such; in yet others a different series of anabolic processes leads to the formation and excretion of uric acid. These points are summarized in Fig. 2.

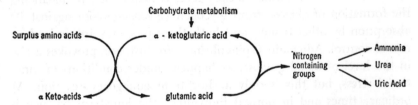

Fig. 2—To illustrate deamination and formation of excretory products.

The excretion of ammonia is characteristic of aquatic animals as a whole. These creatures enjoy an abundant supply of water which can flush away ammonia from the blood as fast as it is formed. Now ammonia is a very toxic material; it is lethal to rabbits, for example, at a concentration of only 1 part in 10,000 parts of blood. Urea and uric acid, by contrast with ammonia, are comparatively innocuous, and in terrestrial animals, whose water supply is usually more or less seriously restricted, the dangers of ammonia poisoning are evaded by the production, not now of ammonia, but of urea (in mammals and amphibia) or of uric acid (in birds, snakes and lizards). This is an interesting example of biochemical adaptation to environmental conditions.

Metabolism of Fat and Carbohydrate

Fats and carbohydrates, together with surplus proteins, are mainly of importance as energy-yielding materials or "fuel," and in the ordinary course of events the energy requirements of the body are met by the "combustion" of a mixture of fat and carbohydrate. In normal individuals metabolism proceeds smoothly enough, but in certain diseases, notably diabetes, there is a breakdown in the normal balance between carbohydrate and fat metabolism and much has been learned about normal metabolism by studying these abnormalities.

The carbohydrate requirements of the tissues are met by glucose carried in the blood. This arises from glycogen stored in the liver. Normally the concentration of glucose in the blood is approximately 1 gm per liter and in the normal, healthy adult varies within very narrow limits. This normal, steady level is maintained by balancing the formation of glucose from glycogen (glycogenolysis) against its absorption by other tissues, and both these processes are under hormonal control. Adrenalin (epinephrine), for instance, provokes a rise in the level of blood glucose, as happens under conditions of emotional stress, but this is only a short-term emergency reaction. At ordinary times and in normal individuals the long-term balance is held by the antagonistic action of two other hormones, insulin, secreted by the islet cells of the pancreas, and a so-called diabetogenic hormone produced by the anterior part of the pituitary gland.

In diabetes the blood glucose rises to very high levels, partly because of overproduction by glycogenolysis and partly because of the impaired power of the liver to manufacture glycogen from it. Injections of insulin correct this symptom and do so by encouraging the storage of glucose in the liver in the form of its polymer, glycogen. The diabetogenic hormone has precisely the opposite effects. If administered to normal individuals, it encourages glycogenolysis and discourages glycogen formation and storage, and it is by balancing the effects of these two hormones one against the other that the level of blood glucose is regulated in normal individuals. Carbohy-concentrations of these two hormones rather than by the absolute drate metabolism, therefore, is controlled by the *ratio* between the amounts of either. The characteristically high level of blood glucose found in diabetes is commonly due to deficiency of insulin production, but can be due equally to overproduction of the diabetogenic hormone. Whichever is the case, the injection of insulin, either by remedying a deficiency of insulin formation or by counteracting an overproduction of diabetogenic hormone, can bring the blood sugar to a normal level and restore normality of carbohydrate metabolism in general.

The presence of abnormally large concentrations of glucose in the blood of diabetic subjects is the reason for what is perhaps the best known symptom of this disease, the presence of "sugar" in the urine. This is because the kidneys have only a very limited power of holding back glucose and, when excessive quantities are present in the blood, are unable to retain the excess.

In itself the excretion of glucose in the urine is wasteful of glucose, which is an important fuel material, and is highly inconvenient because its excretion is attended by the formation of large volumes of urine, which leads in its turn to a correspondingly intense thirst. Nevertheless, glycosuria as such is not particularly harmful, but associated with it is another urinary abnormality known as ketonuria, a consequence this time of the derangement not of carbohydrate but of fat metabolism.

The katabolic breakdown of the body fats results in the formation of large numbers of small fragments, each of which contains only two carbon atoms. Normally these fragments are completely oxidized to carbon dioxide and water, but their oxidation is dependent upon a concomitant metabolism of carbohydrate. Now in diabetes, carbohydrate metabolism is subnormal and the 2-carbon fragments cannot be oxidized as fast as they are formed; instead they tend to accumulate and are diverted along an alternative pathway. Pairs of 2-carbon units unite under these conditions to give a group of substances known collectively as ketone bodies, viz., acetoacetic and β-hydroxybutyric acids, together with traces of acetone. All three of these are rather toxic compounds, quite apart from the fact that two of them are acids, and the accumulation of these in the blood is largely responsible for the dangerous clinical factors in untreated diabetes. The rise in concentration of these ketone bodies results in their appearance, together with that of glucose, in the urine of untreated diabetics.

Important evidence regarding the normal lines of metabolism has thus been obtained by experimental studies of diabetic subjects and we can now return to consider some of the main lines of metabolism in normal animals. The formation of 2-carbon fragments from fatty acids is a somewhat complicated operation involving a considerable number of chemical reactions which need not be considered here in detail. The same is true of the breakdown of glucose and glycogen, which yields as an important intermediary product a simple compound, pyruvic acid which contains three carbon atoms. These and certain other facts already mentioned concerning the metabolism of amino acids can be summarized diagrammatically as in Fig. 3 for the purposes of the rest of our discussion.

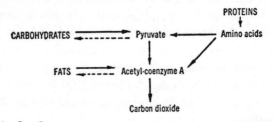

Fig. 3—Summary of some main lines of metabolism.

Ultimately, as the diagram indicates, *all three of the main classes of food stuffs are converted into a common intermediary,* viz., a derivative of the 2-carbon substance known as acetyl-coenzyme A, *and are oxidized away along a common pathway.* Pyruvate, arising from glucose and glycogen by a process known as glycolysis, loses one carbon atom as carbon dioxide and yields acetyl-coenzyme A. Glucogenic amino acids yield pyruvate, for it is at this point that their metabolic pathway joins that of carbohydrate, and hence give rise to acetyl-coenzyme A. Ketogenic amino acids also yield acetyl-coenzyme A, this time more directly, and join the pathway of fat metabolism at this point.

It is worth noticing, before we go further, that carbohydrate can be and indeed is synthesized from pyruvate, and fat from acetyl-coenzyme A (dotted arrows in diagram), but once the step leading from pyruvate to acetyl-coenzyme A has been traversed, no reversal is possible under the conditions that obtain in animal tissues. Consequently, while carbohydrate can be converted into fat, fat is not convertible into carbohydrate. Protein, however, can give rise to both carbohydrate and fat.

The Citric-Acid Cycle

The discovery of the nature of the common oxidative pathway and that of the mechanisms involved was due largely to H. A. Krebs, a Nobel prize winner, recently appointed to the chair of biochemistry at Oxford University. This has been one of the greatest recent triumphs in biochemistry. In simple terms it can be described as follows and summarized as in Fig. 4. The mechanism is somewhat involved but can be followed if Fig. 4 is carefully studied.

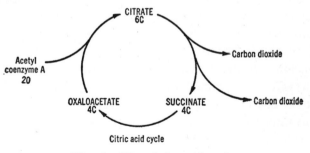

Fig. 4—The citric acid cycle.

Each molecule of acetyl-coenzyme A, with its two carbon atoms, unites with a molecule of a 4-carbon compound, oxaloacetic acid. The product, citric acid, with six carbon atoms, is then degraded step by step by a complex system of enzymes and coenzymes, loses first one and then a second carbon atom, each in the form of carbon dioxide, and leaves a residual 4-carbon substance, namely succinic acid. Further enzymic manipulations of the latter lead back through a series of successive reactions to the regeneration of oxaloacetate, with which the cycle began and which can then take up a further molecule of acetyl-coenzyme A. In this way a very small quantity of oxaloacetate can be used over and over again and can participate in the breakdown of relatively large quantities of acetyl-coenzyme A. Each pair of carbon atoms entering this cyclic system in the form of acetyl-coenzyme A, no matter what its origin, emerges in the form of carbon dioxide, *the common end product of oxidation of fat, carbohydrate and protein alike.* This important mechanism is known as the citric-acid cycle.

Energy Metabolism

The foregoing pages have presented an outline of some of the main features of the "how" of katabolism and, indeed, investigations of the "how" were in progress for many years before there was anything more than the most superficial of answers to the question of "why." Why, in fact, do living organisms make use of the complicated and often lengthy, step-by-step mechanisms they do when the same eventual results could be obtained by simply throwing the materials on the fire? If, ten or fifteen years ago, one asked a biochemist why living organisms oxidized this substance or that to carbon dioxide, the chances are that he would have replied "to get energy, of course." But that "of course" only served to conceal a massive ignorance of the mechanisms whereby chemical energy tied up in the food molecules is made accessible to the organism and how, having been made accessible, this energy is harnessed and transformed into mechanical work, as it is in muscle; or into electricity, as it is in the peculiar electric organs of certain fishes; or into light, as it is in fireflies; or into any other of the large number of energy-expending activities that are invariably associated with the business of living. To these problems we are beginning to find some answers, though much still remains to be done.

Mostly these problems center around a somewhat complex compound, adenosinetriphosphate, known familiarly though by no means contemptuously as ATP. Muscular contraction, electric discharge, light production and a whole host of synthetic biochemical reactions and processes are known to be more or less immediately associated with the breakdown of ATP into ADP (adenosinediphosphate), and

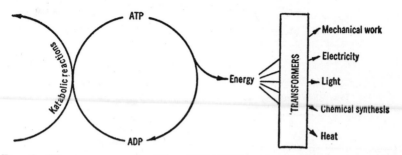

Fig. 5—*The energy cycle. The ATP/ADP cycle resembles a dynamo, driven by a motor in the form of katabolic reactions. Energy generated by the dynamo is drawn off and passed through the appropriate biological transforming devices to do mechanical, electrical or other work.*

this breakdown, in its turn, is known to be associated with the release of large amounts of energy. Each molecule of ATP thus broken down yields a perfectly definite unit packet of energy which might be called a "biochemical quantum." Now if this energy is set free by a simple, straightforward chemical method such as acid hydrolysis, it appears in the form of heat. If the breakdown takes place in a muscle, however, the energy appears for the most part in the form of mechanical work. Evidently the muscle contains some system that can act as a transformer of chemical into mechanical energy. As yet the precise nature of this "transformer" is not fully understood, but at any rate it can be stated that the contractile portions of the muscle act as an enzyme that specifically catalyzes the breakdown of ATP into ADP and, moreover, that *they shorten as they do so.*

If then the breakdown of ATP is at the back of energy-consuming processes as a whole—and there is every reason to think that it is— it follows that, since the amounts of ATP present in living tissues are comparatively minute, fresh supplies of this substance must be constantly forthcoming from somewhere or other. And, in fact, the formation of ATP seems to be practically the sole aim and object of katabolism as a whole. An example of one such sequence of reactions is shown in Fig. 6.

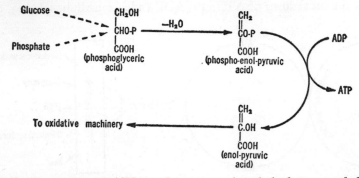

Fig. 6—*Formation of ATP in the course of carbohydrate metabolism. The "energy-rich" phosphate is written as* ~ ℗ *instead of the more usual* — ℗ *which represents an "ordinary" or "energy-poor" phosphate.*

The katabolic breakdown of, say, glucose is a step-wise process and at each step a new compound is formed from its immediate predecessor in the procession. At certain of these steps phosphate is taken up from the surroundings and incorporated into the new molecule, which then undergoes some perfectly definite and as a rule comparatively simple, enzyme-catalyzed reaction such as oxidation or dehydration. As a result, about the theoretical basis of which we know very little indeed and which therefore cannot be very clearly described, a portion of the chemical energy of the new product becomes intimately associated with the phosphate radicle, converting what was formerly an "energy-poor" phosphate radicle into one that is "energy-rich." Next there ensues a reaction between this energy-rich product and ADP in which the phosphate radicle, *together with the energy with which it is associated,* is transferred to the ADP so that a new molecule of ATP is synthesized and available for whatever effector activity is required of the tissue. Here again we come upon a process that is essentially cyclical in character, ATP and ADP undergoing a constant interchange, energy from katabolic reactions being used on the synthetic side of the cycle and transformed into one or another kind of biological work on the other.

Most important among the energy-yielding reactions of katabolism are those which collectively make up the citric-acid cycle, particularly those which bring about the oxidation of certain of the intermediates. For example, the oxidation of each molecule of the 4-carbon compound, succinate, is attended by the synthesis of two molecules of ATP from ADP. Smaller yields arise from processes such as glycolysis, and one ATP molecule is probably formed each time a 2-carbon unit is detached from a fatty acid. All in all, so efficient is the energy-capturing machinery of the body that, of the chemical energy which enters the animal body in the form of food, somewhere between two-thirds and three-quarters can be "trapped" in the form of ATP.

Obviously enough, food in the form of fats, proteins and carbohydrates must be provided to an animal in amounts large enough to furnish the energy it expends in the course of its everyday life. It will lose weight on less and get fat on more. Furthermore, if we know the energy expenditure of a given individual, animal or human, it is possible to calculate its minimum requirements in the matter of food. Elaborate experiments have been made in which animals and humans have been kept in confined quarters surrounded by apparatus which enables their total heat production to be measured with a very high degree of accuracy. Many such determinations have been carried out and the energy output of men lying at rest, men riding stationary bicycles, sawing wood, reading and doing other kinds of work are accurately known. The energy yields of many different kinds of food, measured again as heat, have also been determined, and when the amount of energy dissipated as heat by an individual doing work of some kind is compared with the amount of heat which would be generated by the combustion of the amount of material metabolized in the course of the experiment, the figures agree very closely indeed. Data of this kind form the basis of the calculations of calorie requirements which were so much in evidence a few years ago.

Vitamins

Whereas green plants, and together with them a few groups of bacteria, can synthesize everything their life requires from water, salts, carbon dioxide and some simple nitrogenous compound such as nitrate, organisms of other kinds are unable to achieve this. Animals in particular are synthetically deficient in the sense that they are unable to produce many of the substances required for the maintenance of their substance or machinery. These must be obtained from the food. For example, we have seen that animals cannot produce all the amino acids they require; for the so-called essential amino acids they must rely on their food. In the end this means that they rely upon the green plants, directly if they are herbivorous, indirectly at second- or third-hand if they are carnivorous. These essential amino acids are needed largely for the maintenance of body structure and for the synthesis of enzymes and a number of hormones, but over and above the essential amino acids there is a long list of nutritional requirements for which again animals have to rely upon their food and again, in the long run, on green plants. These substances are the vitamins.

The daily requirement for most vitamins is of the order of milligrams or fractions of a milligram per kilogram of body weight per day, but deprivation of any one of these substances leads to one or other kind of deficiency disease. That certain diseases can be cured by suitable modifications of the diet has, of course, been known for many centuries at least. For example, Hippocrates knew that night blindness, an early sign of vitamin A deficiency, can be cured by eating liver, a tissue that is relatively rich in that particular vitamin. Hippocrates' knowledge has an echo still today, for it is usual to provide the pilots of night-flying airplanes with ample supplies of vitamin A. Another long-familiar deficiency disease is scurvy, which is preventable and curable by vitamin C (ascorbic acid). Interestingly enough the early signs of vitamin C deficiency include extreme irritability and bad temper, and it will be recalled by readers of sea stories that outbreaks of scurvy on board ship were frequently preceded by mutinous tendencies among the crews. Captain Cook protected his crews against scurvy and, incidentally, earned for them the sobriquet of "limeys" by insisting on the provision and consumption of lime juice on his ships, the lime, in common with other citrus fruits, being as we now know a rich source of vitamin C.

It seems strange today that the establishment of the vitamin concept was delayed until the early years of this century. The notion that diet can influence disease was dismissed as nothing more than an old wives' tale by many (and the medical profession was no exception) who should have known better. The final conviction that had hitherto been lacking came mainly from certain experiments of the late Gowland Hopkins, for fifty years professor of biochemistry at Cambridge and one of the pioneers—perhaps the greatest—of biochemistry as an independent science. Young rats were chosen as subjects; young because, as they were still rapidly growing, their nutritional requirements would be large and they would be all the more likely to show the effects of any dietary deficiency to which they might be subjected. All the animals received a diet, adequate in amount, but made up from carefully purified fat, protein and carbohydrate, together with water and salts. One half of the animals received in addition a few drops of milk daily while the other half did not. The group without milk grew less rapidly than normal and later stopped gaining weight altogether and became exceedingly ill. The group receiving milk grew well and at a normal rate. Then, with a stroke of the genius so typical of Hopkins, the diets were switched over. The animals that formerly grew well stopped putting on weight after a few days and fell sick, while the remainder rapidly improved in health and began again to grow. This beautiful experiment demonstrated as conclusively as could be wished that there exists in milk some substance or substances of which extremely small quantities are required for normal growth and for the maintenance of the health and vigor of animals kept on a purified diet that was adequate in every other respect. Few remained unconvinced thereafter.

This experiment is representative of one of the two main procedures used in carrying out experiments on the nutritional requirements not only of animals but also of microorganisms such as bacteria. Starting with a diet or culture medium known to be inadequate to support the normal life of the experimental subjects, various likely substances can be added until the diet or medium becomes adequate. Alternatively one can start with a diet that is known to be adequate and remove one constituent after another until it becomes inadequate. The latter method has been used in many animal experiments and comparable experiments have been carried out on bacteria. Many bacteria can only be cultured in the laboratory on complex media. Many milk-souring organisms, for example, normally live in milk but can be cultured on suitable synthetic media, always provided that they are supplied with riboflavin. This substance is present in milk and if it is removed the bacteria are no longer able to multiply. It might be thought that if a cheap method could be discovered for removing this substance from raw milk the often troublesome phenomenon of souring could be avoided, but if this were done it would be undesirable in another way, for riboflavin is a vitamin for animals as well as for these particular bacteria.

Other experiments on other kinds of bacteria have brought to light the existence of a large number of bacterial vitamins or "growth factors." Not all bacteria have the same nutritional requirements and in this respect they differ markedly from animals, all of which, large or small, vertebrate or invertebrate, have substantially the same vitamin and other nutritional requirements. It is however noteworthy that the bacterial vitamins, where necessary, are usually identical with vitamins required by animals, suggesting that different though these minute, unicellular organisms are in every way from animals, their metabolism must probably be organized on a similar general plan.

Organisms that require this or that vitamin are said to be "exacting" for the particular substance concerned, and although animals as a whole are very exacting, some bacteria, notably some of those responsible for certain kinds of blood poisoning, are even more exacting than are the animals. Some of them require to be provided with about twenty amino acids and half-a-dozen or more vitamins, all of which are normally present in animal tissues. Bacteria with such extensive nutritional requirements as these are likely to find everything they need only in the tissues or tissue exudates of a living animal and so are commonly parasitic and, as a general rule, are highly pathogenic at the same time since they frequently produce powerful toxins. Some of these bacterial toxins have now been isolated and found to be enzymic in nature. One of those produced by the gas gangrene organisms, for example, is an enzyme that digests and liquefies the tissues in the vicinity of the infected area, thus providing a rich medium for the growth of the bacteria and allowing them to spread rapidly and extensively through the tissues; but this is by the way. Before leaving the bacteria and their nutritional requirements, however, mention may be made of a bacterial vitamin that is required by most streptococci, namely *p*-aminobenzoic acid, and to this we shall refer again presently.

The Functions of Vitamins

A good deal is known today not only about the multiplicity and chemical identity of the vitamins but also about their functions. For instance, vitamin A is now known to yield by oxidation a derivative which, in combination with the appropriate protein, forms visual purple, a retinal pigment that is particularly concerned with vision in dim light. Again, vitamin D is required to facilitate the absorption of dietary calcium, though how it does so is not known. In its absence bones are not properly or even sufficiently calcified, so that they bend under the weight of the body, leading to rickets in the child, and, after prolonged deprivation in adults, to the hideous deformities of osteomalacia. On the larger scale, the provision of vitamins A and D in the form of cod-liver oil and of C in the form of orange juice to every child in the United Kingdom during the years of the Second World War virtually banished rickets from the country, reduced the incidence of dental caries and produced what is probably the finest and best developed generation of children to be found outside Utopia. And this in spite of the rationing of fats, proteins and carbohydrates.

From the more biochemical point of view, most interest attaches to the B group of vitamins. Here the old alphabetical system of nomenclature has been virtually abandoned and the numerous substances covered by the old title of "B complex" are now known by their chemical trivial names. Some at least of the functions of most of them are already known. Thus thiamine (B_1) forms part of a coenzyme that plays a major role in the conversion of pyruvate to acetyl-coenzyme A (Fig. 3). Coenzyme A itself is a derivative of pantothenic acid, another of the B vitamins. Nicotinic amide and riboflavin form parts of the coenzymes or prosthetic groups of numerous oxidizing enzymes, several of which, like acetyl-coenzyme A, are intimately bound up with the operation of the citric-acid cycle (Fig. 4). Pyridoxal again forms part of the prosthetic group of the transaminases, the enzymes which catalyze the deamination of the amino acids.

Small wonder then that any deficiency of any one of the B vitamins leads to more or less serious derangement of normal metabolism and to the disorganization of the innumerable natural processes that depend upon and are indissolubly linked with it. Probably there remain yet other functions of these vitamins still to be discovered. It is even conceivable, though perhaps not very probable, that there are other vitamins as yet undiscovered, but in the meantime there are few fields of human endeavor that have already done more, and can do more still, to promote the health and efficiency of the whole human species, no matter what its race, its color or its creed.

Hormones, Antibiotics and Bacteriostatics

Among its other interesting and important achievements are those which biochemistry has contributed to pharmacology and therapeutics. The discovery of hormones, primarily an achievement of physiology, provided the raw materials for a vast amount of biochemical research which led to the eventual isolation, identification and, in some cases, the synthesis of these important bodies. Some of these substances are comparatively simple, others exceedingly complex. Adrenalin and thyroxin are two of the simpler ones; both are derived from the amino-acid tyrosine. Insulin on the other hand is very complex, being a protein, though a comparatively simple substance as proteins go. Mention has already been made in this essay of the use of insulin in the control of diabetes and this is but one of many cases in which hormones are employed in the service of medicine. Other examples include the use of thyroxin in the treatment of goiter and the use of the sex hormones in the management of sterility, habitual abortion and menopause. Among the more recent discoveries are the cortical hormones including cortisone, for the value of which in the treatment of arthritic conditions so many claims, many of them unfortunately extravagant, have been made. Side by side with these discoveries have been those of synthetic estrogens such as stilbestrol, compounds which produce the same physiological effects as the natural female sex hormones and which have not only the advantage of cheapness as compared with the natural products but are perhaps less likely to be carcinogenic. They are used, in fact, for the control of carcinoma of the prostrate gland in males, one of the few forms of cancer that can be checked almost indefinitely without surgical intervention.

These are cases in which the biochemist has taken over and enormously developed fundamental discoveries made in related fields of biological science. At least one noteworthy triumph similarly achieved lies in the field of antibiotics. Fleming's discovery of penicillin, originally an accident, came out of bacteriology, but it was only when biochemists came into the field that this important substance was concentrated, purified and eventually marketed in the pure form, for the isolation of the small quantities of penicillin produced by large-scale cultures of the mold, *Penicillium*, requires techniques of the kind developed by biochemists for the isolation of so many other important biological substances. Similar techniques were also used for the later isolation of many other new and potent antibiotics such as streptomycin, terramycin, aureomycin, chloromycetin and the like.

Biochemistry has also contributed much to developments in our knowledge of synthetic bactericides and bacteriostatics. The combined efforts of organic chemists, pharmacologists and clinicians have been concerned since the days of Ehrlich with attempts to produce synthetic chemicals which, while relatively innocuous to human patients, would yet kill off or check the growth of pathogenic microorganisms. In the case of streptococci in particular, the introduction of sulfanilamide and its present-day legion of derivatives has made it possible to cure many diseases of streptococcal origin, many of which formerly were frequently fatal, e.g., pneumonia, blood poisoning of various kinds, gonorrhea and so on. Sulfanilamide is not a bactericide but a bacteriostatic; it does not kill the responsible organisms but does check their further multiplication, leaving the natural leucocytic defenses of the body to pick off the invaders. Biochemists asked why, and it was the application of knowledge and concepts gained by the study of what is known as the "competitive inhibition" of enzymes that provided an explanation for the mode of action of the sulfonamides.

The reason appears to be that sulfonamide-sensitive organisms require p-aminobenzoic acid as a growth factor or vitamin. Little is known about the part this substance plays in the metabolism of bacteria but it is certain that in its absence they fail to grow and may even die. Presumably therefore p-aminobenzoic acid forms an important part of the metabolic machinery of the cells. However, certain other substances which resemble p-aminobenzoic acid in structure but are unable to discharge its functions, can also gain access to the site at which p-aminobenzoic normally acts. If such a substance and p-aminobenzoic acid are both present, they compete for possession of the site and on the outcome of this competition the fate of the cell depends. Sulfanilamide is such a substance. Provided that it can be applied at sufficiently high concentrations, as is possible because of its relatively low toxicity, it is able to compete with and exclude the essential p-aminobenzoic acid and can thus put an end to the growth and multiplication of the microorganisms. This notion of "competition" between a natural vitamin and an artificial structural analogue is an exact parallel of the phenomenon known to biochemists for many years as competitive inhibition.

The same notion has been widely extended. Already a large group of "vitamin antagonists" or "anti-vitamins" have been synthesized and their action tested on various bacteria. Unfortunately, few of these have proved sufficiently nontoxic for therapeutic use, though many have proved to have powerful bacteriostatic or even bactericidal properties, and this remains a very active and very promising field of biochemical research.

Conclusion

Such then are some of the facts that have been established by the application of chemical methods and concepts to living subjects; in short, by biochemistry. Every kind of living material—animals, plants and microorganisms of every kind—is a legitimate object for biochemical study. Indeed, biochemistry is perhaps more a way of thinking, a way of attacking biological problems, than a mere "subject." There is room for biochemistry and yet more biochemistry in every branch of biological science, in clinical medicine and in veterinary practice today, and, on the academic side, perhaps it is to biochemistry that we may look for a reunification of all the biologies into the one vast and universal Biology which time and inevitable departmentalism have so industriously dismembered in the past.

BIOLOGY

WARDER CLYDE ALLEE

about

Warder Clyde Allee

Dr. Allee died in Gainesville, Florida, on March 18, 1955, shortly be-fore his seventieth birthday, after writing this contribution. He was one of the country's leading students of animal ecology and behavior. He will be remembered no less for his integrity, his elevated outlook on human relationships and his courage in adversity than for his dis-tinguished professional achievements.

When I originally asked Dr. Allee to send me a few biographical notes about himself he sent me the following graceful account. I give it exactly as he sent it.

"I was born and grew up on a small farm in West Central Indiana not far from the Wabash River. My mother, who was 98 in De-cember 1954, was born and is still living on the same farm, a part of which her maternal grandfather had bought from the government when he emigrated from North Carolina in the early 1800s. We lived on the outer fringe of a sizable Quaker settlement. I was grad-uated from the Friends Academy the day after my seventeenth birth-day and began teaching that fall in a one-room country school called Frog Pond.

"I taught grade school for three years, was graduated from Earl-ham College in 1908, taught high-school biology during my senior year and for two years more, and received my Ph.D. in zoology summa cum laude at the University of Chicago in 1912. Summers spent in research and teaching at the Marine Biological Laboratory in Woods

Hole, Massachusetts, on Cape Cod, furnished my most important professional experience for the following nine years—much more important than the winters of those years, during which I held successive teaching posts at the University of Illinois (where I taught botany), Williams College in Massachusetts, University of Oklahoma and Lake Forest College in Illinois.

"Then followed 29 years of teaching zoology at the University of Chicago, with research there and at Woods Hole, and with interesting and somewhat lengthy study trips to Panama, California, and Utah.

"Age 65 brought compulsory retirement at Chicago and immediate appointment as head professor of biology at the rapidly developing University of Florida.

"Conspicuous activities have included the initiation of the founding of Ecological Monographs and Physiological Zoology, the latter by the University of Chicago Press. I have been on the editorial board of Physiological Zoology from the start and managing editor since 1930. I was invited to Paris, France, in 1950 with all expenses paid to take part in a colloquium.

"My long years of work with the Chicago Regional Committee of the American Friends Service Committee early brought me into close working contact with Miss Jane Addams of Hull House, with Rufus Jones and Clarence E. Pickitt of Philadelphia, and with many more, particularly with people from distressed countries in many parts of the world.

"I mention with hesitation, since I need no sympathy, that after an extremely active youth and young manhood, for years I have been a paraplegic confined to a wheel chair."

Dr. Allee was married in 1912 to Marjorie Hill, and had two grown daughters. His first wife died in 1945 and eight years later he married Ann Silver. Besides the places mentioned in his account, he taught at Utah Agricultural College and the University of California, and was Harris Foundation lecturer at Northwestern University (1938) and Prather lecturer at Harvard (1953). He was a member, among others, of the National Academy of Sciences, the American Academy of Arts and Sciences, the Philadelphia Academy of Science, the British Ecological Society, the Florida and Illinois Academies of

Science. He wrote more than 150 journal articles and his books, to mention only a few, are Jungle Island *(with M. H. Allee, 1925);* Animal Aggregation, a study in general sociology *(1931);* Animal Life and Social Growth *(1932);* Ecological Animal Geography *(with R. Hesse and K. P. Schmidt, 1937 and 1951);* The Social Life of Animals *(1938);* Principles of Animal Ecology *(with A. E. Emerson, O. Park, T. Park and K. P. Schmidt, 1949). One of his best known books,* Cooperation Among Animals, with Human Implications *(1951), deals with a theme close to his heart and considered in the following essay.*

BIOLOGY

WARDER CLYDE ALLEE

How did life originate? This most serious and searching question in all biology is usually avoided, especially in short essays. We actually know so little about how life began that much time is required for repeating and repeating our own uncertainties. This was not always true. I knew in my boyhood on a back-country Indiana farm that life had been created by a kindly, very wise, so-capable "Mr. Jehovah," and that was that. It is a far cry from a religion leading to that point of view to the one outlined later in the present chapter.

Many, not at all content with such a solution of the problem, are still puzzling away at the proper answer, which, I repeat, remains unknown. One of the better guesses is that when the earth was much younger its atmosphere contained no oxygen and the upper layer of ozone had not developed. Under those conditions all the ultraviolet rays of the sun reached the surface of the earth, including those of the short ultraviolet region of the sun's spectrum. Given a favorable temperature, moisture, and the needed concentration of inorganic chemicals, these energy-rich ultraviolet rays could supply the driving power needed for the formation of molecules closer to being alive than were any others then in existence.

This suggestion has received considerable, though not conclusive support, from a simple experiment reported in 1952 by Stanley Miller, then a graduate student in chemistry at the University of Chicago. Miller arranged a simple set of glass tubing and a flask in which he placed water, partly as vapor, and three gases such as were present in the early atmosphere of the earth. He then tightly sealed all openings. In addition to water vapor the gases were hydrogen, ammonia, and methane, which is the scientific name for marsh gas. These were made to circulate past a weak corona light produced by a constant electric discharge. Such a discharge was probably present when the earth was young. It was rich in ultraviolet rays as well as in other kinds of energy.

At the end of only a week's time, the water contained amino acids although none were present at the start, and none had been introduced. Amino acids are the "building stones" of proteins, and protein is basic for living protoplasm. This experiment did not produce life from nonliving matter. It does lend strong support to the idea that the organic compounds that serve as the basis of life were formed in some such fashion.

The exact nature of the first somewhat lifelike molecule, just like the processes by which it came into being, is unknown. It might have contained phosphorus, and the energy required for making a simple protein-like linkage could have been supplied from a single phosphate bond. All this synthesis would have taken place before the development of green chlorophyll, which is able to form the sugars and starches required by most present-day plants and animals.

All living organisms probably evolved from some such beginning, and all biology, in its diverse phases, traces back to these scarcely living particles. Some excellent students of the subject use biology as the covering name for the consideration of more general principles that involve both plants and animals. Material dealing mainly with plants is delegated to botany; that concerning animals to zoology. These in turn are broken up into smaller specialities such as protozoology, entomology, and mammalogy, which are still further subdivided.

A second standard division of biology is based on the type of study being made rather than on the kind of organism. As a result the discussion is broken into such categories as morphology, which treats of form and structure; physiology, which deals with functions of living things, or of their parts; ecology, which concerns relations between organisms and their complete environment; cytology, the study of cells; genetics and evolution, which have a chapter devoted to them in the present book, and many more including biogeography. Respectable, and even lively, books are available on each of these subdivisions.

Excellent summarizing essays on biology have been written using these topics as a working outline, witness for example the comprehensive survey in recent printings of the *Encyclopaedia Britannica*. This approach has not been used here primarily because of my feeling that it is too didactic for a book of this kind, that it would hurry the reader along and burden him with too many facts. Then, too, although I have great respect for the bodies of knowledge in each of these fields, and, year after year, I continue to be much interested by the research discoveries in many of them, much of the accumulated information, even in my own special field of ecology, frankly bores me.

I have adopted, therefore, a much less formal and systematic presentation, which concentrates on the material that catches and holds my mature, critical interest somewhat as it did in my youth.

I propose to say nothing about the difficult problems of classification (it is relatively easy to tell a cow from a tree but no expert really knows how to draw the line between one-celled plants and the simplest protozoan animals). However I shall discuss a more important area of uncertainty, the border zone between living and lifeless matter that has never been alive. The principles of ecology will be dealt with. Some of my experiences in a tropical rain-forest in Panama will help to illustrate them. In examining the behavior response of animals to their surroundings, I intend to consider the contributions of learning and adaptation, as well as inherited instinct, to complex behavior patterns. This leads to a subject which has long preoccupied my thoughts, the subsocial and social life of nonhuman animals, and of man. Three aspects of sociality require attention: the simple types of organization, the widespread tendencies toward the beginning of co-operation, the relative biological importance of proto-co-operative, and their opposite, disoperative effects. Finally, I should like to take up the relation between biology and religion, that is, a scientifically oriented religion which accords with my own interpretations and conviction. It is the unity rather than the traditional conflict between biology and religion—(a unity supported by recent biological findings)—that I intend to examine.

This is the discursive and somewhat personal path I mean to follow; perhaps in this way I can succeed in communicating some of the excitement of biology that continues to grip me after fifty years of study. I return now to the main thread of the discussion.

A thought-teasing suggestion is that an early kind of life was viruslike. At least we know that living, growing virus can form into apparently lifeless crystals, which start to grow again when placed in suitable surroundings. Thus apparently lifeless crystals of the virus causing tobacco-mosaic disease will grow if placed on a live tobacco leaf under proper conditions. However, there is always the objection that modern viruses live only as parasites, which appears to mean that they have undergone a long evolutionary degeneration. Perhaps their parasitic habit shows, however, that they are really so simple, as were their ancestors before them, that living as parasites is the only way they can survive in the modern complex world.

If life did originate somewhat as I have sketchily suggested, there is at least one potent reason why it is not continuing to be formed so today. Now, the suitable niches are all occupied by efficient living forms such as bacteria that would kill off newly formed, simple, living molecules by feeding on them.

Other possible relations of the viruses are suggestive. It is a well-known laboratory process in modern organic chemistry to shift the location of ions within the molecule. Indeed, a given kind of ion, hydrogen for example, may be replaced, say by sodium, in routine laboratory work, thereby changing the properties of the whole compound.

The viruses that are capable of being crystallized are tempting objects on which to try similar chemical techniques in the hope that the altered virus may present highly significant changes in its basic properties. Perhaps such man-produced shifts in the arrangement of ions may, for example, change a virulent disease-causing virus into a related form that is entirely harmless to the same host, and so cause virus evolution to take place.

These simplified, condensed suggestions regarding the origin of life and the chemistry of virus bring us to a conclusion of great and basic importance. Living matter, for all its complexities, consists of the same sorts of substances that compose the nonliving world. No new, special chemicals are required, and many of the basic techniques and procedures developed for different phases of chemistry can be applied successfully to the study of living structures and processes.

It is a long jump from particles that are barely living, if that, to the complexities of modern plant and animal life. Even the simplest one-celled plants, known as algae, and their counterparts among animals, the protozoans, are remarkably complicated physical-chemical systems. Hints toward bridging the gap between particles that seem to have only the beginnings of being alive and the most generalized plants or animals will not be discussed here. However, the somewhat similar problems raised in trying to cross the large gaps between different kinds of living things are dealt with in Julian Huxley's discussion of evolution, and in references cited by him.

Life, the central theme of this chapter, is hard to define. But living beings do have some common characteristics, the listing of which almost makes a definition of life. These are:

1. All can change other matter into protoplasm thus assuring the maintenance, growth, and repair of their bodies. All living things also destroy material, even of a part of their own protoplasm, and make use of some of the energy that is released.
2. All grow by complex internal processes.
3. All reproduce their kind.
4. All continuously adjust to their environment.
5. All show at least a foreshadowing of co-operation.

No one of these characteristics will separate the living from the lifeless. At least partial transitions occur for each one, yet the total of all five does become a relative, if not an absolute definition of life. Living beings are not sharply and distinctly set off from lifeless matter, and the physics and chemistry of living protoplasm, although more complex, are not really different from similar relations of nonliving stuff. This conclusion accords with modern ideas of how life originated. Although complete identity is not yet finally demonstrated, the assumption of similarity between lifeless and living matter forms the fertile working hypothesis of present-day biology.

The relation between plants and animals and their whole environment, including one another, forms the currently almost popular and very important field of ecology. Some of the underlying principles of ecology are summarized briefly in the following paragraphs. The simplest principles deal with the physical surroundings rather than with plants and animals. A pigpen is more easily described than the pigs living in it, though pigs are much more interesting and important than their pen.

Living processes are normally impossible in a vacuum. To be sure crystallized virus, or spores, seeds, and small forms, if surrounded by coverings that cannot readily be penetrated, survive prolonged exposure in a vacuum. But active living beings require an environment with which they can establish close working relations.

Living forms are under the influence of their surroundings, and, in turn, they influence them. Thus there is good evidence that the oxygen, which forms a fifth of the air today, was first produced, as it is still formed, by green plants as a by-product of the photosynthesis that makes sugars and starches.

Needed elements of the environment must be present above some minimal amount to be of use to a given plant or animal. This is known as the principle of the minimum. For example, although oxygen forms approximately twenty per cent of the atmosphere, it is only slightly soluble in water where, under good conditions, only about a half of one per cent of dissolved oxygen is available for respiration; often even less is present. As the dissolved oxygen content of the water falls lower and lower, it becomes more and more of a limiting factor. The principle of the maximum applies to the opposite condition in which richness rather than scarcity becomes the limiting condition. Too much rather than too little is present. Such a condition is shown with heat, but normally does not occur in relation to oxygen, except for the so-called anaerobic bacteria and a few other organisms that are oxygen intolerant. The associate principle of the optimum, when neither too little nor too much is present, can easily be made apparent. In a complex environment containing many important aspects, the ecological optimum may not be the best condition for the particular plant or animal so far as any one factor is concerned, and yet be the optimum for the whole community.

One of the most exciting principles of ecology deals with the remarkable fitness of the environment for life as we know it. In theory it is possible for a form of living stuff to have evolved on the cold outer planets, where the temperature is much, much lower than it is on the earth. There, ammonia might be the key compound, as water is with us. Ammonia has a considerably lower freezing point than water. It is markedly less fit as a basis for life since, among other considerations, it forms firm chemical compounds much more readily than does water.

Life could also exist at a much higher temperature than characterizes the earth's climate. A living system is possible at too high a temperature for carbon to be the common, basic organic element as it is with us. Silicon might be substituted under such conditions, although silicon is less fit than is carbon to form the basis for the complex physiology of life.

I still find it literally astounding, as a group of us put it a few years ago in a so-respectable and so-scientific book called *Principles of Animal Ecology*, that the surface of a solid body such as the earth—placed as it is, neither too close to nor too far from an energy-giving sun—does actually provide an excellent general environment for the living organism. It was possible for the late biochemist Lawrence Henderson of Harvard to maintain that this is basically "the best of all possible environments for life." This conclusion, published in 1913, has not been successfully contradicted to date, although, obviously, not all of earth's habitats, deserts, for example, are ideally fit places for life in general. Apparently, believe it or not, we live in what approaches being fundamentally, the best of all possible physical worlds.

There are ever so many more ecological principles, far too many for consideration here though each is significant, and the matters summarized can be interesting, too. Discussion of one more will suffice at this point. A whole set of principles centers upon light, and one of the most striking of these states that many reactions to light by both plants and animals are stimulated to occur when the intensity of light multiplied by the length of exposure reaches a constant value at or above the threshold of stimulation. The working of this principle is well illustrated in photography. Beyond the upset value for the photographic film, the more intense light calls for shorter exposure to produce a given effect. Oat seedlings, which turn toward the light equally if exposed to 0.00017 candle-meters (one candle power of light at a meter's distance is one candle-meter) for 23 hours, 18 minutes, will give the same strength of reaction if stimulated by 26,520 candle-meters for 1/1000 of a second. In each instance the product of the two values is approximately the same in candle-meter seconds, 26.3 to be compared with 26.5. Similarly, the horseshoe crab, *Limulus*, of the Atlantic coast south of Maine, in the presence of a concentrated source of light in a dark room, turns and moves away from it. When exposed to light from two sources that differ in intensity, it will turn and move away in a direction determined by the angles at which the two beams reach the eyes together with the product of intensity and duration of exposure to the lights.

In one of the first experimental series with the horseshoe crab, out of 48 individuals tested, all but ten reacted in fairly diagrammatic fashion; these ten gave unpredictable results. This introduces another principle. It is remarkable and significant that although 38 of these highly complex animals behaved in their reaction to light as though they were slow-moving guided missiles, the other ten reacted in an unpredictable manner. As we used to say at the University of Chicago, the reaction of those ten illustrated what we called the Harvard law of animal behavior, which holds that under controlled conditions animals do as they damn please. The facts are real; the name is a teasing joke.

Ecology, and other parts of biology are like that. Life sciences are not exact as are physics and chemistry, although they have certain fairly exact phases. Perhaps a sample of living conditions will make clear what I mean. For many of us there is a great pleasure in getting out into the field and observing life as it is lived there. Some three decades ago when I was young and vigorous, I spent a well-remembered brief period in the Canal Zone in Panama. There on Barro Colorado Island I drove my share of a set of long spikes into a tall tree, with Negro workmen doing the others. The tree rose out of a dense tropical rain-forest and towered above the forest canopy.

The spike ladder enabled me to climb through marked changes in climate. There was almost no air movement at the forest floor; it amounted to less than a mile a day during the windy dry season. Overhead, in the forest canopy, the wind moved at the rate of ten miles a day; farther overhead, entirely above the canopy, it was probably moving 24 times that fast.

The temperature was nearly or quite the same at top and bottom of the tree at night or under dense clouds. In the canopy, and in the bigger sunflecks on the ground, it ranged at least 18°F. higher during the day than it was in the heavy shade at the tree's base. The evaporation rate was some six times as fast in the tree tops as on the ground, and the intensity of light in and above the tree tops ranged from 25 to 500 times that on the forest floor a hundred feet below, or more.

The majority of animals in that tropical rain-forest—and there are large numbers of many different kinds of them—live on the forest floor where, apart from the easily avoided sunflecks, the environment is remarkably constant. Ants are the most characteristic animals present, though not nearly so exciting as jaguars or monkeys. The upper forest has the hazards of life in the trees added to the much more extreme daily changes in living conditions. I was distinctly disappointed both in the numbers of individuals and in the numbers of forms to be found higher and higher in the tree. Again ants were most numerous. Mainly they belonged to different species from those on the ground.

It is hard work collecting animals in the upper, or monkey, region of the forest. They can be shot, using dust shot for insects, birds and small lizards, for example. Even then they are not yet in hand and may never fall through the thick foliage to the ground. I well remember a sleek, short-legged, apparently slow-moving, lizard that repeatedly slipped away from my free hand. He handled himself very well as did other much larger lizards, birds and monkeys. I was at a disadvantage moving cautiously among the branches some 70 to 80 feet above the ground. I felt a distinct handicap in my lack of a prehensile tail. Certainly the animals are different in the different forest levels, as strikingly different as are the immediate environments in which they live.

Plants and animals, especially animals, reveal many of their ecological relations by their behavior toward both living and nonliving things about them. We have already seen that in certain of their reactions they may resemble physical and chemical systems, both in principle and even in many details. Also they may show more complicated types of behavior—too complicated to have been analyzed as yet into physical and chemical phases. Superficially viewed, the reaction of the horseshoe crab moving away from light illustrates both aspects, until one tries to break the diagrammatic movement, which resembles that of a guided missile, into its finer elements, with the legitimate goal of trying to find the simplest nerve-muscle components of the behavior complex. As yet, the best efforts yield only vague approximations at this level. Neither the machine nor the supermachine emerges too clearly.

Consideration of the behavior of plants and animals extends far beyond the limits usually set for ecology and, in fact, stretches the conventional limits of biology, not only toward the basic sciences, but also toward philosophy. One rather complete outline of the content of animal behavior recognizes a primary division into unlearned behavior on the one hand, and learned patterns on the other. These two major types of reactions have many fundamental similarities. Unlearned patterns do not usually run their courses automatically and mechanically. In addition to fixed and unchanging components, given as a result of some inherited tendencies released by a proper stimulus, even inherited behaviors contain a variable element that may be more or less adapted to the particular situation. Horseshoe crabs crawling fixedly away from light adapt to the inequalities of the surface over which they crawl. Conversely, a certain amount of inherited behavior enters into every form of learned activity.

An act is at one and the same time normally a function of unlearned or constant behavior and of learned or variable elements. In its more complex phases the inherited, constant activities are called instinctive, which is a much-abused word with many different shades of meaning. Under many conditions the variable, learned phase may produce an appropriately modified reaction that fits surrounding conditions; under other circumstances it results in an unexpected response to the given situation.

Analysis of an action into these two parts lacks reality. Constant and variable activities must not be taken as two more or less opposed natural agencies pulling the organism now in this direction, now in that, as they battle for supremacy. Rather, they are two different phases of the same whole. In inherited, innate, instinctive reactions the "constant" elements are greater than the "variable" ones; in intelligent behavior the relation is reversed.

Two bits of instinctive behavior that I saw myself may be helpful and interesting. Years ago, near the Marine Biological Laboratory at Woods Hole on Cape Cod, I was trotting back from a noontime swim in a hurry for food when I saw a wasp dragging a caterpillar across the uneven surface of the dusty road. The caterpillar was alive but had been stung into a complete paralysis.

I stopped to watch. The wasp turned before she reached the rude sidewalk. She passed near a low sturdy weed up which she climbed and draped the limp caterpillar over a low fork some few inches from the ground.

All this time the wasp was being followed by a small tachina fly, which would lay her own egg or eggs on that of the wasp. I knew that the wasp would eventually bury the caterpillar and lay an egg on it. The egg would hatch into a grublike larva, which would eat the still living, paralyzed caterpillar, only to be eaten itself by the grubs of the tachina fly.

I knew all this, and also knew that wasp and fly were reacting according to inherited behavior patterns, and that there was high probability, amounting almost to certainty, that neither had any foresight of the outcome.

The wasp descended from the weed and proceeded a few feet to a small burrow, which was a fraction of an inch wide and about that deep. She had dug the burrow before stinging the caterpillar. She entered and enlarged the little cavity, digging vigorously, and throwing the dirt, like a dog, out between her hind legs.

After a short time the wasp left the enlarged burrow and returned along the way she had come. However she did not remember the weed-climbing incident and did not locate the caterpillar immediately. Meantime the tiny tachina fly had stayed near the caterpillar instead of following the wasp on her digging activities. Finally the wasp found the weed, climbed it, brought down the caterpillar and renewed her slow progress to the burrow. Now the tachina fly followed, again keeping about a foot to the rear.

The wasp dug a bit more, dragged the caterpillar into the burrow, and deposited her egg. At that moment the tachina fly darted forward, dove into the burrow, presumably laid her egg or eggs, emerged, and flew away. The wasp filled the hole, leveled off the nearby ground and she, too, flew away.

In another instance, in a different part of the country, after the wasp filled the burrow she leveled off the ground for a few square inches making the spot similar, so far as I could see, to the bare ground elsewhere except for its being darker from the moisture which would soon dry. Still she hovered near giving the impression that she was not yet through. After a short time she settled down on a fallen cluster of three pine needles still held together as they had grown on the tree. It took hard work for her to drag the bundle of needles to the drying site of the burrow where she deposited them near the center of the small litter-free spot. The wasp then flew away as though entirely finished. The place where she had deposited the pine needles looked as casually littered as was the ground nearby.

All these complicated patterns were excellent examples of unlearned behavior, both by wasp and tachina fly. Yet mixed in with instinctive responses, which were dominant, there was evidence of adjustment to the existing irregularities in the surface of the dust, on the part of the crawling, burdened wasps. They each made changes in the size of the burrow, and in the behavior centering upon the weed or pine needles. The long pause of the tachina fly near the caterpillar hanging draped over the weed was similarly a distinct variation from her normal, simple instinctive pattern.

Such complex examples of unlearned behavior are well known. Simpler patterns are much more common and are shown even by single-celled protozoans, which also give evidence, at least in certain cases, of the beginnings of learned behavior. The unlearned, inherited patterns evolved as did structure; they are deeply ingrained —I sometimes say they are built in—and can be modified only by evolution, whereas learned responses are much more plastic. Both occur in the communal reaction of animals to each other, among nonhuman forms, as well as in man.

The subsocial and social life of animals shows two major tendencies: one toward aggressiveness, which is best developed in man and his fellow vertebrates; the other toward unconscious, and in higher animals, toward conscious co-operation. With various associates I have long experimented upon both tendencies. Of these, the drive toward co-operation, for reasons that will soon become apparent, is the more elusive and the more important.

Aggressiveness in the defense of territory is widespread, particularly among vertebrates. Many fishes show a high development of territorial defense, especially in the breeding season. Both intruding and defending fish seem to recognize boundary lines. The animal in its own territory normally fights harder than when it is the invader; further, its aggressiveness tends to become less spirited with increasing distance from its own territorial center. A few amphibians, many lizards, birds and mammals, including man, defend the boundaries of areas they occupy.

Fighting is often involved though animals of diverse kinds use warning displays both to prevent invasion of their territories and to repel an invader. The singing of location-holding male birds frequently has this effect, and song may be substituted for actual combat, somewhat as bands of howling monkeys engage in howling contests when near their common borderline.

The male tends to be more active than his mate in territorial defense; often she takes no part at all in such activities. Aggression of this kind is definitely related to that resulting in dominance hierarchies.

Social orders of dominance are clearly developed in many small flocks of hens. Frequently hen A pecks B, both peck C, and so through the flock, without B pecking back at A, or any of the hens pecking her superiors. The individual with lowest rank pecks none and is pecked by all. Variations also occur. In the most common one, A pecks B, B pecks C, and C, surprisingly enough, pecks A, thus forming a pecking triangle. The higher rank between a pair of hens is won by an individual simply standing her ground when meeting a stranger, or by threatening, or, more rarely, by winning a fight. Once established the order tends to persist.

I have studied nip orders in fish, peck orders in several species of birds, fight orders in lizards, mice, and in dogs, hook orders in cows, and various kinds of dominance orders in humans. In some species, supremacy is gained now by one and now by the other individual of a given contact pair. (After many pair contacts, it is possible for the observer to know which one wins out most frequently.) In other species the dominance is absolute.

The peck orders among hens give a fair illustration of the self-centered phase of group biology and show one form of the individual struggle for existence. This kind of social organization illustrates an important part of Darwin's theory of evolution.

High position in the social peck order confers privileges. We know that top-ranking animals feed more freely, and that high-ranking males of rhesus monkeys, sage grouse, common chicken, and other species have more ready access to females. Low social rank may lead to semistarvation in common domestic hens, to reduced sexual drive among cocks, to being forced out of coveys in California quail. Among many species, it forces the low birds in the peck order into inferior territories.

With some animals, high social rank carries responsibilities for leadership, or for guard duty; in other instances no correlation between social rank and social service has been found. With many other animals, as in groups of men and women, the true leaders do not necessarily hold high social rank. The leadership-followership set of relations are more nearly related to co-operative tendencies than they are to aggression.

Aggressive behavior, for all its dramatic interest and frequent importance, is not basically as significant as are the group-centered tendencies toward co-operation, which may well be called proto-co-operation. Among lower organisms, the beginnings of co-operation are entirely nonconscious. Natural co-operation in its simpler forms implies merely that the relations among cells forming a plant or an animal, or among individuals within a group, are of more help than harm.

At all levels in the animal kingdom, from the protozoans to insects and to man, and under a variety of conditions, there is safety in numbers, always providing that the number is not excessive. The dangers of overcrowding are well known and can easily be shown. The equally real dangers of undercrowding are often less easily seen.

Mass protection from cold is common, especially among warm-blooded animals. Grouped animals protect one another from many poisons and from other harmful chemicals. A concrete example of the greater safety in larger as compared with smaller numbers may be helpful. Among college students at X, or perhaps better F, university, a group of students who drive out to a drinking party may suffer little or no harm if the party is large, and the supply of alcohol is not too generous. In contrast, a few students consuming the same amount of alcohol run grave risks of automobile accidents on the way home, not to mention other adverse effects that are possible.

Living sponges literally can be torn cell from cell, as by squeezing them through the meshes of a common linen handkerchief. Providing enough cells are present, those falling in the water near each other fuse and grow into new sponges. In one carefully tested case, clumps of about 2000 cells formed new sponges; those of 40 to 500 cells died. Somewhat similarly, if a natural population is decreased until only a few remain alive, the species is in danger of dying out in that locality unless others move into the area from elsewhere. The species may become extinct even though in theory enough animals are present to reproduce themselves and persist. The heath hen is a good example. It died out completely in 1932 after a long last stand on Martha's Vineyard off Cape Cod.

Many animals and plants can produce a change in unfavorable surroundings, if enough are present, so that the group can survive. Some may die off in the process, but by dying they may produce such changes that those living with them, or others following, survive better and even thrive when they could not do so under the initial unchanged conditions.

It may well be that the first living particle in the world lived only a moment, or at any rate for a very short time. In disintegrating it could have neutralized a part of the poison that killed it. As a result, and for a brief interval, that particular tiny niche might have favored the continued existence of the next living particle to be formed therein.

Some vital processes are slowed down by increased numbers so that all present have a better chance to live. Spermatozoa of many sea-dwelling animals afford an example. Marine forms often have separate sexes that shed eggs and sperm into the sea where fertilization and development occurs. Scattered spermatozoa lose their ability to fertilize eggs sooner and live for a shorter time than when they are massed together.

Many biological processes carry on at a higher rate of speed in the presence of populations of optimal size and density. Such activities are slowed down both in overcrowded and in undercrowded populations. The length of time between first divisions in fertilized sea-urchin eggs follows this rule. Various kinds of protozoans show increases in the rate of sexless reproduction, if the right number are present, rather than too many or too few. Many divide more frequently when two asexual individuals live in the same small—really tiny—laboratory niche as compared with the rate shown by their isolated sisters in the same amount of liquid. Sexual reproduction may well have evolved from such a beginning.

Some protozoans live in colonies. These could hardly have evolved from solitary forms unless the colony of cells that remained attached together after division had shown the beginnings of co-operation to a greater extent than did the ancestral cells, which were scattered singly. The evolution of the many-celled higher animals from the one-celled protozoans was probably based on similar relationships.

Each advance in complexity of plants and animals arose through the natural selection of an increased ability of the individual elements (cells or organs) of the evolving stock to co-operate; the greater natural co-operation came first, and then it increased by selection following variation.

Charles Darwin recognized that a relatively large population is highly important in evolution by natural selection. Today there is growing evidence that evolution proceeds more rapidly in populations of interbreeding animals that are neither too small nor too large. It takes place fastest when a population is broken up into small breeding units, which are not completely separate from each other. Then, if a favorable variation occurs in one group, emigrants can carry the improvement to neighboring small units. Given time, and there is almost an endless supply of time in the world, a useful adaptation can be carried through the whole set of partially isolated groups.

The dependence of living beings on one another is shown by the repeated observation that all living things, from the simplest to the most complex, live in loosely knit communities; this is plainly seen in coral reefs or oyster beds, as well as in colonies of ants and among men. Further, the evolution of truly social animals has taken place independently in such widely separated divisions of the animal kingdom as insects and man. Societies could hardly have arisen so frequently and in groups of such unlike forms if there were not a strong, underlying level of automatic unconscious, proto-co-operation among animals. In nature, no animal is solitary throughout its life history.

As has already been stated, there are two types of social or subsocial interactions among animals: the self-centered drives that lead to individual advancement or self-preservation, and the group-centered, more or less altruistic drives, which lead to the welfare and protection of the group as a whole, or to the persistence of a part of it even with the loss of many individuals.

The germ of the concept of natural co-operation, along with that of natural selection, can be traced back to the early Greeks. Because of the idea of natural selection, and owing to the interpretations of Darwin's followers in the late nineteenth century, the self-centered drives of natural selection, with all nature pictured as being red in tooth and claw, stole the show for several decades. Today, balance is being restored. The picture that emerges from recent studies of social biology is one in which co-operations and their opposite, disoperations, both exist. Both self-centered and co-operative forces occur in nature, and each plays an important role.

The question arises insistently as to which of these opposing tendencies is more basic and powerful. A well-considered answer must be based on both short-run and long-run effects. I know no experiment that tests such matters directly. After much thought, and all the reading and research that I have been able to do, it is my mature conclusion that co-operation is more important. The balance between co-operative tendencies and those that are disoperative may be relatively close. Co-operation loses under many conditions. In the long run, however, the group-centered drives are at least slightly stronger.

If co-operation had not been the stronger force, the more complicated animals, whether insects or birds, or mammals, could not have evolved from the simpler ones, and there could have been no men to worry each other with their distressing and biologically foolish wars. Despite many known appearances to the contrary, human co-operative drives are as firmly based on an animal ancestry as are the disoperative ones that we think of as human evil. Our tendencies toward co-operation, such as they are, are as innate as our tendencies toward thinking. We could do well with more of both.

Now I come to the more delicate part of the task that I have undertaken. In order that my possible personal bias, if any exists, may be apparent, I should say that I am a citizen of the United States of America, with generations of American ancestors. Further, I am both a mature biologist and a working, though highly unorthodox, member of a religious organization. As I see it, our present-day European style of civilization is based primarily on religion, on other forms of tradition, and on science. The arts furnish color and interpret human behavior and thinking. Philosophy busies itself, or should, with trying to understand and explain the whole. The functioning of modern civilization, if it is to be properly effective, calls for the co-operation of all these elements.

Today, as in the past, religion wastes valuable time and energy quarreling with science about the relative importance of each, and over the proper division of opportunities and recognition, a quarrel that scientists now largely ignore. Philosophy invades the fields of both. Too often art becomes cynical and irresponsible, and philosophy scolds all and sundry, sometimes in no friendly voice, for the general unwillingness to let philosophy direct the whole.

Philosophy insists, even yet, on its discredited, age-old claim of having a special short cut to knowledge. Certain philosophers scold science, the most recently revitalized influence in civilization; and strong elements of modern religion, having attempted to use science to establish their claims, try to carry on alone in some of the most vital activity and thinking of our times.

Here, as elsewhere in human efforts, it is easier for closely knit elements in a situation to develop frictions among themselves than it is to disregard relatively petty internal troubles and make common cause against serious opposing forces. The enemies of the better aspects of our none-too-perfect civilization are strong enough to require united efforts from the arts, philosophy, science, and religion if they are to be properly met. Perhaps plain speaking from a somewhat aberrant friend of all these elements of modern social life may be helpful.

Religion has much to learn from science in objectivity, in willingness and courage to follow evidence faithfully, and even in judging what constitutes valid evidence. Particularly religion can learn from science the advantage of giving up the thundering "Thus saith the Lord" in favor of the more humble, and essentially more effective summary of "This appears to be the evidence." In short, religion can profit by becoming intellectually more sound without losing for a moment its proper emphasis on the deep emotions of man. And science has much to learn from religion. I mean from real religion, not from the semi-science of theology, which, too often, consists mainly of esoteric playing with words or the juggling of selected ideas.

Religion is ill-served by past and present emphasis on mystical and supernatural improbabilities. I hesitate to use the word "God" because of the wide variety of meanings attributed to it. Even so, "God" is a possibly permissible name, if one must have a name, for the personification, or, perhaps better, the abstraction, of all the best that mankind has been able to think, and feel, and do, of all the beauty we have created, together with all the natural beauty we can appreciate, and of all the love anyone has been able even to imagine. Such a conception transcends tradition and mere emotion; it has both power and dignity. God may be much more than has just been indicated; I do not know. This statement is by no means final; however, it is as close an approach to the truth as my knowledge of real evidence permits me to make at the present time.

Science has much to learn from a religion with some such concept of God, a religion characterized by social consciousness and honest thinking, combined with propaganda of the deed. More specifically, we scientists can profit by being more humble in the face of our immense ignorance even within our own fields of special study. We can also tone down our excessive pride in the discoveries we have been able to make, which are small in the face of the unknown.

Scientists can profit by a frank admission of awe and admiration for the great beauty of the objects and processes that we study, the charm of which often escapes us because of our focusing on detail. We will profit by being less certain that the more unattractive the interpretation, the closer the approach to truth. We will gain in the long run by working in our chosen fields more quietly. Science and mankind, and religion, too, for that matter, would profit if all men would live closer to the ideals expressed and practiced by the more devoted men of religion, and science.

I would make these suggestions in stronger language were it not for the fact that from a fairly wide and close relationship with many kinds of people, individual exceptions aside, scientists in general, and biologists in particular seem to be the best people I know. This may be an expression of prejudice based on similarity of experiences and on congeniality of temperament. I am inclined, however, to regard the differences between my scientific and my other friends as real, and to attribute it to the training furnished by effective exposure to the methods of science.

The biological sciences impose an especially effective discipline in that they combine an impressive need for precision in detail with a large content of mystery. The combination is the more effective in that a mistake in judgment concerning the mysterious, unanalyzed elements often is exposed relatively soon by some new, more penetrating measurement. The continuous checking of ideas against sound, objective evidence does something to make conscientious followers of the scientific method essentially more honest and less given to self-deception than are those skilled in the manipulation of ideas or words.

Despite my belief in the goodness of my fellow biologists, I admit that even study in laboratory or field, including good research work, does not necessarily bring forth some of the higher types of altruism.

When asked to recommend someone to teach biology in a deserving though struggling Negro college in the United States or in Africa, or in remote ill-equipped, much-needed laboratories in China or India, I have learned to turn to students with a strong religious background for those with vision enough to see that the opportunities may, in the long run, repay the sacrifices.

Let us take another approach. No one passes much time without being reminded that we are living in a world and in a country where international relations are based on war, or on threats of war. We need to examine frequently our responsibilities under current conditions for, like other animals, we men and women do not live in a vacuum insulated from the impacts of our time. For most, particularly for those who are fully mature, we should continue at our present jobs, or at something closely similar. The younger generation needs as many steady points of reference as possible. This is apparent when they come, as many do, to talk themselves quiet in the presence of a sympathetic, calm, older person in whom they place some confidence. In addition to helping maintain intellectual honesty and competence, we need to give full play to all activities making for emotional maturity and stability. We need also to know that the natural human fate is not to engage in a struggle for existence based on man's fighting tendencies combined with those of our animal ancestors, softened only by slight checks imposed by more or less artificial rules for human conduct.

The biological support for the doctrine of the inevitableness of war is now opposed by strong evidence indicating that the idea of a ruthless struggle for existence is not the whole, or even the major, teaching of current biology in regard to social philosophy and social ethics. This newer evidence, which I have outlined above, does not cast doubt on the existence of the human vices of pride, covetousness, lust, anger, gluttony, envy, and sloth. Neither does it remove indications that these find natural roots in behavior of nonhuman animals.

The newer biology strengthens decidedly the older evidence for a biological basis for the human virtues of faith, hope, and love. It supplies renewed indications that men have also inherited and improved on these tendencies through a long evolution. Modern findings strongly suggest that, as in all animal behavior, with its combination of learned and innate elements, the present high state of the seven capital sins just named is an expression of man's learned devilishness as well as of his inherited behavior patterns. The former belief that these sins are man's inevitable response to his inherited nature is no longer tenable.

We have come a long way in the present chapter, all the distance from considering how life may have originated, exclusively as a natural event, to a glance at some current phases of human thought and action, still without bringing in anything supernatural. It is impressive to realize that life has evolved from a barely living molecule until one animal—man—can think out a rough working pattern of his whole world and of much of the universe. The evidence is not all in and our ideas are far from final. Much research and thinking needs to be done, but the prospect for further progress is hopeful. Man's glimpse, in the large, of the advance from the first living particle to the best human thinking is the most important insight in biology, or in all of science.

EVOLUTION AND GENETICS

JULIAN HUXLEY

about

Julian Huxley

Julian Huxley, brother of Aldous, son of Leonard and grandson of the famous Thomas Henry Huxley, was born in London, June 22, 1887. He received his early education at Eton and Balliol College, Oxford, where he specialized in zoology. From 1912 to 1916 he taught at the Rice Institute in Houston, Texas, and in 1919, after military service in Italy, returned to Oxford as a fellow of New College and Senior Demonstrator in Zoology. He held the chair in zoology at King's College, University of London, 1925-1927, and the Fullerian professorship of physiology at the Royal Institution, 1926-1929. In the 1930s and '40s Huxley was active in many different scientific and educational enterprises, ranging from supervision over the making of biological films and service as secretary of the Zoological Society of London to membership on the General Committee of Lord Hailey's African Survey and adviser on East African education. Recognition of his contributions to education and his exceptional devotion to the cause of social betterment came with his appointment as first Director-General of the United Nations Educational, Scientific and Cultural Organization (UNESCO) in 1946, a post he held for two years.

Huxley's researches in biology have established his position as one of the world's foremost authorities on evolution. (He is since 1938 a Fellow of the Royal Society and has received many other academic awards.) He combines broad scientific knowledge and scholarship

254

with a profound critical and philosophical faculty. This cast of thought is displayed in his scientific papers and books no less than in his prolific writings for general audiences. Among his publications are Essays of a Biologist (1923), Essays in Popular Science (1926), Animal Biology (*with J. B. S. Haldane*) (1927), *and* The Science of Life (*with H. G. and G. P. Wells*) (1929), *all of which show his exceptional gifts as a popularizer of science;* The Captive Shrew and Other Poems (1932); Evolution: The Modern Synthesis (1942), *a masterly scientific work surveying great masses of data and various theoretical aspects of the subject and unifying them into a comprehensive interpretation;* Scientific Research and Social Needs (1934); TVA: Adventure in Planning (1943); Man in the Modern World (1947); Heredity, East and West (1949).

Now 68, Huxley's energy seems rather to increase than to diminish as he grows older. In 1953-4 he made an eight and a half month trip to Hawaii, Fiji, Australia, Java, Bali, Manila, Singapore, India, Ceylon, Pakistan, Iraq, Persia, Syria and Lebanon. He returned from this journey, which was punctuated by innumerable lectures and conferences, to greet the publication of his book, From an Antique Land, *an account of his travels in 1948 in the Middle East, with sections on its history and archaeology, and his own handsome color and black and white photographs.*

In 1954, also, he finished a long scientific paper on "Polymorphism and Evolution," started a new book on his most recent journey, and set off again on a visit to the United States to speak at the Columbia Bicentennial and to lecture all over the country on "Evolution and Human Destiny" and similar subjects.

Huxley was married in 1919 and has two sons. In light of his immense literary and scientific output, his professional travels and many other duties, it is hard to imagine he has any time for recreations; nonetheless, he lists several in Who's Who—*whether wistfully or as a report of activities pursued is not indicated—including bird-watching, swimming and "travel."*

EVOLUTION AND GENETICS

JULIAN HUXLEY

Life can be studied from two distinct points of view. These can be rather crudely summed up in the two words *mechanism* and *process*, or by means of the two questions "How do organisms work here and now?" and "How do organisms change in the course of time?" Most studies in anatomy, morphology, physiology, systematics, and ecology are trying to find answers to the first question, while those in evolution, embryology and most of genetics are concerned with the second.

In what follows I shall be discussing various aspects of this second question: how living matter reproduces itself, how it varies, how it becomes organized into different forms, how it is acted upon by selection, and how it becomes transformed in the course of time— in other words, genetics in the broad sense, together with evolution regarded as a process.

The work of the last forty years has made it clear that these two fields are complementary. We cannot understand evolution unless we understand the process of hereditary transmission, and we shall not transcend a limited and static view of the mechanism of heredity unless we study how it may be altered in the course of evolutionary time.

This was not always so. Biologists could not begin exploring the evolutionary implications of genetics before the fact of evolution had been established, nor could they begin to understand the bearing of genetics on evolution before the mechanism of heredity had been discovered. The first took place less than a century ago, the second less than half a century.

I shall therefore start by treating the two subjects separately, beginning with genetics. Genetics is the science concerned with heredity —the way in which life and its characteristics are transmitted down the generations. It is really extraordinary how many superstitions and false notions prevailed in the past on this subject.[1] Thus in antiquity it was believed that quite highly organized animals such as flies, bees, frogs, and even mice, could be "spontaneously generated" out of mud or putrefying matter—in other words that there was no mechanism of material transmission of living substance from one generation to the next. This notion was killed, so far as higher animals go, in the seventeenth century by Redi, the Florentine naturalist, physician and poet, who proved that maggots did not appear in meat when it was screened to prevent blowflies laying their eggs in it; but it survived in regard to microscopic organisms like infusorians and bacteria until dealt its deathblow by Pasteur barely a century ago.

Another widespread superstition was that maternal impressions could influence the characters of the offspring. In the Bible, Jacob is stated to have caused the birth of piebald and spotted sheep and goats by making the expectant mothers look at "pilled wands"—twigs on which stripes and patterns had been cut. In 1920, my wife, who was carrying our first child, was warned by our maid not to look at a large and ugly fish in the aquarium at Plymouth for fear that this should influence the baby's appearance.

An even more widespread error is the belief in the inheritance of "acquired characters." This phrase, by the way, proves somewhat of a stumbling block to many laymen: they ask, not unreasonably, whether all new characters that appear in evolution are not "acquired." However, the point is a purely semantic one. "Acquired characters" in this connotation are defined as characters acquired by the individual during its lifetime as the result of environmental agencies, or of use or disuse of organs. Characters of the former type include the tanning of white men's complexions by sunlight, the excessive vegetative growth of green plants in nitrogen-rich soils, the goiter induced by lack of iodine, or the succulence of plants in saline conditions; among those of the latter are the enlargement of muscles by

[1] See C. D. Darlington's recent book *The Facts of Life* (1953) for a pungent and learned account of prescientific myths and theories of reproduction and inheritance.

hard exercise, learning, the improvement of sensory discrimination by practice, and the growth of tendons in relation to the mechanical stresses they are called on to support.

The theory of evolution by means of the inheritance of acquired characters is often called Lamarckism, after the great French naturalist Lamarck, whose main works were published early in the nineteenth century. Although he believed only in the evolutionary importance of characters individually acquired through use and disuse, as the result of deliberate effort (or lack of it), the term Lamarckism is commonly extended to cover the inheritance of all "acquired characters."

Today we know that acquired characters in the above sense are never inherited, and indeed are not heritable. Any character of an individual animal or plant is always the joint product of heredity and environment. If there is a sufficient alteration *either* of the hereditary constitution *or* of the environmental conditions, the character will be altered. Furthermore, the hereditary constitution, as we shall see, consists of a highly elaborate system of material self-reproducing units or *genes*, each with its own specific chemical nature. During early life, this system interacts with its environment to set in train the processes of development, and these in turn give rise to the individual organism with all its visible "characters." Thus any direct effect of environment upon a character is exerted on a late stage of a developmental process, not on the genes underlying it. For instance, sunburning acts on the processes of pigment-formation in a man's skin, and cannot possibly affect the genes in the sperm-producing cells of his testes, since there is no mechanism for the transfer of specific or self-reproducing material from any organ of the body to the reproductive organs.

Indeed, it might have been deduced on general grounds that devices would have been evolved to *prevent* the hereditary constitution from being affected by environmental changes; for the primary function of heredity is to transmit a standard self-reproducing system which is adapted to the average conditions of the species' environment. If every extreme of hot or cold, of dry or wet, were able to alter the genes, the standardization would be lost and the orderly system would be disorganized.

We now know that a few environmental agencies can affect the genes directly. But these are all of particular potency, like X-rays, or ultraviolet radiation, or a few special chemical substances; and what they do is to cause the genes to mutate, by altering their chemical structure, with consequent alteration of their effects on development. No case is known where the effects of any environmental agency on an individual character are the same as those which it may cause the gene to exert by making it mutate.

As a result of the new point of view made possible by our new knowledge of the mechanisms of reproduction, heredity, and development, biologists have largely ceased using the phrase "acquired characters." [2] Instead they speak of such characters as *modifications* (of the individual), and classify visible variations into two radically different types—those due to modification in this sense, and those due originally to mutation, in the sense of an alteration in the genes.

In passing, this modern approach enables us to dismiss the old question of whether heredity or environment is the more important. The answer is *neither*; for both are essential, though in particular circumstances one or other of the two components may be more effective. Thus if environmental conditions are kept uniform, as when a sample of seed is grown in a plot of uniform soil treated with the same fertilizers throughout, any differences in the resultant plants will be due to hereditary differences in their genetic constitution. Conversely, if heredity is made uniform, by using seed from a pure line, any differences in the crop will be due to environmental differences, in soil or cultivation or fertilizer.

Normally, of course, neither heredity nor environment will be uniform, and then careful analysis will be required to discover what part of any difference between individuals is assignable to differences in heredity and what to differences in environment. This applies, for instance, to human statute or scholastic ability, or to differences in yield between crop-plants grown from imperfectly purified seed in a variable environment.

Another superstition prevalent among animal breeders is that of te-

[2] In order to make the inheritance of acquired characters comprehensible (as well as to have some model for hereditary transmission in general), Darwin advanced his theory of pangenesis, in which he postulated the existence of minute living particles or "gemmules," which were supposed to be detached from all bodily tissues and then to be transmitted in heredity. Later research, however, showed that no such mechanism exists.

legony, or the supposed influence of a previous sire on the offspring from a later mating. Although this is entirely groundless, it has led to many valuable female animals being rejected for pedigree breeding, because they had earlier been mated to "mongrels."

These myths and errors have now been dispelled by the advance of knowledge. The basis for a scientific theory of heredity was laid when, during the mid-nineteenth century, it was finally established that reproduction always takes place by the development of a piece of living substance detached from the parent. Sexual reproduction involves the complication that two pieces of living substance—in this case, single cells—are detached from the two parents, and then unite to form one. The cells which thus unite are called *gametes* or marrying cells, and the product of their union (the fertilized ovum in higher organisms) is called a *zygote*.

The next step was the demonstration that the essential element handed down in reproduction consists of a set of visible cell-organs, the chromosomes, which in each species occur in characteristic shape, size and number. Elaborate machinery exists for ensuring that each time a cell divides, the chromosomes too reproduce themselves, the original set becoming doubled and then dividing so as to produce two identical sets, one of which passes into each daughter-cell: this is called *mitosis*. In the process called *meiosis* or reduction, which occurs during two cell divisions before the gametes (sperms and ova in higher animals) are produced, the number of chromosomes is reduced to half, so that the gametes are *haploid*, i.e., with one instead of two of each kind of chromosome. With the fusion of the gametes at fertilization, the double or *diploid* number of chromosomes is restored, so that the zygote possesses two complete chromosome sets.[3]

Thus although the contributions of father and mother to the offspring (zygote) are extremely unequal in terms of cells (gametes)—the tiny, tailed, active spermatozoon or sperm from the one side and the bulky, inert, and often enormous ovum or egg from the other—yet they are equal in terms of chromosomes, each providing one com-

[3] In a few cases, e.g., the sex chromosomes, a chromosome-pair may be unequal, one member being reduced or absent in one sex. Thus in our own species, men have one large (X) and one smaller (Y) sex-chromosome, while women have two equal X's.

plete haploid set. Since observation shows that fathers exert as much effect as mothers on the nature of their offspring, the chromosomes were thus revealed as being almost certainly the organs of heredity, or at least as its material basis.

This self-reproducing system of chromosomes, operating by means of mitosis, meiosis and sexual union, was speedily shown to be a general characteristic of organisms, whether plant or animal, multicellular or unicellular, high or low in organization. In recent years it has been demonstrated in bacteria, and a simpler prototype of it appears to exist even in the submicroscopic viruses, on the borderline between living and nonliving.

Meanwhile in the 1860s, the first step was taken toward understanding the invisible organization underlying this visible mechanism. The Abbé Mendel, by a series of brilliantly conceived experiments, made it clear that the inheritance of certain characters must be mediated by units—factors or determiners of heredity—which are transmitted from parent to offspring, and recombined in all possible ways in the sexual process.

His results lay unheeded for 35 years. But as soon as they were rediscovered in 1900, biologists in many countries began to work along the same lines. Within a decade, it had been established that mendelian inheritance, depending on unit-factors and obeying Mendel's laws, was a general phenomenon; it occurred in every kind of animal and plant in which experimental breeding could be practiced; and today the list has been extended to include not only higher organisms, but also mosses and molds, unicellular fungi like yeasts, the minute and simple bacteria, and even viruses.

Furthermore, before 1930 it had been shown not only that mendelian inheritance was of general occurrence but that all inheritance (apart from a few cases of so-called cytoplasmic inheritance, by means of particles transmitted in the general protoplasm of the cell), was mendelian—in other words dependent on the transmission and recombination of discrete unit-factors.

In the early days of mendelian research, attention was naturally focused on large or sharp character-differences, such as albinism, or red versus blue flower-color, or hornlessness in cattle, which were easy to distinguish and to follow in inheritance; and for a time it

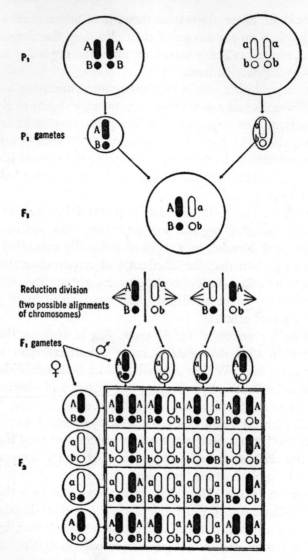

Diagram showing independent assortment of two pairs of chromosomes, A-a and B-b. Note that at the reduction division there are two possible alignments of chromosomes producing four types of gametes. By random union these produce the sixteen different chromosome combinations shown in the F_2 checkerboard. (From Principles of Genetics, *by E. W. Sinnott and L. C. Dunn, by courtesy of McGraw-Hill Co., New York.)*

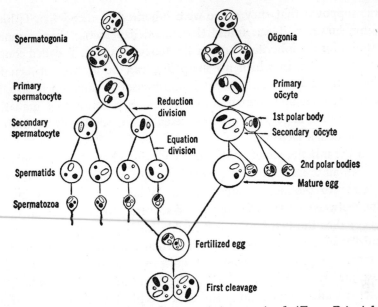

Diagram of spermatogenesis and oögenesis in an animal. (*From* Principles of Genetics, *by E. W. Sinnott and L. C. Dunn, by courtesy of McGraw-Hill Co., New York.*)

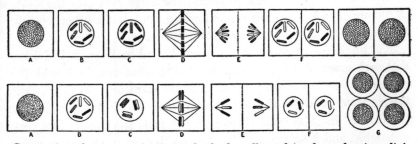

Comparison between mitosis in the body cells and in the reduction division which precedes the formation of the reproductive cells. The individual chromosomes are differently marked. In ordinary mitosis (upper row) it is evident that the chromatin is divided equally between the two daughter cells (F left and right). In the reduction division (lower row) the chromosomes do not split but align themselves in pairs (C and D) and one member of each pair goes to each pole (E), resulting in the formation of two cells (F), each with half as many chromosomes as the body cells. These by a subsequent equational mitosis give rise to four functional gametes (G). (Modified from Sharp.) (*From* Principles of Genetics, *by E. W. Sinnott and L. C. Dunn, by courtesy of McGraw-Hill Co.*)

was supposed that they alone were inherited in mendelian fashion. Later, however, it was found that mendelian factors were responsible also for the inheritance of small differences and of so-called continuous variation, in which no sharp line can be drawn between the characters under investigation.[4] In most cases of variation in size, for instance, including human stature, there is a continuous gradation from small to large; and yet size differences are genetically determined by mendelian factors.[5]

In the inheritance of continuously varying characters, a number of factors, all or most of them producing quite small effects, combine or interact to produce a larger effect. What is more, such interaction between separate factors was discovered to be a general occurrence: thus the two factors responsible for the very distinctive "pea" and "rose" types of comb in fowls, when both are present together, interact to produce a comb of quite a new shape, the so-called "walnut" type. Or again, the "hooded" pattern of rats, in which the foreparts and a stripe along the back are black while the rest of the animal is white, depends on a single mendelian factor. But the effects of this can be altered by a number of so-called modifying factors, some of which can combine to extend the black area over the white of the upper and even some of the lower surface, while others operate to restrict it to the head or even to the snout alone.

The original idea of the early Mendelians like Bateson had been that each mendelian factor corresponded to some one distinct visible character; and in fact they often used the term unit-character, as if the characters and not the factors responsible for them, were directly transmitted in inheritance. However, the facts soon made this view untenable, and it was eventually realized that every visible character depends genetically on several or many separate mendelian factors. Thus the mendelian factors, or genes as they were later called, though they behave as separate and separable units in regard to their transmission, interact and co-operate in regard to their effects on characters. Spatially they are like a row of beads on a string; but functionally

[4] Though it took the mendelians over a decade to discover this, Mendel himself had prophesied it in the 1860s.
[5] As previously pointed out, they are not *entirely* so determined, since environmental condition (such as amount of food) may also affect size.

they combine to form a single organized system. This organized system we call the gene-complex.

Meanwhile the important phenomenon of mutation had been discovered. New characters—such as white eye-color in place of the normal red in the fruitfly Drosophila—appeared in breeding stocks of various animals and plants, sometimes in pure-bred strains—and then proved to be inherited in mendelian fashion. It soon became clear that the mutant characters were due to changes taking place in the hereditary factors—in most cases presumably slight changes in chemical constitution or molecular organization.

Since the hereditary factors are self-reproducing, the mutated factor will reproduce itself and be transmitted in its new form to later generations.

"Spontaneous" mutation of this sort was found to be a general phenomenon, occurring in all organisms. It is, however, very infrequent. The rate of mutation for most factors varies from much less than 1 to about 50 per million: thus the mutation producing severe hemophilia ("bleeding") in man occurs only in about 30 of every million eggs or sperm produced, though the gene concerned has one of the highest mutation-rates known.

In 1927 Muller made the important discovery that mutations, including many of those occurring spontaneously, could be artificially induced by means of X-rays, and that the mutation rate was then enormously increased. Similar artificially increased mutation has later been produced by various other agencies.

It soon became clear that all characters which are inherited in mendelian fashion owe their origin to past mutation. Mutation in fact is the source of all heritable variation, and therefore provides the raw material for evolutionary change.

Mutation can be of various kinds. The commonest kind is gene-mutation, which alters the nature of single genes or hereditary factors; but there are also chromosome-mutations of various sorts, some involving rearrangement of parts within or between chromosomes, others involving the addition or subtraction of whole chromosomes, and still others the addition or subtraction of whole chromosome-sets. But all mutations are capable of self-reproduction, and all produce some effect on the characters or properties of the organism.

In the second decade of this century a further decisive step had been taken. The genetic system composed of the hereditary units deduced from breeding experiments had been equated with the visible mechanism of the chromosomes, and the "unit-factors" themselves had been identified as material particles—tiny sections of the chromosomes, each with its own particular location in the system, to which the name of *genes* was given. As a result, whenever sufficient genes had been studied in breeding experiments, it became possible to make maps of the genetic system, showing the position of the various genes in the different chromosomes.

This was truly a spectacular achievement. But the most important points established were the facts that inheritance is particulate in its nature—that is to say, is mediated by the transmission of definite bits of self-reproducing matter—and that it is co-operative in its operation, that is to say the separate hereditary particles or genes combine or interact to produce their effects, and are all organized into a single functional system, the gene-complex. With this realization, not only did genetics find a firm scientific basis, but the relations between genetics and evolution were put on a new and satisfactory footing. As discussed more fully later, R. A. Fisher, the English statistician and geneticist, in his great book published in 1930, the *Genetical Basis of Natural Selection*, was able to draw the most far-reaching theoretical conclusions from this central fact of particulate inheritance and the detailed data concerning its operation.

Recently, considerable progress has been made in what is sometimes called physiological genetics—the study of how the genes operate on the processes of development to produce their effects on the characters of organisms.

Remarkable discoveries have recently been made concerning the chemical nature of the genes or, what amounts to the same thing, the chemistry of self-reproducing (self-copying) matter. The self-reproducing gene-units of heredity consist of a combination of certain kinds of protein with a particular sort of nucleic acid in which the nucleic acid seems to act as a sort of chemical template, enabling the gene to impose its own precise form and organization on the materials from which it builds up a copy of itself; and the essential capacity for self-copying seems to depend on a peculiar structural organization, in which two identical chemical strings are intertwined spirally with each other, making chemical connection by means of their side-chains, but with the two members of the double spiral running in opposite directions ("head to tail") instead of parallel.

Genes must now be regarded as self-copying chemical molecules or super-molecules of very large size (with molecular weights of a million and over) and very great complexity of organization. Indeed, their organization is so complex that various external agencies, like X-rays, or spontaneous internal rearrangements, can produce slight alterations in it, such as a change in the number or position of the atoms in one of its numerous side-chains. If such an alteration is not too great, the gene will reproduce itself in the new altered form. It is these alterations that we detect as genetic mutations.

The study of heredity is thus leading to discoveries about the mechanism of self-reproduction, and so, since "life" is merely a general term to denote the properties of self-reproducing matter, is pointing the way to the discovery of the nature of life itself.

Before turning to discuss evolution, I will attempt to sum up as briefly as possible our present views on the mechanism of heredity.

Heredity always has a physical basis. In every organism, plant or animal, the genetic mechanism consists of a number of genetically separable unit-particles, the genes, arranged in a definite order along the visible cell-organs called chromosomes. For some part of the life history in all organisms, and for almost all of it in all higher plants and animals, there are two complete sets of chromosomes and genes in every cell, one derived from the mother, the other from the father. (In some cases, the cells of certain tissues double or quadruple the number of their chromosome-sets.) The number of different kinds of genes is very large—at least several hundreds even in bacteria, and up to several thousands or possibly tens of thousands in higher animals such as flies or men. Each kind of gene can exist in a number of slightly differing forms called *alleles*, which produce different effects. Thus in rabbits, three alleles of one gene determine different color-types—total albinism, partial albinism of the "Himalayan" type, white with black points, and full color respectively. The different alleles must have arisen by the mutation of one original gene.

The number of different kinds of chromosomes in a set is much lower—from one to rather over a hundred. The way in which the chromosomes behave in cell-division (mitosis), in preparation for sexual union (meiosis), and in sexual union (fertilization) determines the way in which genes are inherited and results in the genetic "laws" of segregation (Mendel's First Law), free assortment (Mendel's Second Law), and linkage. Segregation is what happens to pairs of alleles lodged in the same chromosome. Thus, in Mendel's classical experiments, a tall strain of peas, carrying a pair of alleles for tallness (T T) were crossed with a dwarf strain (tt). The offspring all contained one T and one t allele, but all appeared tall, since T is dominant in its effects. But in meiosis, T and t *segregated* so that the gametes were all either T or t in equal numbers. Since fertilization is at random, the next generation consisted of 25 per cent TT, 50 per cent Tt, and 25 per cent tt plants. The tt plants were again dwarfs and had *segregated* out pure from their hybrid parents.

Free assortment describes what happens to two (or more) allele-pairs all lodged in different chromosomes. Each pair segregates independently of the rest, so that new *recombinations* of genes and characters are produced. Thus in the second generation from a cross between tall green-seeded and dwarf yellow-seeded peas, Mendel obtained tall yellow-seeded and dwarf green-seeded plants in addition to the parental types.

Linkage is what happens to two or more genes which are lodged in the same chromosome. Their segregation is not independent, for the closer two genes are on the chromosomes, the more likely are they to segregate together, the less likely to become separated at meiosis, or to "cross over" as it is technically called. It is by ascertaining the cross-over percentages of different genes that geneticists can map their relative position in a chromosome.

Such a mechanism, it can be seen, has a number of important biological functions, and its operation explains many apparently unrelated and puzzling phenomena. The fact that it is composed of self-reproducing matter provides for constancy of constitution and character in time, even in face of great diversity of environmental conditions. The further fact that it consists of a large number of separable self-reproducing particles or genes accounts for the familiar but at first sight surprising observation that members of a single family may differ strikingly in their inherited characteristics. This is of course a consequence of the independent segregation of genes in sexual reproduction, which results in the recombination of any mutants (genetic variations) present in the population.

Mutation in its turn arises from the fact that the self-copying process is not always exact: inexact copying, where the inexactitude is spontaneous or caused by cosmic rays or other external agencies, results in the production of a self-reproducing mutant gene. There are thus two kinds of genetic variation, the first due to new mutation, the second to recombination, which may produce new combinations of existing mutants. Between them, these two sources of genetic variation provide the raw material for evolutionary change.

The further fact that most mutants are recessive to their normal or wild-type partners allows a species to build up a reserve of potential variability while preserving an effective constancy of character. This reserve variability may be of very different extent. Sexual reproduction with regular outcrossing increases it; but both inbreeding and the dropping of sexual reproduction, as in parthenogenesis or apomixis or asexual (vegetative) reproduction, decreases and may totally abolish it.

Sex itself is illuminated by our genetical knowledge. In origin it has nothing to do with sexual differentiation, the difference between males and females of a species; its basic and universal function is to provide the species with greater genetic variability. Neither segregation nor recombination can occur in nonsexual reproduction. Sex brings together alleles from different strains. It thus increases variability and evolutionary plasticity, by combining mutants which would otherwise remain imprisoned in the separate lines in which they first arose. Sex thus permits the formation of a common pool of variability for the whole species.

Finally, it enables us to understand many of the facts about species. For Darwin, the great problem was the origin of new species from old; once this had been accepted as a fact, the further problem presented itself of how species attain and maintain their specific distinctiveness.

We can now say definitely that not only differences between species, but also those between genera and higher taxonomic categories, arise in the same way as differences between subspecies and minor intraspecific varieties. All spring from the same sources of variation— mutations of various kinds and their recombinations—and are brought about by the same mechanisms—natural selection combined with some degree of isolation. The only difference is a quantitative one: more mutations and a longer span of time are required to bring about the greater amounts of difference.[6]

The second question, of how related species maintain their distinctiveness and remain separate biological entities even when they inhabit the same area, can also now be answered. They remain distinct because of some incompatibility to effective interbreeding. Sometimes the incompatibility depends on differences in behavior: the female of one species will not mate with the males of another. Sometimes it depends on timing: the flowering or spawning of related species of plants or aquatic animals takes place at different times of year. Often it depends on some incompatibility in the genetic mechanisms: the two gene-complexes are incapable of co-operating in development; or if they can so co-operate, as in the mule, they cannot co-operate in the maneuvers of meiosis, so that no functional gametes are produced; or if functional gametes are produced, many of the offspring resulting from fertilization are nonviable, defective, or sterile. To put the matter in a nutshell, if the differences between a new species and its relatives come to be too great in any aspect of reproduction, incompatibility follows.

This is so in the great majority of animals; but in a few animals (e.g., some fish) and a considerable number of plants, quite distinct species, if brought together, will intercross and can still produce fertile offspring. This only occurs with species which normally inhabit different regions; whenever two closely allied species overlap geographically, they possess some barrier to effective interbreeding, and this has undoubtedly often been strengthened by selection, in order to prevent the biological waste involved in intercrossing.

To sum up, the essential achievement of the science of genetics has

[6] Goldschmidt (1940 and later writings) still maintains that the large differences involved in what he calls macroevolution require a different *type* of mutation, a "macromutation" of large extent and radical effect, as against the ordinary mutations involved in small-scale "microevolution"; but he is now virtually alone in this contention.

been the discovery of the universal mechanism of inheritance. This is the gene-complex. It consists of hundreds or thousands of genetically separable units, the genes, but these interact and co-operate in development so that the gene-complex functions as a highly organized and integrated whole. The genes are lodged in orderly arrangement in the chromosomes, which provide the machinery for transmitting the gene-complex with quantitative accuracy, and for ensuring the recombination of different alleles in sexual reproduction.

Finally, the occurrence of occasional mutation provides the heritable variation that gives species their reserve variability and constitutes the raw material of evolutionary change.

When we come to evolution, including the past origin and future fate of existing animals and plants, we are confronted by an array of myths, superstitions and errors equal to those concerning heredity.

The commonest myth is probably that of creation—the idea that all organisms, including man, were created in their existing forms out of nothing, or out of raw materials like earth and water, by a god, at some definite moment in time. This is the myth found in Genesis, but variations of it occur in the mythology of many tribes and peoples.

An opposed but equally erroneous myth is found in some eastern religions—the idea of an endless cycle of recurrence, accompanied by transmigration of souls into different kinds of animals, by way of justice—punishment or recompense as the case may be—for the actions of the soul in its previous existence.

Often the idea of creation at a given date in the past was applied only to higher animals and plants, while lower forms were supposed to be spontaneously generated here and now.

Coming to the early nineteenth century, when the idea of evolutionary transformation as opposed to once-and-for-all creation began to be seriously entertained, we find Lamarck indulging in the erroneous (but still persistent) belief that there was but a single ladder of nature or trend of advance from lower to higher, and in the superstition of the inheritance of acquired characters. In spite of Darwin's demonstration of natural selection as a natural and inevitable mechanism, by which evolutionary change could be brought about, many wishful thinkers preferred, like Samuel Butler, to rely on the Lamarckian idea of the inheritance of the results of will and effort; or, like Michurin and Lysenko, on the neo-Lamarckian idea of the inheritance of environmental effects; or, like Bergson and Bernard Shaw, on a mystical or vitalistic *élan vital* or Life Force; or, like some paleontologists, on the almost equally mysterious inherent trends that were supposed to produce "orthogenesis" or predetermined straight-line evolution in a given direction.

The scientific study of evolution did not begin until after Darwin's publication of the *Origin of Species* in 1859. There were two reasons for this. First, Darwin presented an enormous mass of evidence which made it clear that transformation must have occurred. And secondly, he proposed for the first time a mechanism by which it could have occurred, in the shape of natural selection. It was of this key-concept that T. H. Huxley wrote "My first reflection, when I first made myself master of the central idea of the *Origin*, was 'How extremely stupid not to have thought of that!' "

Darwin himself extended the idea of evolution to include the origin of man from apelike ancestors (1871) and the evolution of mind and behavior as well as of bodily structure and physiology (1872). Meanwhile an immense amount of attention was devoted to the study of individual evolution or development, which we call embryology or ontogeny; and remarkable paleontological discoveries began to be made, confirming in the most striking way Darwin's deductions that the evolutionary advance of a group of animals and plants is brought about by its radiation into a number of separate lines or lineages, in each of which transformation is gradual and tends toward the improvement of the lineage for a particular way of life.

The concept of evolution was soon extended into other than biological fields. Inorganic subjects such as the life-histories of stars and the formation of the chemical elements on the one hand, and on the other hand human subjects like linguistics, social anthropology, and comparative law and religion, began to be studied from an evolutionary angle, until today we are enabled to see evolution as a universal and all-pervading process.

But before discussing evolution in this extended sense, I must mention a few more milestones in the study of biological evolution. During the latter half of the nineteenth century, the comparative study of morphology, embryology, geographical distribution and paleontology, had provided a broad picture of the relationships and probable evolution of the main groups of animals; while the intensive work of the great naturalists had brought to light the range and complexity of the detailed adaptations achieved by natural selection. Furthermore, fossil hominids more apelike than modern man had been discovered, together with a remarkable sequence of his and their stone implements; and in the present century a series of further finds have now bridged the gap between *Homo sapiens* and the anthropoid apes, or at least provided an adequate set of steppingstones.

In 1900, the event occurred which was destined to exert the greatest influence on evolutionary theory since Darwin's day—the rediscovery of Mendel's work, which soon led to the conclusion that the inheritance of mendelian characters must be particulate, dependent on a set of material unit-particles transmitted from parents to offspring. By about 1915, it was becoming clear that almost all inheritance was particulate, that the particles involved were the genes arranged along the chromosomes, and that the raw material of evolutionary change consists of the mutations or self-perpetuating variations which from time to time occur in the hereditary material. At first, for the simple reason that the earlier geneticists had naturally preferred to work with pairs of characters showing large and striking differences, the facts of Mendelism did not seem to fit in with Darwin's belief in continuous gradual evolutionary transformation, but rather with de Vries' idea of sudden large jumps or quanta of change. However, it was soon discovered that the great majority of mutations actually utilized by organisms are of small extent, and that frequently a number of genes with small effects combine to form the genetic basis of a given character. And this idea of the functional interrelation of genes was later generalized, until, as already mentioned, the idea of the gene-complex was born—the realization that the hereditary constitution is not a set of separate gene-units, each exerting its effect in isolation from its fellows, but a highly organized whole, whose parts operate in closely adjusted interrelation with each other, so that for instance a particular gene transferred to the new genic environment provided by a different gene-complex, may and usually does produce quite different effects on the visible characters of the organism.

It speedily became clear that selection acting on gene-complexes of this type could produce apparently continuous transformation of animals and plants in their evolution. And finally, in 1930, R. A. Fisher laid the foundations of modern evolution theory with his notable book *The Genetical Basis of Natural Selection*. In this, he not only demonstrated mathematically how selection acting on small mutations of the extent and frequency known to occur in nature, could produce gradual and continuous transformation, but also proved that evolutionary transformation could not take place on the basis of the "blending inheritance" postulated by Darwin and most of the biometricians, but required a particulate mechanism.

Fisher further demonstrated the theoretical impossibility of Lamarckism involving the inheritance of acquired characters, or of orthogenesis involving an inherent urge or will or tendency to evolve in a particular way, playing or having played any significant part in bringing about evolutionary change.

Such theoretical demonstrations of impossibility may be of great importance for the development of science—for instance the impossibility of constructing a perpetual motion machine; the impossibility of heterogenesis, or the production of one kind of animal by a quite different kind; the impossibility, according to Einstein's special theory of relativity, of bodies moving with a velocity faster than light; or the impossibility of alchemy in the traditional sense.

Fisher's demonstration of the impossibility of Lamarckism and orthogenesis acting as agents of evolutionary change means that we need waste no more time and energy on these subjects, but can concentrate on the study of natural selection. Thanks to the work of Fisher, ably extended by men like Haldane and Sewall Wright, we can now confidently say that natural selection is overwhelmingly the main agency of evolutionary change, and the only agency of evolutionary direction.[7]

[7] When a few individuals are isolated, say on an island, they are not likely to contain all the alleles possessed by the species as a whole. Further, in very small populations, alleles may occasionally be lost from the gene-complex, resulting in what Sewall Wright calls "drift." The resultant changes in character of the population will be random, not directional or adaptively related to the environment. But those nonadaptive statistical accidents play only a very small part in the evolutionary process.

Natural Selection is the phrase used by Darwin to denote what might more accurately be called the differential survival of variants in relation to the conditions of life.

Given the basic facts of life—self-reproduction and mutation—this follows as an inevitable consequence. For instance, if a mutation gives rise to a mutant which has an average chance of survival only one-half of one per cent higher than the allele from which it arose—that is today, if on the average 200 of the mutants survive and reproduce themselves in each generation as against 199 of the original—then in a biologically short period, it will replace the original form as the normal type of the population. Natural selection thus works not by all-or-nothing elimination, involving 100 per cent death as against 100 per cent survival, but by slight average extra survival over a number of generations; further, it may be concerned with all kinds of characteristics, from ability to escape detection to speed in pursuit, from passive armor-plating to greater intelligence, from extra viability or biological "toughness" to higher fertility or success in mating.

For reasonably rapid evolutionary change to take place, it is clearly necessary that favorable mutations occurring in separate stocks or lines should be capable of being brought together and combined in a single line; this is of course achieved by means of sexual recombination.

The picture becomes more complex when we find that mutants which are unfavorable when acting alone may sometimes be favorable when combined, or that a mutant which is selected against in one set of circumstances, is favored when conditions change (as happened with the black mutants of many moths in areas which became industrialized).[8] It is for such reasons that the reserve store of recessive mutant gene found in all outcrossing species is so important; it provides a reservoir of potential variability which can be drawn upon as the occasion demands.

In Fisher's epigrammatic phrase, natural selection is a mechanism

[8] A considerable number of species of moths in Britain and western Europe have become melanic (black or nearly so) in industrialized areas during the past 100 years. This was due to the fact that the melanics survive better than the normals in unfavorable conditions, such as for instance the contamination of their food-plants with smoke. The normals have the advantage of being protectively colored, and in rural conditions this outweighs the extra hardiness of the melanics.

for generating an extreme degree of (apparent) improbability—improbability of such a high order that it could never have been produced by chance alone without the aid of natural selection, any more than monkeys tapping on typewriters could ever produce a play of Shakespeare. Given the facts of life and the known extent of biological time, such apparently improbable results as the protective resemblance of a Kallima butterfly to a dead leaf, or the evolution of organs of stereoscopic color vision like our own eyes, become comprehensible and scientifically explicable.

The study of how selection acts on the organisms in different circumstances led, among other things, to the realization that their gene-complexes evolve adaptively just as much as do their bodies and their behavior; and much study, largely initiated by Darlington, was devoted to the problem of the evolutionary effects to be expected from gene-complexes of different types.

In particular, it became clear that the retention of a genetic system promoting outbreeding will favor variability and therefore evolutionary flexibility in the face of any change in environmental conditions. On the other hand, the change-over to one of the many systems promoting inbreeding or rendering outcrossing difficult or impossible, will increase immediate fitness in the sense of close adaptation to the existing environment, but is likely to lead to failure and probable extinction in the evolutionary long run.

Meanwhile the notable discovery by Muller in 1927 that genes could be artificially induced to mutate by means of X-rays, at a rate many times higher than that of natural mutation, led to a huge crop of new research. Among other notable results, it was found that chromosome-doubling (polyploidy) could be produced by means of the chemical substance colchicine, thus giving rise to many plants and some animals with four instead of the normal two complete sets of chromosomes; and this has enabled plant breeders to make many otherwise impossible fertile crosses between species with different numbers of chromosome-sets, and so to initiate various new lines of artificially directed evolution. (A hybrid between species with four and two chromosome-sets has three chromosome-sets and is sterile. For a fertile cross, the two parents must have the same number of chromosome-sets.) More importantly, it was discovered that many other agencies besides X-rays, some of them physical like ultraviolet radiation, others chemical like mustard gas, are capable of inducing mutations, and that certain of these mutations appear to be caused only by certain agencies. This discovery was later turned to practical account, notably in the production of strains of the mold *Penicillium* giving much higher yields of penicillin than those found in nature.

Of late years, a great deal of research has been carried out on unicellular microorganisms, including bacteria. This has had two main results of importance. First, it has enabled us to discover in many cases how genes act and what they do, because in microorganisms there is normally no long and complex process of development, and a gene is often directly concerned with the production of some chemical substance required in the cell's basic metabolism. And secondly, reproduction is so rapid that it has permitted us to study in the space of a few weeks or months, evolutionary effects of mutation and selection which in higher organisms would require decades or even centuries.

Then, during the last two decades, the viruses, those strange entities which occupy a position intermediate between the living and the nonliving, have also received much attention. It has been discovered that these subcellular organizations (it is better not to beg the question by calling them organisms), even when capable of being crystallized in pure chemical form, exhibit the basic phenomena of genetics—they are composed of a number of separable self-copying units analogous to genes; they exhibit genetic variation analogous to that produced by gene-mutation; and in some cases when two different varieties are mixed, the offspring exhibit a recombination of characters analogous to that produced by the sexual process.

In the very different but equally important field of paleontology, the present half-century has seen great activity, notably in the unearthing and analysis of trends or lineages of fossil animal groups, thus giving us for the first time a reasonably accurate and detailed picture of the actual course of evolution in different groups in various circumstances and in various periods of the earth's history.

Finally, there has been in the last fifteen or twenty years a remarkable movement toward a synthesis of the various disciplines relating to biological evolution. This has been undertaken by paleontologists like George Gaylord Simpson, by taxonomists like Ernst Mayr, by geneticists like Theodore Dobzhansky, and by general biologists like myself, and has been promoted by the founding of special journals devoted to the subject, like *Evolution*, so that we are now witnessing the rapid growth of a unified science of evolutionary biology.

Furthermore, with the adoption of the evolutionary approach in nonbiological fields, from cosmology to human affairs, we are beginning to realize that biological evolution is only one aspect of evolution in general. Evolution in the extended sense can be defined as a directional and essentially irreversible process occurring in time, which in its course gives rise to an increase of variety and an increasingly high level of organization in its products. Our present knowledge indeed forces us to the view that the whole of reality *is* evolution—a single process of self-transformation.

Further analysis speedily reveals that this universal evolutionary process is divisible with three main sectors or phases—the inorganic or cosmological, the organic or biological, and the human or psychosocial. Each sector has its own characteristic mechanism of self-transformation and its own maximum rate of change, and each produces its own characteristic type of results.

The inorganic sector is almost infinitely the largest in spatial extent and in mass, as it comprises the entire universe of galaxies and intergalactic space, with the exception of the few small areas where living matter has developed. The methods of change operating in it are very simple, being confined to physical and occasional inorganic chemical interactions. The resultant processes of transformation are in general extremely slow, so that the life-history of a star is to be measured in thousands of millions of years. Finally, the resultant products never attain to any but very low or simple levels of organization. At the submicroscopic end of the scale, matter in the cosmological sector exists for the most part on the atomic or subatomic level, though it occasionally comes to be organized in the form of molecules or of simple chemical compounds; while on the grand scale, the complexity of organization goes no further than the simple spiral pattern of the galaxies, and the concentric structure of the stars.

In correlation with this, the inorganic sector has given rise only to a very limited variety of products—on the one hand the various types of subatomic particles, the different chemical elements, and a quite small range of chemical compounds; and on the other hand, the few kinds of stars, together with their occasional appendages such as comets and planets, and the still fewer kinds of galaxies or spiral nebulae.

In the biological phase[9] the time-scale is still very extensive, though somewhat less so than that of the cosmological phase—nearly 2000 million years since the first appearance of life on earth as against about 5000 million years or somewhat less for the age of our own galaxy.

The amount and rate of change produced, however, is immensely greater. If we think first of variety, we find that biological evolution has produced organisms as diverse as starfish and roses, men and toadstools, tapeworms and oak trees, birds and bacteria, with an amazing range in size, in method of working, and in organization and plan of construction. There are now in existence about a million and a half distinct and separate species of animals and plants, all of them presumably derived from one original form.

Equally amazing is the degree of detailed adaptation achieved. We need only think of the wings of a hover-fly, the eyes of a falcon, the luminous lures of deep-sea angler-fish, or the mechanisms of orchids for securing cross-pollination by insects.

Most remarkable of all, however, is the rise in level of organization. The earliest organisms must have been submicroscopic units, of the same order of complexity as modern viruses; and for tens or hundreds of millions of years life did not rise above the unicellular level. In contrast with this, we find that later evolution has produced organizations of such almost miraculous elaboration as the flying birds, the gigantic plankton-feeding whales, the temperature-regulating mechanism of higher mammals, the societies of ants and bees, and the human cerebral cortex—the most complex system of which we have any knowledge.

This vast increase in the tempo and amount of change has been

---

[9] I am restricting myself to the biological phase on this planet, since here only do we have any firm knowledge of it. There is, however, the scientific probability that life (complex self-reproducing and self-varying matter) has been produced on a number (several hundreds or even thousands) of other planets in our galaxy.

made possible, as I have already indicated, by the availability of a new method of self-transformation—natural selection.

The actual course taken by biological evolution has now been revealed in detail by fossil evidence in a number of groups such as horses, trilobites, elephants, ammonites, and various types of dinosaur; and with reasonable accuracy in a larger number, such as most other mammalian orders, including the primates with man himself, and many groups of fish and reptiles; while it can be deduced in broad outline in many other types, both plant and animal.

We find the following general results. First, each new group proceeds to break up or diverge into a number of different lines, each of which becomes increasingly specialized, or improved for a particular mode of life. This process of divergent specialization operates at various levels. Thus the higher or placental mammals have diverged into a number of Orders—the carnivores for active catching of large prey, the insectivores for small prey, the bats for flying, the rodents for gnawing, the ungulates as herbivores, the primates for tree life, the whales and porpoises for a fully aquatic existence. Each of these in turn has diverged into a number of finer specializations—the carnivores, for instance, into seals, sea-lions, cats, dogs, weasels, bears, etc., and these smaller groups have repeated the process, which ends up with the formation of separate species each adapted to its own special niche: thus the cats have produced the lion, the tiger, the lynx, the bobcat, the fishing cat, the puma, the leopard, the jaguar, the ocelot and various other feline species.

In the great majority of cases this process of divergent specialization sooner or later comes to an end: the type becomes stabilized at a certain level, and after that remains constant in essentials, though still often capable of minor alterations on that level, alterations which are merely variations on an existing theme, and do not radically change it or introduce a new theme. The classical example is that of the horse family, the Equidae. This, after nearly 50 million years of gradual and steady specialization or improvement of limbs for speed and of teeth for chewing vegetable food,[10] became stabilized in its

---

[10] In the latter half of this period, the more successful branch of the family specialized for running on open plains, and for chewing hard flinty-stemmed plains grasses rather than woodland leaves.

definite form around five million years ago; and since then has merely rung the changes on this form by evolving into the various species of zebra, true horse, and wild ass.

As T. H. Huxley pointed out three-quarters of a century ago, natural selection is the only agency capable of producing change or the absence of change according to circumstances. But before discussing this point further, I must deal with the subject of so-called dominant groups.

In the actual course of evolution as revealed by fossils, we find a succession of these dominant groups, each of them arising at a certain period of evolutionary time, rapidly becoming more successful and abundant through divergent specialization, and finally becoming stabilized in all or almost all of its branches. Meanwhile the previously dominant group, from among whose more primitive members the new successful group has originated, is much reduced in numbers and in variety, many (and sometimes all) of its branches becoming extinct.

The classical example is that of the land vertebrates. Before the Devonian, a little over 300,000,000 years ago, there were no land vertebrates: all the backboned animals in existence were fish (or of more primitive fishlike types). In the Devonian, the amphibians effected a partial colonization of the land.

After the comparatively short period of some 70 million years, the reptiles rose to dominance, in virtue of the improvements in bodily organization and reproduction (dry scaly skin and large-yolked shelled egg) which permitted their full conquest of the land. The amphibians declined in importance, but the reptiles blossomed out into a fantastic array of specialized types—dinosaurs, crocodiles, plesiosaurs and ichthyosaurs, tortoises, pterodactyls, and many others.

However, at the close of the Mesozoic, after over 150 million years of reptilian supremacy, the two new groups of the birds and the mammals rose to joint dominance on land, in virtue of their new capacity for keeping themselves at a constant high temperature, their much greater parental care of their young, and, especially in the higher mammals, their improved brains. The majority of reptilian types became extinct, and during the Cenozoic the birds and mammals radiated out into an exuberance of specialized lines. After about 60 million years this phase was brought to an end by the Ice Age, and by the rise of the latest dominant type in evolution, Man. As before, with the rapid expansion of the new type was correlated widespread reduction and extinction of the previously dominant types, especially the mammals. We need only think of the fate of mammoths, sabertooths, giant sloths and giant wombats, or more recently, of aurochs and quagga, passenger pigeon and great auk.

Essentially similar successions of dominant types are found in aquatic vertebrates, in aquatic arthropods, in mollusks, and in insects.

Two general points need stressing. First, each new dominant type owes its dominance not to any specialized adaptation but to some new mechanism of importance in general biological organization. And secondly, stabilization after rapid improvement and expansion is the fate of most dominant types as of specialized lines. Thus the reptilian type seems to have exhausted all its possibilities of major advance during the Cretaceous, though considerable changes were still possible within the reptilian level of organization (e.g., those leading to the evolution of snakes). And the birds have not shown any improvement *qua* flying machines for at least 20 or 30 million years, though they have been improved for a diversity of habitats and ways of life.

Even ants, which are in many ways the highest type of invertebrates, became stabilized over 35 million years ago; the ants which we find beautifully preserved in Baltic amber are specifically but not even generically distinct from those alive today.

Thus the great majority of animal and plant groups, large and small alike, are restricted in their evolutionary possibilities. After a longer or shorter time, they become stabilized at a certain maximum level of biological organization. On this level, they may continue to evolve, producing new variations on their basic organizational theme. These variations may be quite considerable, as in the previously mentioned case of the evolution of the snakes, whose construction opened up new ways of life to its possessors. But this, though an important novelty, was achieved on a purely reptilian level: the snakes show no improvements in basic organization such as characterized either birds or mammals.

Very occasionally, such basic advances and improvements are achieved; and they then make possible the rise of a new dominant group on a new level of biological organization. Evolutionary progress takes place by a series of such steps from lower to higher levels of organization.

Restriction of evolutionary possibilities may be due to a number of rather different causes. In the first place, specialization for a particular way of life leads to a cul-de-sac. This is partly because the mechanisms concerned eventually reach a state at which further change in the same direction would be disadvantageous; thus in the horses, further elaboration of the grinding pattern of the molars would produce a "millstone" too finely patterned for efficient grinding of the grass-stems on which they feed, and the reduction in the number of their digits can obviously not go below one! Furthermore, the specialized type soon becomes so well-adapted to one mode of life that it cannot change to another: too many mutations would be simultaneously required to enable it to climb out of its old evolutionary groove into a new one.

Improvements in general efficiency or organization also tend to a limit. Thus it would apparently be of no biological advantage for a bird or a mammal to evolve a greater accuracy in regulating its temperature; and the fact that the units of vision in a vertebrate are single cells, and therefore must be above a certain diameter, makes it impossible to construct an eye with an acuity of vision greater than that of a falcon.[11]

Sometimes the restriction is indirect. Thus the breathing mechanism of insects, by means of minute tubes or tracheae taking air direct to the tissues, while very efficient at small sizes, rapidly becomes less efficient with increasing bulk, with the result that an insect the size of a rat could not function at all, and in fact none exist larger than a mouse. This limitation of total size in turn limits the size of the brain and the number of nerve-cells in it; and this again limits learning capacity and mental plasticity. Thus the adoption of the tra-

---

[11] In the compound eyes of insects, the units of vision, the ommatidia, have a larger minimum size, which restricts the acuity of vision and resolving power to a considerably lower level.

cheal system of respiration by insects restricted their possibilities of intelligence, and therefore of their competing with man for the position of new dominant type.

When we survey the biological panorama as a whole, we see that evolution is from one point of view the realization of the possibilities of living substance: evolutionary advance and progress involve the successive realization of new possibilities. Further, we are driven to the rather surprising conclusion that some time during the late Cenozoic, probably about five million years ago, all the purely material or physiological possibilities of life had been actualized and had reached the upper limit of realization. Though it is difficult to prove such a universal negative, it certainly holds good, as already mentioned, for visual acuity and accuracy of temperature regulation, and also for many other features, such as size in land animals, speed of locomotion, elaboration of instincts, digestive and mechanical efficiency, and protective resemblance; and its general applicability is rendered probable by the fact that the evolutionary level of all major groups of animals seems to have become stabilized by this period.

One major avenue of advance, however, remained—the further realization of mental possibilities. It was this direction which was taken by our earliest hominid ancestors and led to the emergence of our own species as the latest dominant type of evolution.

With the advent of man, evolution on this planet enters the human or psychosocial phase. Man's distinctive property of conceptual thought, with its objective correlate in the shape of true speech,[12] assured him his position of biological dominance by providing him with a totally new method of evolutionary change—the method of the cumulative transmission of experience.

By means of spoken and still more effectively of written language, man can do what is possible to no other organism, namely transmit the results of experience to later generations and do so cumulatively. This constitutes a second mechanism of inheritance, in addition to

[12] By *true speech* I mean a method of communication which employs arbitrary symbols (words) to denote things or ideas, instead of one which, like all others employed by animals, uses innately-determined sounds or gestures to signify emotional or behavioral states.

that of biological genetics. What this exclusively human mechanism transmits is not a system of material units as in biological inheritance, but a system of knowledge, ideas and attitudes. We may sum up the essential difference between the three sectors of evolution by saying that whereas evolution in the biological sector depends on its new property of the self-reproduction of matter, in psychosocial evolution it depends on the self-reproduction of mind.

The result is that in the psychosocial sector evolution is preponderantly cultural, not genetic. While the intrinsic genetic character of man, mental as well as bodily, has not changed appreciably since the end of the Paleolithic, those of his societies and cultures have done so. What is more, this cultural evolution has proceeded at an unprecedented rate, many hundred times greater than even the fastest changes found in biological evolution; for the new mechanism of transmission of experience immensely speeds up the processes of change. Furthermore, because the transmission of experience is cumulative, the rate of change can show an acceleration instead of a steady maximum, and this is precisely what we find: it is common knowledge that the rate of change in human affairs has risen since before the dawn of history, and is now proceeding at an almost explosive speed, a speed at which major changes in ideas and material conditions often succeed each other faster than do human generations—something unprecedented in previous centuries.

This acceleration of cultural evolution obviously depends on two main factors—improvements in the methods of acquiring new experience, and improvements in the mechanism of transmission of experience once acquired. The invention of writing and later of printing are examples of the second, while the use of the scientific method and its application to an ever-widening range of subjects are examples of the first.

As a result of this high and accelerating rate of change, we find that in the less than 10,000 years since the discovery of agriculture, psychosocial evolution has produced a degree of variety and a rise in organizational level comparable with those achieved by biological evolution in the last 1,000,000,000 years—a period a hundred thousand times greater.

Innumerable examples of human variety come to mind once one

begins to think of the different types of society, the artistic and scientific achievements of different cultures and individuals, the different religions and ideologies, that have come into being since the beginning of the Neolithic. During the same period, the highest level of organization has risen through the following main steps. First, food-gathering and hunting tribes; then agricultural village communities; small urban communities; early civilizations with cities, the use of metals and writing, with widespread commercial transport organizations, and with the dawn of systems of organized scientific and technological knowledge; later civilizations, with moderate technological advance, including printing and ocean-going ships; early scientific civilizations with restricted use and application of science (paleotechnic); and modern scientific civilizations with deliberate and extended use and application of science (neotechnic). Finally, the last few decades have seen the first beginnings of organization on the world level.

This is not the place to discuss the psychosocial phase of evolution in detail. But it is worth while pointing out a few of the ways in which it differs from the biological phase. First and foremost, as already stressed, is its radically different method of self-transformation. This at once implies that we cannot apply the conclusions drawn from biological evolution directly to human affairs. Genetic change due to the automatic working of natural selection, for instance, is now only of subsidiary importance in the psychosocial sector. However, genetic change guided by conscious purpose could come to be extremely important: it is already clear theoretically that we could appreciably raise the average of desirable genetic qualities in man, such as health, vigor, intelligence, and various special aptitudes. Practically, however, this would require not merely more scientific knowledge, but a radically changed attitude to the problem.

Meanwhile the facts of cultural diffusion and culture-contact make it evident that cultures and societies evolve in quite different ways from those available to the rigidly separate lines of biological evolution. In human evolution, cultural elements can diffuse and interpenetrate other societies; the genetical elements of biological evolution are incapable of diffusing and interpenetrating other organisms.

Another extremely important difference is this—that whereas major evolutionary advance in the biological sector appears to have reached its limit, the psychosocial sector is in an extremely early phase of its evolution, with enormous possibilities of change and advance still unrealized. The new dominant type constituted by man is in a very young stage of its evolution, corresponding more or less with that reached by the mammals in the early Eocene.

A further radical difference is that whereas all dominant (and other) biological types rapidly diverge into a large number of separate lines—orders, families, genera and species—man has remained biologically a single unit. The incipient divergence which gave rise to the major races or subspecies of *Homo sapiens* was early counteracted by a process of convergence, due to man's incurable restlessness, which has brought together representatives of different racial groups, and to his tolerance of diversity in mating; and this convergent intercrossing, which has proceeded with an increasing rapidity in modern times, has kept mankind as a single species or interbreeding group.

Cultural and ideological divergence proceeded much further in man than did genetic divergence, giving rise to a huge array of distinctive cultural "species": the vertical difference between ancient Assyrian and modern American culture is as important as that between an amphibian and a mammal, and the lateral difference between, say, Eskimo and Melanesian society is as great as that between a snail and a shrimp. But this too is now being counteracted by a process of convergence. Science is potentially universal, and its technological and medical applications are spreading rapidly all over the world. Psychosocial evolution is surely heading toward a single unitary pool of knowledge and ideas, and ideological convergence is clearly the goal to be aimed at. On the other hand, this ideological and scientific unity should equally clearly be combined with the maximum amount of cultural richness and diversity.

Another distinctive character of man is the much greater importance of the exceptional individual in cultural than in biological evolution. This is shown not only by the effects which exceptional individuals like Napoleon or Genghis Khan or Lenin may exert on the course of history, but more importantly in science and the arts, where fundamental discoveries and enduring masterpieces are always the work of exceptional individuals.

Population also constitutes a distinctive human problem. Not only have the total human population and its absolute annual increment increased more or less steadily since the end of the Paleolithic, but also its percentage (compound interest) rate of increase. Before the Neolithic, this must have been well below 0.1 per cent per annum; by the late seventeenth century, it had reached 0.25 per cent; and in the eighteenth century, 0.5 per cent. Within the last few decades it passed one per cent for the first time. It is now well above that figure and still going up.

In animals, excessive population is regulated by death from famine, disease, or climatic extremes; man is unique in being able to regulate it consciously—by infanticide or abortion, as in many primitive societies, or by deliberate birth control. Probably the most important task now before man is to discover a simple and cheap contraceptive and to embark on a world policy of population control.

Another grave modern problem, made more urgent by the invention of the various types of atom bomb, is the prevention of war, coupled with the task of harnessing atomic energy for constructive purposes, while shielding the human germ-plasm from its deleterious effects. But this is an immediate, political problem in the forefront of public consciousness, and it would be out of place to discuss it in detail here.

It is more important to set down some of the general implications of the evolutionary approach to human affairs. I would first of all remind my readers that evolution in the psychosocial sector—human history in the broad sense—is an extension of the general process of evolution, but that it operates with the aid of a quite new mechanism and produces quite new kinds of result.

Evolution can be envisaged as a progressive realization of intrinsic possibilities. Man is the latest dominant type in biological evolution, and the first (and up till now the only) dominant type in psychosocial evolution. His destiny is to act as the agent of the evolutionary process on this planet, by enabling it to realize new and higher possibilities. This he can accomplish only if he utilizes to the fullest possible extent the new mechanism of self-transformation which his ancestors achieved—the employment of cumulative experience in the service of conscious purpose. Biological evolution, though it often displays direction, is directed from behind, by the blind and automatic force of natural selection: psychosocial evolution can be, to a lesser or greater extent, directed from in front, by the anticipatory force of conscious purpose. Thus the long-range task of the human species is to establish a fully conscious common purpose, based to the fullest possible extent on scientifically established knowledge.

If we hope to sum up the situation epigrammatically, we can say that, with the advent of man, conscious purpose was able for the first time to exert an operative effect on evolution; and that through the new knowledge acquired during the last hundred years, the evolutionary process was able for the first time to become conscious of itself. The next decisive step in evolution will accordingly be the fuller development of that self-consciousness. In particular it will be the conscious clarification of the future in the light of the long evolutionary past and of the study of human potentialities. Once this has been done, greater realization of possibilities rather than higher productivity, fulfillment rather than efficiency, will become the overriding aim.

PSYCHOLOGY

EDWIN G. BORING

Edwin G. Boring

Edwin G. Boring was born in Philadelphia in 1886 and after local schooling went to Cornell to study electrical engineering. In 1908, having got his degree, he spent a year with the Bethlehem Steel Company finding out, as he says, that what he had wanted all along was physics or "some kind of science" and not engineering. Thereupon he went back to Cornell for graduate work in physics but "got caught by psychology, perhaps because I was allowed with little training to do a tiny bit of psychological research on learning in protozoa." His first job in the science he finally chose as lifework was a Cornell assistantship in psychology at $500; this supported him while he worked for his Ph.D., which was awarded in 1914. The day after he got his degree he was married—his wife is also a psychologist. He stayed on to teach at Cornell until America's entry into the First World War when he was assigned by the Army to give intelligence tests to recruits at Camp Upton, Long Island. For a brief period after the war Boring held a professorship in psychology at Clark University, but in 1922 he moved to Harvard where he soon became professor and director of the renowned Harvard Psychological Laboratory, a post he held for twenty-five years (1924-1949). Boring says he went to Harvard determined "to get its psychology out of the clutches of its philosophers": in this aim he was successful, furthering it by his experimental work and by the publication of more than 200 articles, some describing his researches (he remarks that his experiments *have done most to show "why the full moon looks large on the hori-zon"), some theoretical, some historical.* His best known work is the History of Experimental Psychology, *published in 1929 and revised in 1950, a fascinating book which has done a great deal to make Ameri-can graduate students in psychology aware of the background of their specialty. He has also written a history of experimental work in the psychology of sensation and perception. He is a member of the Na-tional Academy of Sciences and former president of the American Psychological Association.*

Boring is 69, but has not retired. "I cannot decide," he says, *"whether I would like to retire so as to have more time to do the things in psychology I am chafing to do or whether I want to keep closer contact with the Harvard Psychological Laboratories so that I can keep on being stimulated as I am now. I'd like to do both." Bor-ing is primarily an experimentalist, yet there is no branch of psychol-ogy alien to his understanding. He has the breadth of outlook and hospitality to ideas which mark the true scientist.*

PSYCHOLOGY

EDWIN G. BORING

On Tuesday morning, October 22, 1850, Gustav Theodor Fechner was lying in bed in his home in Leipzig, Germany, wondering what science could do to combat the growing materialism of the age. Fechner was a German scientist and scholar, a man of broad outlook, of substantial erudition and of patient and thorough habits of work. He had been a professor of physics at the university in Leipzig, but for ten years now he had been ill and incapacitated for work. Perhaps in part because of this illness and perhaps also in part because he was getting older—he was forty-nine in 1850—his interest had become fixed on the nature of the spiritual, the nonmaterialistic world.

It occurred to Fechner that morning—this is one of those rare occasions when an important scientific insight can be dated almost to the exact hour of its occurrence—it occurred to him that, if you could show how the spiritual and the material are related, you would be demonstrating that there is after all only one world and that the opposition between the two would then disappear. He recalled the experiments of E. H. Weber, the physiologist, sixteen years earlier. Weber had shown that the just noticeable difference between the intensities of two sensations—between the brightnesses of two lights or the heavinesses of two weights—occurs when the difference between the intensities of their stimuli is a fixed proportion of the stimuli. If you can just barely distinguish the difference in weight between 29 and 30 ounces, Weber found, then you will also be able just barely to distinguish the difference between 58 and 60 ounces and also between 29 and 30 drams (1 dram=⅛ oz.).

Such a fact was just what Fechner needed. Here he had an observable relation between spiritual events (psychic processes, sensations) and material events (brain processes or the external stimuli which cause them). It is clear that Fechner was greatly stirred by his new insight, excited enough to spend the next decade of his life in careful experimentation, relating the intensities of sensations to the corresponding magnitudes of their stimuli. He came presently to believe that, if the intensity of a sensation is to be increased by equal steps, the magnitude of its stimulus must always be increased by a constant ratio, i.e., sensation intensities of 4, 5, 6, 7, 8 might be aroused respectively by stimulus magnitudes of 5, 10, 20, 40, 80.

In 1860 he published his great work, *Elements of Psychophysics*, showing how to measure sensations, and, in doing so, he believed that he had resolved the conflict between materialism and spiritualism. The world, however, thought otherwise. It noted instead that Fechner had actually succeeded in measuring mental phenomena and had thus opened the way to a quantitative science of the incorporeal events of consciousness. So often the contribution of a great man to the history of thought and discovery is something other than he had intended!

We need not go into the history of these matters. Fechner was not alone in his novel researches nor was his thought entirely new. Away back in 1760 a Frenchman, Bouguer, had anticipated Weber's discovery. The great Helmholtz, physiologist and physicist, was busy measuring visual and auditory sensations while Fechner was at work, and a younger man, Wilhelm Wundt, was getting ready to "found" the new scientific psychology, that is to say, to give it a name ("physiological psychology," later to be called "experimental psychology"), to write the first systematic handbook of the new science (in six huge editions from 1874 to 1911) and to create the first formal psychological laboratory (in Leipzig in 1879). Suffice it to say that, when psychologists quote the timeworn sentence, "Psychology has a long past but a short history," they mean that, although psychology began with the Greek philosophers two thousand years ago and continued as mental philosophy alongside natural philosophy for a very long time, the new experimental psychology did not claim scientific status for itself until the middle of the nineteenth century. In those early days it was usually called "physiological psychology," because it took over all the problems of sensation that the physiologists had been working on ever since they discovered that motor and sensory nerves are different. So it comes about that our present interest lies almost wholly in the achievements of the last one hundred years.

The present nature and range of experimental psychology is to a very considerable extent a consequence of psychology's history. The largest body of modern established fact lies in the field of sensation and perception, simply because that is the oldest interest, the topic in which research had already been started by the sense-physiologists before the new scientific psychology came into being in the 1860s. At first there were no satisfactory ways of measuring learning and memory, but Ebbinghaus, inspired by Fechner's success with sensation, published the first measurements of learning in 1885. He found that you can measure learning by counting the repetitions necessary just barely to master a given material or skill, and that the memory for such learning can be measured by noting how many fewer repetitions are required to master the same material or skill again at a later date, when forgetting has weakened but not entirely destroyed the original learning. These early methods, crude as they were, showed that memory and learning can be studied experimentally and also revealed the general nature of the functions for learning and forgetting. Modern methods, using as subjects children and adults, rats and pigeons, are more complicated as well as more precise. Pigeons, for instance, can learn certain rules for obtaining food by pecking at a button. They peck away all night, rewarded systematically with food by a machine, with their peckings all recorded on a tape. Thus learning, in an age of electronic gadgets, has become the most active field in experimental psychology.

The new psychology of observation and measurement had, by the end of the century, moved on from the investigation of the problems of sensation and perception to the study of learning; yet it remained insufficient for a complete description of man's thought and conduct. Men are activated by motives, by intentions, purposes and wishes, which are something more than learning and indeed affect learning as well as thinking and acting. It is not really possible to understand about human nature until one gets at the causes of its action. Psychologists did not know how to go ahead until they came upon the fact that psychology has to deal with unconsciousness as well as consciousness. Then they began to make a new kind of progress with what came to be called "dynamic psychology," the psychology of motivation, most of which works unconsciously.

No one did so much to promote this new research as Sigmund Freud, whose psychology of wishing first came to attention about 1900. Freud himself was not a conventional experimentalist. His laboratory was the consultation room, and also the bedchamber, where people had their dreams. A dream may be a partial revelation of what was previously a wholly repressed wish—that was his great discovery at the turn of the century. So often man does not know what he wants, especially when the unknown wish finds itself in conflict with some other socially approved wish. For instance, a man might hope, without consciously admitting it, that his father would die so that he could inherit his patrimony, and at the same time wish to have his father remain in good health because he is fond of him and admires him. Then the suppressed wish for his father's death might be half revealed in a dream and ultimately be brought completely to light by the laborious techniques of psychoanalysis. Even if the wish were not revealed at all, its existence could make the wisher feel guilty without his knowing why. For such reasons Freud developed the conception of the unconscious as the repository for repressed wishes.

The experimental psychologists were not quick to accept Freud's brilliant contribution to psychology, but they soon discovered independently that the key to creative thinking lies in the unconscious, in the predisposition with which the thought-problem is approached, a predisposition that is usually unconscious both before and during its operation. When later experimental psychology took up with the new concepts of a developing psychoanalysis, psychology had rounded itself out, at least so far as the mind and behavior of the individual were concerned. There was still waiting for advancement social psychology which deals with the interaction among people.

The first generations of scientific psychology were therefore perception–learning–motivation, and the range and stability of each of these important fields can be seen now to be roughly proportional to its age. Motivation, the youngest field of study, is the least secure.

Now that we have briefed ourselves on experimental psychology's three most important topics, we finally get around to asking the basic question: "What is psychology about?" The answer to that question is different in 1950 from what it was in 1900. In the first half-century of scientific psychology's existence it was understood that consciousness was the object of study in psychology, consciousness and the manner of its dependence on the brain. Two hundred years earlier, in 1650, the philosopher-physiologist Descartes had made the distinction between mind and matter clear, and everyone thereafter continued to accept his basic view. Mind, said Descartes, is unextended substance; it lives in the body but takes up no space there; it may even be immortal and live on when the body dies. Matter, on the other hand, is extended substance; it occupies space; the body, the nerves and the brain are matter. Mind and brain interact. The nerves create sensation in the mind. The will directs muscular movement of the body. Fechner's psychophysics was actually a study of the relationship between consciousness and external stimulation, but he would have liked, had he known how, to study "inner psychophysics," as he called the relation between consciousness and the brain. Altogether there was, up to 1900, no very serious doubt about what psychology was attempting.

Then psychology discovered unconsciousness! It was a gradual process, this discovery, one of those developments which make you realize that the thinking of cultivated men and the progress of science are often determined by unrecognized forces at work in the culture at a particular time. The *Zeitgeist*, as it has been called, the atmosphere of the times, plays its role in insight and discovery and often accounts for the simultaneous independent discoveries, familiar to every historian of science.

So Freud in Vienna was elaborating his concept of the Unconscious, discovering that wishes and motives may determine the thought and action of a person without his knowing what his own motives are. At the same time Külpe, an able but less well-known psychologist in Würzburg, was discovering that thinking itself, creative problem-solving, is largely or even entirely unconscious! Men form correct inferences without being able to say afterward how they formed them. His evidence was so little anticipated that years passed before its significance was grasped and still more years before it was related to Freud's simultaneously developed conception.

In America, meanwhile, John B. Watson was founding behaviorism, a school which argued that behavior, not consciousness, is the subject matter of psychology, that consciousness, even though it may exist independently of behavior, may nevertheless be safely ignored —and should be ignored—since the method of introspection, which had been used to get descriptions of consciousness, had proved unreliable. Actually Watson came to this conclusion because he had been pursuing psychological research on the sensory discrimination and the learning ability of rats, where behavior is what is directly observed and consciousness can only be inferred. Quite naturally he proposed that psychologists should extend to human subjects the methods that had proved successful with animals. So it was that these three synchronous trends—Freud's, Külpe's and Watson's— converged. Motive is usually unconscious, said Freud. Thought and creative insight, when brought under experimental control, turn out to solve their problems and reach their goals automatically, depending on an unconscious predisposition which controls their course: this was Külpe's contribution. In both cases you know about thought only from the eventual behavior or conduct of a motivated thinker. Behavior is the chief datum. Still later Watson made the point that not only motivation, but also learning and discriminatory sensation, can be studied as behavior in animals without regard to consciousness.

The victory of behavior over consciousness as the primary datum of psychology is perhaps not yet complete the world around, but there are two factors which have favored it in the past and are likely to promote it in the future.

The first of these is to be found in the spirit of America. Experimental psychology began in Germany and for the first half-century Germany led, with America a close second. In no other nation was development so rapid as in these two. By 1920 America had gained the lead. The use of psychological tests in World War I accelerated the American development. Then Hitler crippled German science and after that the demands for psychology in World War II forced the science far ahead in the United States. In 1917 the American Psychological Association totaled 336 members. In 1955 it had about 13,000, having increased steadily, like compound interest, at the rate of ten per cent per annum since its founding in 1892. But America is a practical country, a pioneer country in which settlers not so long ago wrested their living from stubborn nature. That is why America took so readily to a practical philosophy like pragmatism and at first put engineering ahead of science. So Americans were more concerned with what people do than with what goes on privately inside their heads. For that reason behaviorism found a ready acceptance in the New World, as it could not in a Germany accustomed since Kant to idealism; and, with America gone behavioristic, classical psychology could but surrender to majority rule. The small minority who clung to consciousness as the chief subject matter of psychology was for the most part sequestered in Europe, far away from this astonishing multiplication of psychologists in America.

The other influence that favored the identification of behaviorism with psychology was more subtle and also more effective. Watson had said that, after all, introspection *is* behavior, a kind of verbal behavior. Later P. W. Bridgman, the physicist, was to argue for operational definitions of scientific concepts, for the notion that a scientific datum like distance or an atom is defined wholly by the operations that are used to identify or describe it in scientific observation. The Vienna School of logical positivism provided for this view a philosophically sophisticated background. Then, about 1930, the American psychologists took up with it. Consciousness thus became that which is reported in introspection, and thus any language that an organism uses to describe its own characteristics. So a rat reports on its capacities by the errors it makes in learning a maze, and an ape by its insightful behavior in piling two boxes, one on top of the other, to enable it to reach the suspended banana. Similarly man reports on his sensory capacity by pressing a key when he sees a certain color and not pressing it when the color is slightly different, and on his learning ability by making only so many errors when he tries to repeat a list of nonsense words after saying them over twenty times.

The fundamental principle here is that science deals only with public information, and, whatever private consciousness may be like, it gets into science only by publication of some sort—by the words or gestures or other behavior of the organism to whom the consciousness belongs. Even the unconscious is tapped by the psychoanalysts only through the use of words or other behavior. This bit of behavioristic logic put the American psychologists at ease, allowing most of them to go all out for behaviorism. Introspection still exists in psychoanalysis, in social psychology, in the study of perception, in psychophysics, but nowadays we know that introspection is a kind of behavior; it is communication by physical signals which mean something crucial about the organism—the organism that was conscious in the 1850s but is only behaving in the 1950s.

So now it is conventional to say that psychology studies behavior, even though, quite often and quite properly, it seems to be talking about conscious experience.

With the general area of psychology thus mapped we can turn to some of the more important fields of psychological research, sampling each for the kinds of facts and laws which have emerged within it by the use of the experimental method: in other words a sampling inventory of the new experimental psychology that is now only a hundred years old.

1. *Psychophysics.* Psychology's long attack on the problems of sensation is best illustrated by examples from psychophysics, the discipline that Fechner founded in his unsuccessful attempt to spiritualize nineteenth-century materialism. Psychophysics includes the determination of thresholds—both the absolute threshold, which is the least stimulus that can be perceived, and also the differential threshold which is the least perceptible difference between stimuli. A great mass of research on the absolute thresholds reveals the human being as an astonishingly sensitive indicator of small changes in the physical world.

In vision the threshold for light is about 0.3 microwatts for a large stimulus a meter square in the center of the field of vision when the eye is most sensitive because it has been left in the dark for half an hour. That is the power that would raise a 3-gram weight one-hundredth of a millimeter in one second. Not very much power. Nevertheless it is about a thousand times as great as the threshold out at the extreme edge of the visual field where the value is only about 0.0003 microwatts. If the light is concentrated on a tiny area, as it is for the image of a star, the threshold is still lower, something like a hundred million-millionths of a watt. An erg is the energy required to raise one gram a thousandth of a centimeter, yet such a threshold star would have to shine on a human eye for forty years before it had delivered an erg of energy to it. Actually the human retina at its edge is thirty thousand times as sensitive as the most delicate radiometer which physicists use for detecting radiant energy.

Is the ear less sensitive than the eye? No; if anything, it is just a bit better. If you compute the maximal sensitivity for each under the very best conditions, you discover that the power that will just affect the retina of the eye—a star on a dark night seen out of the corner of the eye—is about 0.000,000,010 microwatts, whereas the power that will just affect hearing—at middle tonal pitch which is the most sensitive region—is about 0.000,000,004 microwatts. Those figures may not, however, be exact. It is better to say that both eye and ear are amazingly sensitive when conditions are right. Then the eye can perceive a bare half-dozen quanta of light, a quantum being the smallest unit of light that a modern physicist can conceive of. If the threshold for the ear were reduced to one-quarter of the value indicated, it would be possible to hear the movements of the molecules of the air, to perceive a movement of the air less than the diameter of a molecule of hydrogen.

All the evidence points to the fact that smell is as accurate and rich a sense as sight and hearing, that man may still have the olfactory capacity of some of his smell-minded mammalian ancestors. Catarrhal conditions may limit his sensitivity, and modern Western culture tends to turn attention away from smell. Nevertheless it is possible for a clear nose to smell one part in fifty thousand million of the putrid substance called mercaptan, to perceive as little as 0.000,000,-000,002 grams of this substance.

The other senses, such as taste, pressure, cold and warmth, are not so keen as these three, but their thresholds are still surprisingly small. In general, the psychologists have discovered that man has a greater capacity for fine perception than he ordinarily uses. In World War II, when the senses had to be used to the limit in the competition for victory, some of the ways for obtaining maximal sensitivity were worked out in careful research. An airplane night flier, to take one example, needs to know just what conditions will make visual sensitivity greatest, and also the situations in which even the best vision can fail him, the situations in which he must rely on other information if he is to escape disaster.

There is one exception to the above generalization: man employs visual space perception to the full limit of his capacity. The human eye can perceive as a black line a very dark distant wire against a very bright background when the width of the wire subtends at the eye only one second of arc. A second of arc represents on the retina about one-fifteenth of a thousandth of a millimeter and that is only about one-fortieth of the distance between the separate nerve endings. How is it possible to get such fine perception? On the retina the image of the wire is just a long straight blur, due to the optical imperfections of the eye and the random scattering of the tiny sense organs; but the brain translates such a long continuous blur back into a black line with edges sharp against its background. So the brain restores some of what the eye loses.

Man uses the visual portions of his brain to their limit. In hearing, the two halves of the brain pretty nearly duplicate each other. One half—either half—is needed for hearing and the other is a spare. The loss of the auditory center on one side does not greatly impair hearing. In vision, on the contrary, both halves are needed. The visual center in the left half of the brain works for the left halves of both retinas, which do the seeing for the right half of the field of vision (since the eye is a camera which reverses the perceived field, right for left). Any injury to the visual area in either half of the brain necessarily results in a spot of blindness.

You often hear it said that all science is empirical, that psychology and physics both go to the same experience for their primary data. That is true. The physicist Ernst Mach once wrote a book to show that both psychology and physics are different kinds of analysis of the same kind of sensations. But physics is wise. It is not interested in the sensations themselves but in what they indicate, and so it uses the most accurate kinds of sensations for its supply of information, that is to say, it uses visually perceived lines. That is why you hear it said: "Yes, physics is empirical; it is an empirical science of scale readings," for, whenever possible, physics reduces its scientific observation to the visual perception of a scale. The ear may be able to perceive a little less energy than the eye under optimal conditions, but no perception in any of the human senses is so effective as the eye when it comes to perceiving spatial pattern and spatial difference.

2. *Perception.* In recent years there has been interesting experimental work on what has come to be called object constancy. The human brain has built into it various properties which enable it to correct immediate sensory impressions in such a way that the man who owns the brain gets a truer perception of the outside world. Helmholtz called these corrective mechanisms "unconscious inference," because the brain assembles a variety of data in order to build up the best and truest perception.

A good example is 3-D perception in the modern stereoscopic movies which show depth. Here you have two pictures, one taken from the point of view of the right eye and the other from the point of view of the left eye. A tridimensional scene looks different when viewed from different angles, and it would be possible to measure the discrepancies in two such pictures so as to compute the depths in the third dimension trigonometrically. The brain, however, normally makes that computation for the disparity of view between the two eyes instantaneously, so that we see the depths just as they are, or exaggerated if the two pictures are taken from points farther apart than the separation of the two eyes. You can take successive pictures of the ground from an airplane, view each picture stereoscopically with the proper eye, and see the perspective of the distant scene below that you would get if your eyes were a hundred yards apart and 40,000 feet above the ground. The important point to note here is that the brain and the two eyes together get a truer perception than can either eye alone, for together they make up 3-D vision, whereas each retina alone has only 2-D vision.

One of the most familiar and best understood cases of object constancy, where the brain corrects the eye in the interests of truth, is what is called size constancy. If you are looking at a man 20 feet away and he walks off to a distance of 40 feet, his image on your retinas shrinks to half its original height, but the perception of him does not shrink. He looks just as tall, and will continue to look just as tall if he walks away to 200 feet. Certainly a chap who is six feet tall when twenty feet away does not get to seem seven inches high (one-tenth as tall) when 200 feet away. The brain, however, needs information or it cannot perform this calculation; it needs to "know" the distance. If you deprive it of all its clues to distance, let it use only one eye, render invisible all perception of objects that would provide the clues of visual perspective, work with unfamiliar objects, like faint disks of light in complete darkness, then object constancy fails and a disk twice as far away does indeed match the size of a near disk of half the diameter. But give the brain its necessary data and it does its corrective job unconsciously and instantly.

3. *Reaction.* Even though the psychologists of the late nineteenth century were primarily interested in consciousness, certain crucial facts of behavior did not escape them. Reaction time was one of these. Indeed, the pioneer work in this field was performed by the astronomers long before there was any scientific psychology as such.

In 1796 the Astronomer Royal at the Greenwich Observatory dismissed his assistant because the assistant could not make accurate observations of the times of stellar transits, that is to say, he could not estimate accurately, while listening to the ticks of a seconds-clock, the fraction of a second at which a star, seen in the field of the telescope, crossed a given cross hair. Actually all the Astronomer Royal knew was that he and his assistant did not agree, and twenty-five years later a German astronomer named Bessel undertook to examine this situation further by comparing his own observations with those of another equally distinguished astronomer. The two men differed by almost a whole second, an astonishingly large amount. That led the astronomers to begin the study of individual differences between observers—"personal equations," they called them—in order that they might correct the observations of one man to agree with the observations of another.

Another twenty-five years went by and electric currents had become available for scientific use, and electromagnets, and electrically operated chronoscopes which would measure time-intervals to a thousandth of a second. Then it became possible to measure absolute reaction times, to see how long it took an observer to press a key after a signal had been given. The astronomers at first had been able only to compare one observer with another; now they and presently the psychologists could measure the actual time for a signal to be perceived and for a movement to be made in response to it. These reaction times, studied intensively in the psychological laboratories, turned out in the 1870s and 1880s to vary with the individual reactor, with the sense-department for which the signal is given, with the degree of complication in the stimulus or the reaction, and ultimately with the preparatory attitude of the reactor.

The times of the simplest reactions were of the order of one or two tenths of a second, and it was found that there is a sensory type of reaction, when the reactor is prepared in advance to make sure of the nature of the stimulus before he reacts, and also a motor type of reaction when he is set to respond as quickly as possible without waiting for full cognition of the stimulus. The sensory type takes something like 0.2 seconds and the motor type nearly as little as 0.1 seconds. The quicker motor type is, however, less accurate. It may be touched off by the wrong stimulus or go off prematurely without any observable stimulus. The false starts in the hundred-yard dash are of the motor type.

Historically this discovery marks the beginning of the experimental psychology of motivation because it shows how an initial predisposition—to perceive the stimulus accurately or to go off just as quickly as possible—can affect subsequent psychological events. Predispositions are attitudes, are essentially wishes or needs or motives. They have their effects on almost every psychological event and, as we have noted, are more often unconscious than not.

The modern uses of reaction times are many. If, in a test of memory, an association comes more quickly by a few hundredths of a second, it is judged to be stronger. The association test for crime detection and for the recovery of repressed ideas makes use of the converse fact that it takes time to inhibit the strongest and most immediate response which, if given, would reveal the guilt or the repression. Reaction time is used to measure degree of attention: a distraction is really working if it slows down time of response. Airplane pilots, chauffeurs and the operators of many kinds of machines are tested for reaction times. The best chauffeurs have intermediately long times; accidents increase when their times are too slow or too fast.

4. *Learning.* As we have already seen, the experimental study of learning did not begin until Ebbinghaus' researches in 1885. The British philosophers had already established without experiments certain laws of association, which were to all intents and purposes laws of learning. The chief of these was the law of frequency of contiguity, and Ebbinghaus based his work on this principle, that the more often two ideas are together in consciousness, the more often a new arousal of one will rearouse the other. To get fairly uniform material with which to work he invented nonsense syllables, three-letter items like BAP, WEG, FID, TOX, RUV, and had his subjects (himself for the most part) repeat series of these syllables until they just barely knew them. Actually he found that frequency of happening together does not work in any simple manner. If you double the length of a series of syllables, you have to repeat it oftener to learn it, that is to say, you have to increase the frequency of the contiguity between each pair of successive syllables. The adding of extra syllables weakens the connection formed between the others.

What holds for ideas may also hold for behavior, as Pavlov, the Russian physiologist, found out when he discovered the conditioned response at the beginning of the new, behavioristic twentieth century. If you teach a dog to recognize the sight of food so that his mouth waters when he sees it, and if you then sound a tone regularly just before he sees the food, he will presently anticipate the food; that is to say, his saliva will flow when he hears the tone and before the food appears. The salivary response to the sight of food is said then to have been conditioned upon the sound of the tone, and the conditioning is, in part at least, a result of the frequency of contiguity between the hearing of the tone and the seeing of the food.

In this manner you can investigate all the laws of learning and memory, as well as all the laws of sensation. You can find out by experiment how faint a tone can become and still remain a conditioning stimulus, and how well the dog can discriminate between one tone and another by salivating for the proper frequency and not salivating for a slightly different frequency. Pavlov called such a conditioned secretion of saliva "psychic juice," because most of the facts of learning and perception could be investigated in this manner. Later, when Watson founded behaviorism, he took over the facts and method of conditioning as a chief contribution to his new psychology that ignored consciousness.

It is impossible to say whether psychology's swing away from the data of consciousness toward the data of behavior has been largely due to the suitability of animal subjects—rats, pigeons, monkeys and apes—for experimental work on learning and sensory discrimination, or whether causation has worked the opposite way. In either case learning has been the live fresh topic in experimental psychology since 1930 and most of the work has been done on animal subjects. One prominent investigator even dedicated his magnum opus to the white rat and he might have added, as so many authors say of their wives, "without whose help this volume could never have been written." The rat learns the path to food through a maze, shows how he remembers what he has learned, demonstrates the aid or hindrance which knowledge of one maze is to learning another, or the effect of learning another on the memory of the first—all of these situations being paradigms of what happens to learning and memory in college or in industry. The rat reports upon his sensory capacities by learning or failing to learn to jump across a small abyss to a properly marked door. If he hits the correct door it opens and he is fed, but the wrong door is locked and makes him plunge uncomfortably down into a net. The pigeon learns to peck away at a button, often more than ten thousand times an hour, receiving food when he pecks in accordance with some prearranged schedule, for example, every fortieth peck or every ten seconds. A pigeon can learn either of such simple rules and adjust his pecking to them. Rat and pigeon—they are perceiving, discriminating, learning, cognizing, remembering.

One of the great advantages of using animals for subjects is that their brains can be operated upon, specific regions of the neural tissue removed or destroyed, and the effect upon learning or sensory discrimination noted. The two chief discoveries about the brain as the organ of what psychology studies—consciousness or behavior—have been these. (1) It is not safe to predict from lower animals to man. The lower forms need the cerebral cortex less than does man. For instance, removal of the visual brain areas in man renders him completely blind, whereas their removal in the rat makes it unable to distinguish spatial patterns but permits it still to discriminate differences in illumination. (2) Even in man not all the cerebral cortex is essential to learning and memory. A great deal of tissue can be destroyed, especially in the frontal regions, with little interference in the capacities of the person losing the tissue. Such losses make even less difference in lower animal forms. A dog with one cerebral hemisphere gone is astonishingly able, and even with both gone, although he lives a dull life without initiative, he gets along if he has a nurse to make sure that food gets into his mouth. On the other hand, a man with no cerebrum dies. As to where memories are kept or in what manner they are stored no one has an intelligent guess. The answer to this question has long been sought and still eludes the insight of even the most brilliant investigators.

5. *Emotion.* There has been plenty of talk about emotion ever since William James in 1884 proposed the extreme hypothesis that we do not cry because we are sorry but are sorry because we cry. He was trying then to impress on his audience the fact that a thoroughgoing emotion always has in it a great many visceral changes, the perception of which constitutes an essential ingredient of every emotion. He was, of course, writing in the age when consciousness was psychology's main business. The important discovery about emotion came later in psychology's behavioral century. Studies of the emotions of dogs and cats resulted in what is called the emergency theory of emotion. A dog can be said to have an emotion in the presence of a cat, and conversely. A dog in a cat-perceiving state is found to have his sympathetic nervous system innervated. Such innervation has the effect of putting the organism—the dog—on a war footing, ready for violent action. It speeds up his heart, sends more blood to his voluntary muscles and less to his digestive organs, liberates sugar from his liver (the sugar that combats fatigue and increases strength), increases sweating (to keep the body cool under exertion), erects his hair (probably to make him look larger and more fierce), and stops all his digestive processes including the flow of saliva—so that his mouth goes dry. (In India they judge a man guilty if his emotion makes his mouth so dry that he is unable to chew rice.) So to have an emotion is to be prepared for vigorous emergency action.

Digestion can wait for more peaceful times. In this discovery we have the modern behavioral equivalent of James's organic stir-up in emotion, an inventory of the actual physiological changes themselves.

6. *Motivation.* We have already noted that the third historical phase of experimental psychology is the period in which motivation became a problem for scientific attack. The pioneers were, as we have seen, Freud and Külpe, working independently on very different kinds of problems. Still earlier there had been the discovery that reaction time and type depend on the predisposing attitude of the subject before the reaction occurs. Freud worked out a psychology of unconscious wishes, the first thorough dynamic psychology. It was Külpe's student, Ach, who in 1905 discovered the determining tendency, as he called it. A determining tendency is a predisposition for association that is not dependent upon previous frequency of contiguity. It acts, as it were, *de novo.* Ach found, for instance, that all his subjects, since they knew arithmetic, already had three common associations formed for the stimulus of an 8 over a 5. These associations are the sum 13, the difference 3, and the product 40. The sum is the strongest association and the product the weakest. Nevertheless Ach could, simply by asking his subjects to multiply, thus setting up in advance the proper determining predisposition, always get products as associations, never sums or differences, and that without any new practice in multiplying (without more frequency of contiguity). If you ask a man for opposites and give him the word *black* he will almost surely say *white,* but if you ask him for rhymes, then he will say *tack* or *sack.* Determining tendencies do not create new associations; they just make old weak ones, strong. If you ask for a rhyme for *month* you may get nothing; since very few have ever formed the association between *month* and $(n + 1)th$, there may be nothing there to strengthen.

Dynamic psychology does not talk much nowadays about determining tendencies. It speaks principally of needs, drives and attitudes. The rat has a need for food, and food deprivation increases his hunger drive. There is really no such thing as unmotivated behavior, and hunger is the drive usually employed to produce action in animal experiments. Attitudes are prejudices, as the conservative attitude is different from the radical. One experiment has seemed to show that poor boys may actually see pieces of money as larger than do rich boys, a case of an economic attitude's affecting perception. Social psychology and the psychology of personality make broad use of the concepts of attitude and need. Quite early social psychology sought to list the primitive needs or instincts, but it is hard to distinguish between the primary inherited needs and the derived needs acquired through learning and the adaptation of the person to his cultural environment.

In general, the primary needs are physiological, and they may also be vital in the sense that the organism dies if the needs are not supplied. Oxygen is a vital need of the organism, and so are water and food. A man can live for minutes without oxygen but not for hours, for days without water but not for weeks, and for weeks without food but not for months. Sleep is probably also a vital need, but mostly people do not die from sleeplessness; instead they go to sleep. Once an enthusiast, who thought sleep was a habit which he could break by practicing staying awake, actually did remain awake for more than nine days, but then he went to sleep. Sexual desire is a physiological need, activated by hormones in the blood, but it is not vital. Men do not die of sexual starvation. Activity is another physiological need which is not vital. It is these primary needs that drive the organism to action, and, when they are satisfied, the drive ceases until oxygen or water or food or sleep is needed again.

Every theory of action holds that an organism in need is under tension for satisfying the need. If an animal has in its repertoire of habits ways of satisfying a particular need, these habits are reinforced by the need and appropriate action ensues. On the other hand, if the animal knows no solution under the circumstances in which it finds itself, then it becomes restless and proceeds by trial and error until it hits upon a satisfaction. Satisfaction of a need, reaching a goal, always terminates the drive for the moment.

Most human needs are derived, built up within the social environment in which a man lives. Different investigators whose tasks are to assess personalities develop different inventories of needs. One distinguished group found it could get along with a list of thirty needs or attitudes—the abasive, the achievant, the acquisitive, the affiliative, the aggressive, the ambitious, the autonomous attitude, and so on with twenty-three others. Other investigators have other lists. At times it seems as if need for aggression in the face of frustration were so universal as to be primary, but it is obviously not vital, nor physiologically based, nor is it inevitable since frustration can also be met with apathy.

Needs are known to affect the form of perception, the nature of imagination, the degree of sensitivity and the persistence of activity. Every time we speak of wishful thinking or of a convenient memory we are expressing the belief that the existence of a need distorts the normal relation to reality of the person who has the need. Most of the disturbances of personality with which psychiatrists and psychoanalysts deal, those that are classified as functional and not as organic, are disturbances of motivation of this sort.

7. *Ability.*   It is obvious that a man's personality is to a large extent his motivational pattern, the inventory of his needs and attitudes. But his skills, abilities and aptitudes must also be added to make the whole psychological picture of the individual. An aptitude is a predisposition for acquiring a skill. Some people can learn languages more easily than can others; some have more aptitude for acquiring mechanical ability than have others. One kind of aptitude does not assure the existence of the other nor guarantee its absence. In general, however, abilities tend to be positively correlated. Some persons rate high in respect of many different abilities, and some low in respect of many.

It used to be supposed that underlying all abilities there was a common factor which was called general ability or intelligence. While it entered into different abilities in varying degrees, it was thought to have some part in practically all. That view is now becoming obsolete, and, in a sense, the concept of intelligence might be said to be on the way out were it not so firmly rooted in school practices. It is indeed true that a large class of scholastic and academic skills, the bookish abilities of intellectual persons, show a high correlation with one another and with verbal abilities. The factor common to them is better called scholastic aptitude than intelligence, and it is certainly a general factor among the abilities that are important in formal education. It was, of course, on school children and college students that the intelligence tests were originally tried out and calibrated.

The modern tool for the analysis of abilities is factorial analysis. To use it you make up a battery of tests for whatever population you have in mind—school children, soldiers, factory workers—and you try to make the tests as different as possible but presumably covering all the activities important in your investigation. Then you administer them to as large a fair sample of the population as is practicable and treat the result by the new statistical procedures which select the factors common in determinable degrees to various tests, much in the way that physical forces are resolved into independent components by the use of the parallelogram of forces. So you come out with independent factors a, b, c, d, . . . and statements of the degree to which each contributes to every test. Then you examine the nature of these contributions and give each factor the most plausible name you can think of.

America's leading investigator in this field has worked out for eighth-graders and college students the following seven primary basic abilities in intellectual performance: (1) spatial visualization, (2) numerical quickness in arithmetical computation, (3) verbal comprehension of ideas and meanings, (4) word fluency in speech, (5) memory facility for retention, (6) perceptual speed in observing details, and (7) inductive ability to extract a rule common to a problem. The U. S. Army in World War II constructed a General Classification Test for its millions of soldiers. It avoided the word *intelligence* because that term seemed opprobrious in respect of those who scored low. This was a short test and it was based on the first three of the seven factors listed above. It worked well both for selecting the men of high general ability from those of low, and also for distinguishing between verbal aptitude and mechanical aptitude, which is indicated by a high score for spatial visualization.

Here we may stop, for we have had a look at at least one of the more important subjects of investigations in each of the seven most important topics of modern scientific psychology. The reader now knows what psychology is about, what psychologists think about and at what they work.

Modern psychology is not, however, what Fechner was hoping to found on that October morning in 1850 when he had a vision of how to make the spiritual absorb the material in an age of materialism. His vision was sure enough to induce him to carry through an enormous amount of tough psychophysical experimentation during the next ten years of his life, but the world was not looking for a spiritualistic philosophy in 1850. Rather it was ready to snatch at a new science of psychology in the middle of a century which used to be called the scientific age. From Fechner's hands it took what he did not know he had, a new science of mind, for psychophysics must be a science if it measures, and it must be new if it manages to measure anything so incorporeal as sensation. Often in science the importance of research turns out to be something quite different from what its originator expected. In fact, the story of Fechner is the parable for the practice of basic research. If men are left free to pursue knowledge for its own sake, the new discoveries may be useful, yet often useful in wholly unanticipated ways.

What would Fechner have thought if he had had a true view of whither his activities would lead by October 1950? In 1850 it would have seemed that psychology would remain the property of a relatively few scholars in the universities. In 1950 it had become the bread-winning profession of twenty thousand Americans and a few thousands elsewhere, with not more than a third of them in academic institutions. And as for materialism, the new science had gone almost the whole way from what Fechner wanted, for not only had it forgotten about spiritual values, but it had also largely dispensed with consciousness, once its very reason for existence, and had become a physicalistic science of behavior. Perhaps it is well that no true vision of this future was vouchsafed Fechner. He might have been discouraged and never have given us psychophysics. But he would not have prevented psychology; that is sure. History, as Tolstoy has made so clear, is the servant of no Great Man. Fechner was History's agent, not her master. Had he failed her, History would have found another man.

ANTHROPOLOGY

CLYDE KLUCKHOHN

about

Clyde Kluckhohn

*Clyde Kluckhohn was born in Le Mars, Iowa, in 1905. His early
schooling included attendance at the Culver Military Academy
and at Lawrenceville, after which he entered Princeton. Forced to
leave during his freshman year because of illness, he went to New
Mexico to regain his health and spent a year, mainly on horseback, in
the Indian country of the Southwest. "Fortune," he says, "landed
me on the ranch of an educated and intelligent man who had a fairly
good anthropological library and a lively intellectual interest in Indians. I learned some Navaho and came to know more than casually
Indians of a number of different tribes." These experiences are described in his first book* To the Foot of the Rainbow, *which appeared
in 1927. He resumed his education at the University of Wisconsin
where he graduated in 1928. "On leaving the university I was determined," he writes, "not to become a professor and thought of an
eventual career in law, medicine—or cattle ranching and politics."
The award of a Rhodes scholarship enabled him to spend two years
at an English university. While at Oxford he had "the wavering
thought" of becoming a classical archaeologist and in 1930, on returning to the United States, "almost entered the Harvard Law
School." But after another visit to the Southwest and flirting with
the idea of becoming an Indian trader, he finally made up his mind
to become an anthropologist. He attended lectures at the Sorbonne,
wrote another book on the Southwest, studied anthropology at the*

University of Vienna—and while there took the opportunity of being psychoanalyzed "inexpensively"—and won a diploma in anthropology at Oxford.

Kluckhohn began his teaching career at the University of New Mexico as assistant professor of anthropology from 1932 to 1934. In 1935 he joined the Harvard faculty and the next year received his doctorate from the university. When he started teaching at Harvard there were two physical anthropologists on the faculty, the late Earnest Hooton and Carleton Coon; this fact led him to shift mainly to cultural anthropology. In 1946 he was made a full professor at Harvard.

Kluckhohn's professional career has taken a broad and varied course. He has taught all branches of anthropology and has even held classes in anatomy; he has engaged in archaeological excavations in the Southwest, in England and Greece, and has published in this field; he has given courses in linguistics.

Besides his academic activities Kluckhohn has since 1942 spent much time in government and administrative work. He has helped train military government officers, codirected an intelligence and psychological warfare group concerned with Japan, headed the Far East Policy Division of the Office of War Information, done odd jobs for the Office of Strategic Services, the Navy and other government departments, and for a period served on MacArthur's staff in Tokyo. In the fall of 1947 he organized the Russian Research Center at Harvard and he directed it until July 1954. The Center is the largest nongovernmental research institution dealing with the U.S.S.R. in the Western world; it studies all aspects of Soviet policy, with particular emphasis on politics, psychology, economics and sociology.

Among his writings are The Navaho (1947), Personality in Nature, Society and Culture, edited with Henry Alexander Murray (1948), and the prize-winning, Mirror for Man (1949), a popular study of what anthropology can do for world peace by promoting the understanding of and respect for cultural differences. Dr. Kluckhohn is married—his wife is a lecturer in sociology at Harvard—and has a son who is a graduate student in anthropology at the University of Chicago. In his own opinion, his best work is a book on Navaho witchcraft and the concluding chapter in the volume The Excavation of B.C. 51. *His academic distinctions include an honorary degree from the University of New Mexico, the Viking Fund medal for general anthropology and membership in the National Academy of Sciences.*

ANTHROPOLOGY

CLYDE KLUCKHOHN

Anthropology is the study of the similarities and differences, both biological and behavioral, among the peoples of the world from the dawn of human history to the present day. Anthropology excavates and analyzes the remains of past civilizations (archaeology); describes the evolution and present biological characteristics of our species (physical anthropology); traces the development and spread of customs and technologies over the face of the earth, showing how these forms, arts, faiths and tools satisfy the psychological needs of individuals and keep societies together (cultural anthropology); defines the varieties of human speech and the relationships among the tongues of men (linguistics). Its realm is thus immense; its objective is to discover, by systematic and scientific means, the nature of this "human nature" about which we all talk so glibly. How has man come to be what he is? What is constant and what is variable in "human nature?" Can we explain the differences among human groups in terms of biology, of varying physical environments, of the accidents of history? More realistically, what approximate weight can be assigned to each of these factors—both in general and under particular circumstances?

The following more specific questions will illustrate the range of anthropological enquiry:

When and where were various plants and animals first domesticated? By what routes and under what conditions did they spread to other peoples?

Did the great pre-Columbian civilizations of Middle and South America learn how to work metals independently or did they get the idea or even the techniques from the Old World?

Are all types of men, extinct and living, descended from the same ancestors or were there various separate lines of development?

What are the present biological limitations and potentialities of the human species?

How significant are the biological differences among existing human populations?

Is one type of physique more prone than another to specific kinds of organic or mental illness?

Are the religions of peoples living in the tropics similar to one another and different from those of peoples living in the Arctic?

Can styles in art or music be shown to depend upon economic or social organization?

Are the child-training practices of a society reflected in typical adult personality?

Is there any fixed rate at which languages ordinarily change?

Is there a relationship between the nature of a language and the over-all way of life of a people?

The diversity of these questions suggests something about the historical origin of anthropology which has been characterized as "the science of leftovers." The first anthropologists were specialists in geology, medicine, law and biology whose curiosity was intrigued by topics that were somehow left out of the then-existent sciences. Anthropologists today still refuse to be stopped by the artificial conventions that divide up academic subjects. They pay little attention to the line between "savage" and "civilized." There are only three things which unify anthropology:

1. A focus on man in all his variation and similarity.

2. A consistently comparative point of view.

3. A stubborn conviction that history, physique, environmental situation, way of life, and language are all related in discoverable patterns.

HUMAN EVOLUTION [1]

by S. L. WASHBURN

Mammals have existed on earth for 60 million years and man's first mammalian ancestor was a four-footed beast about the size of a rat. In the millennia since then he has developed into the relatively giant biped of today. Paws changed to hands. The sense of smell was greatly weakened, while vision changed from a primitive condition in which each eye worked relatively separately and saw only black and white into the stereoscopic color vision we think normal. The number of young was reduced from several to one at a birth, and the length of life was greatly increased. The method of locomotion changed at least twice and perhaps three times.

The guiding factor in evolution is selection, and for most of human history man's fate was controlled in a way exactly comparable to that of other animals. But with the coming of the Ice Age some of the small-brained bipeds learned to use tools. Thereafter, adaptation, selection, migration, and the size of the group depended on the tool-making traditions as well as on the biological endowment. In the latter phases of man's evolution it is impossible to study the physical changes without investigating the cultural changes with which they are inexorably linked. Especially the great expansion of the brain, which we think of as uniquely human, seems to come after the upright posture and after the use of tools.

Evolution reveals to us how our human nature, the basis for our way of life, was built system by system over the millions of years of primate evolution. When our ancestors had evolved to the point where they could make tools, the process of change took on a new dimension and accelerated. If it were not for tools, mankind might be only a species of tropical bipeds, no more successful than the baboons. It is the importance of

[1] In view of my own lack of competence on this very specialized and tricky subject, I asked Professor Washburn, Chairman of the Department of Anthropology at the University of Chicago, to treat the topic. Very appropriately from the standpoint of this chapter, he stresses the origin of behavior rather than the details of the relationship between man and the various monkeys, apes, and other primates. C.K.

culture in the late stages of human evolution which necessitates the close co-operation of the biologist and archaeologist.

Although specialists agree on the main events of human evolution and their significance, they argue about the precise course of evolution. Has man been separated from the apes and monkeys for many millions of years, or is he a recent arrival, perhaps distinct from the apes for only a million years? Was man ever really an ape or is his origin so remote that his ancestors were more like monkeys? I believe that the close similarity in the arms of man and ape shows that our direct ancestors were arm-swinging apes, perhaps not very different from the living chimpanzee. However, this question cannot be finally decided until many more primate fossils are found, for the precise course of evolution can be revealed only by a moderately complete fossil record. In the meantime, the development of modern evolutionary theory and experimental methods helps to clarify the issues and to narrow the area still subject to disagreement. Further, the discovery of fossils depends less and less on chance and is becoming a planned search. As this process proceeds, the rate of discovery of fossils is accelerated. If the discoveries of the next ten years are as dramatic as those of the last, several of the most debatable issues may be settled.

The History of Man

The oldest-known tools have been found in deposits in South, East, and North Africa, in Europe, and in Asia. The earliest examples of toolmaking known occur in tropical Africa. They are primitive pebble tools made perhaps 600,000 to 700,000 years ago. Many authorities believe that their makers were the first true men whose skeletons have not yet been uncovered. However, the latest scientific review of the subject suggests that they may have been made by ape-men (Australopithecines) though perhaps of a different type from those whose physical remains have been discovered in considerable quantity in South Africa in recent years. The South African ape-men may have killed game with crude weapons such as sticks or bones. There is even some suggestion that they used fire, but this is still quite uncertain. The ape-men and the first true men may have had common direct ancestors, with the true men representing a more progressive line which evolved into larger-brained, toolmaking types.

Organisms and Stages of Cultural Development	Approximate Years B.C.	Subdivision of Geological Time
Ape-men of South Africa	700,000–500,000 (?)	Lower Pleistocene
Earliest Pebble Tools of True Men	700,000	Lower Pleistocene
Lower Paleolithic	700,000–70,000	Lower and Middle Pleistocene
Peking Man	300,000	Mid-Pleistocene
Neanderthal Man (various varieties)	150,000 and later	Mid- and Upper Pleistocene
Middle Paleolithic	70,000–35,000	Upper Pleistocene
Modern Man	70,000 (?)	Upper Pleistocene (?)
Upper Paleolithic	35,000–8000	Upper Paleolithic
Mesolithic	8000–4500 *	Early Post-Glacial
Neolithic	4500–3000 *	Recent
Bronze Age	3500–1500 *	Recent
Iron Age	1500 ff.*	Recent

* For these dates the Middle East is taken as the point of departure. Figures for Europe and most other parts of the world would be later—in some instances a good deal later.

The earliest human skeletons (such as those of Peking Man and the Neanderthaloid races of Europe) reveal variable but uniformly brutish creatures. They may or may not be our ancestors. A few authorities still hold that modern man (who first appears, according to present evidence, about 70,000 years ago) evolved from these brutes. More students would hold that contemporary races carry at least some admixture with the earlier types. A third view is that the Neanderthal men of the Old Stone Age represent merely isolated survivors of a formerly widespread Neanderthaloid group, but that they were eventually exterminated by our own species whom we immodestly call "wise men" (*Homo sapiens*).

Man's brain began to outstrip the ape's brain only after his limbs and trunk had attained full human status. The critical primary adaptation that differentiated men as a distinct group was in the hipbone. The size of the human brain increased as men adjusted to new ways of life. After the use of tools—which presumably gave greater survival advantages to individuals who had large brains—brain size doubled. The range in the cranial capacity of chimpanzees and gorillas is about 325 to 650 cubic centimeters, of the man-apes of South Africa 450 to 650, of Java Man 750 to 900, of Peking Man 900 to 1200, of Neanderthal Man 1100 to 1550. The last range is about that of modern man.[2] Historic man has shown a more or less steady increase in average stature and a decrease in average head length.

As human physique evolved, so did human culture: in technology, economy, art, religion and morals. For the more ancient periods we can only crudely sketch the evolution of tools and of ways of making a living. Archaeologists who specialize in the Old Stone Age distinguish various types of assemblages of unpolished stone tools. Some of these archaeological "cultures" are found only in Europe, or Africa, or Asia; others are no respectors of continents. It is in the last phase of the Old Stone Age in Europe that we first learn something, not only about tools, but also about religion, costume, and art.

The lower Old Stone Age in Europe may have lasted 400,000 years. The upper Paleolithic probably endured less than 30,000. Yet its advances in technology were far greater than were those of the longer period. Man employed a more economic but more sophisticated method of preparing flakes,[3] and fashioned a far greater number of specialized and standardized tools. He used bone, ivory, and antler extensively. He hunted with missile weapons and traps. Among his other inventions were the needle and thread, skin clothing, special fishing equipment, lamps of animal skulls or stone which he used in the dark caves where his paintings are now preserved. The earliest man-made dwellings are found in this era. The location of some settlements suggests a much more complex social life, including collective hunting. There is evidence for magic employed to increase

[2] There is no *conclusive* evidence for *Homo sapiens* (modern man) before the third inter-glacial.

[3] The earliest known tools were cutting instruments, made by breaking a roughly spherical pebble so as to get a sharp edge. Probably a little later are pear-shaped flint "hand-axes" about seven inches long and with detectable edges around their outlines. Contemporaneous—though more frequently found in different regions— were flakes of flint obtained principally by striking one rock with another so that good-sized chips "flaked" off.

the supply of food animals, for private property, and possibly social stratification. Art appears in various forms: finger-tracing, engraving, bas-relief, sculpture and painting. A wide range of red, yellow, brown and black shades are used. No true blues, greens, or whites have yet been observed.

The European Mesolithic (Middle Stone Age) is an adaptation to a radically changed environment but does not differ too strikingly from the later Old Stone Age. Collecting of wild fruits, nuts, berries, and roots is more important in the economic life. Cemeteries show that fairly sizable communities of hunters and fishermen existed. There are indications of head-hunting, of cannibalism, and of some kind of chieftainship. The Mesolithic in northern Europe is as long a period as the whole of recorded human history (about 5000 years), but must be regarded as the final phase of an archaic way of life rather than as the direct harbinger of modern civilization.

Our civilization derives directly from the New Stone Age (Neolithic) of western Asia and Egypt. Men changed from a wandering to a settled life. Formerly the Neolithic period was defined by the appearance in the deposits of polished stone implements and contemporary kinds of plants and animals. Today the significant criterion is taken to be the planned raising of food in contrast to the hunting and collecting of the earlier periods. In various parts of the Near East one finds—rather suddenly at about the middle fifth millennium B.C.—wheat, barley and sickle blades and the bones of cattle, pigs, sheep and goats. Other animals, among them the horse, appear to have been domesticated later and elsewhere. But present evidence suggests that the revolutionary inventions which made possible a new type of economy, town life, and vast changes in social organization and culture generally took place in the Near East during or prior to the fifth millennium B.C. Thus far only a few sites that may be transitional to the food-producing revolution have been excavated, and their dates are at present problematical. The earliest sites with good stratigraphy seem to be Jarmo in Kurdistan (Iraq), Tel Hassuna (northern Iraq), and possibly Jericho. It does seem clear that pottery, metals and writing are later than the domestication of plants and animals.

A food-producing economy permitted a rapid increase in population. This in turn led to the spread of the Neolithic way of life. Colonies (perhaps of younger sons and daughters) had to be planted by land and sea. Within a few thousand years domesticated plants and animals, metallurgy, and town life had gone from the Near East along the shores of the Mediterranean as far as Spain and Italy and up the Danube into Central Europe. Eastward, Neolithic cultures spread to India, China, and elsewhere. Then follows the Bronze Age, which was succeeded by the Iron Age, and in the Mediterranean Basin we have arrived at the fairly familiar territory of classical civilization.

The date of the first entry of man into the New World is still being argued, though there is general agreement that the Eastern Hemisphere was the cradle of mankind. The conservative view is that human beings did not reach the Americas until after the final retreat of the Wisconsin glaciers (approximately 7000 B.C.). Most authorities, however, hold today that man arrived in the new world during one of the interglacial phases of the Wisconsin glaciation, or even earlier. Probably the first settlers in the Western Hemisphere slowly filtered down from the Arctic regions. Ancient sites in Alaska contain grooving tools and thin slivers chipped delicately from prepared flint cores that are very like artifacts characteristic of archaeological finds on the Asiatic-European side of the circumpolar region. Ten to fifteen thousand years ago the whole Arctic area seems to have been thinly populated by bands who had followed the animals clinging close to the retreating ice sheets. These bands gradually spread out in various directions—wherever they found that meat was available.

By 9000 B.C., according to this view, there were hunters in the North American high plains who made tools of distinctive type and rather similar to some of those found at Cape Denbigh, Alaska. By 7000 B.C. human beings were living at almost the southern tip of South America.

A generation ago almost all American scholars stoutly defended a kind of anthropological Monroe Doctrine. Man had reached this hemisphere from Asia via the Bering Strait region not much earlier than 2000-3000 B.C. All subsequent cultural evolution here had been entirely independent until after the arrival of Columbus—with the possible exception of a not very influential earlier contact with Norse voyagers. Attempts such as those of the British anatomist, Grafton Elliot-Smith, to show a connection between Maya architecture and sculpture and the artistic styles of Southeast Asia were howled down. Elliot-Smith wrote a witty defense, "Elephants and Ethnologists," in which he suggested that the Americanists simply refused to see the obvious, but his and other arguments for transpacific connections were hardly taken seriously by American anthropology. There is little doubt that there was a factor of genuine bias here, for some relevant bits of evidence were conveniently ignored. For example, a last stronghold of the proponents of the anthropological Monroe Doctrine was the supposed fact that some of the distinctive features of the Old World Bronze and Iron Ages, such as the wheel, were completely unknown in the New World. Actually, wheeled toys[4] were discovered in a pre-Columbian horizon in Mexico as early as 1887 and Middle American archaeologists have reluctantly come to the conclusion that some Maya pottery was wheel-made.

Today professional opinion is less rigid. Development on these continents is held to be mainly indigenous, but the position of extreme isolationism has weakened. Archaeologists recognize remarkable parallels between cultural elements in Peru and elsewhere in South America and some distinctive traits of cultures in Oceania and Southeast Asia. The archaeological remains indicate that, shortly after the time of Christ, certain Alaskan Eskimos obtained iron by trade from China and Korea. Their art also shows some striking resemblances to ancient Chinese art. Some investigators grant the possibility that Norse adventurers reached central North America two or three centuries before Columbus. Chinese junks may have been washed up on the shores of British Columbia or Washington. There seem to have been movements back and forth between this Northwest coast and Siberia. Few today would maintain that the New World remained sealed off from the Old (except for successive migrations from Asia through the Bering Strait route) for fifteen thou-

---

[4] Little clay animals with semicircular protuberances instead of legs, each perforated to make a kind of bearing. The animals were accompanied by perforated clay disks. Linking the bearings and disks with a stick, the toys can be rolled back and forth on an even surface. A National Geographic Society expedition found (1940) in the state of Vera Cruz two more wheeled pottery toys which had axles running through clay cylinders on which the little pottery dogs (?) were standing.

sand years or more. The disagreements now center upon how much contact there was and how much difference it made to cultural evolution on this hemisphere.

But these are speculations, and we may more profitably return to the facts. There were hunters on the high plains at least 10,000 years ago. Certain cave cultures of New Mexico and Arizona existed at approximately the same time. Some of the earlier simple hunting and gathering cultures changed very slowly, but maize was being raised in the Southwest by at least 1000 B.C. Pottery came nearly a thousand years later. At 1000 A.D. the classic civilization of the Pueblo Indians was full blown. To the far north the Old Bering Sea variant of Eskimo culture has dates as early as 300 B.C. The archaic horizon in Mesoamerica shows pottery, a calendrical system, writing, and well-developed religious cults during a period between roughly 1000 and 200 B.C. The parallels of development between the Andean cultures and those of Mesoamerica are striking. The oustanding exceptions are the absence in South America of writing and of the conception of mathematical zero. The Incas did keep records and transmitted messages by knotted cords (quipus). By the time the Spaniards arrived the Inca and Aztec civilizations were both at a stage which has many analogies to Bronze Age society in Egypt and the Near East.

Dating. Archaeologists employ perforce both relative and absolute datings. A human fossil or an artifact may be placed as earlier or later than others in the same undisturbed deposits. Or, its relative position may be given in terms of local or regional or inferred world sequences. A specimen may be given an absolute date either on the basis of its own properties or those of the deposit in which it was found or by geological or other correlation of the deposit with others whose absolute age has been established.

Astronomy, geology, botany, chemistry, paleontology, geophysics and other natural sciences have all contributed ideas and techniques used by archaeologists to establish absolute or relative dates. The most exciting applications of recent years come from measuring the disintegration products of radioactive elements. The radioactive carbon (Carbon 14) method[5] is based upon the fact that organic materials go through radioactive disintegration at known rates. It has been possible to date some hundreds of archaeological specimens ranging in age from a few hundred years to more than 20,000. The plus or minus error of these dates varies from 100 to 1200 years, but, for the older specimens at least, the method is far more accurate than the techniques hitherto available. However, the Carbon 14 method will not carry us back further than 30,000 years. For most of the Paleolithic we must still rely upon astronomical, geological, paleontological, and geophysical correlations.

It is possible to mention only one other specific technique, that of dating by tree rings.[6] By comparing the rings in a given beam with a master chart one can discover the year in which this tree was cut. If the beam has not been re-used, one can thus determine the year in which a structure was built. Tree-ring dating is reasonably accurate, but a trustworthy master chart cannot be worked out in all climatic areas.

Anthropological linguistics also helps greatly to unravel the relationships of peoples and their movements in time. The newest method of linguistic dating was, curiously enough, suggested by the Carbon 14 technique and involves an application of the same theoretic principle. The fundamental everyday vocabularies of languages change at a relatively constant rate. The percentage of such words retained in common by related languages gives a good estimate of the time elapsed since the linguistic community broke up into two or more segments. One takes several hundred basic words (numerals, father, mother, water, heart, day, night, long, short, and the like) and sees how many are phonetically alike in the two languages being

[5] Carbon 14 (contained in charcoal, vegetable matter, bone and shell) disappears from dead tissue at a constant rate. In about 25,000 years most of it is gone. Therefore, if a fragment of organic matter is found to have about one-half the amount of carbon 14 found in living tissue, the fragment may be estimated to be roughly 12,500 years old.

[6] In a region where there are sharp variations in moisture from year to year, tree rings of varying widths and shapes occur. By examining enough specimens one can construct a patterned sequence over a series of years (from about 1 A.D. to the present in New Mexico-Arizona). The pattern of rings in any particular tree can then be matched against the total sequence to see exactly where it fits in.

compared. Sixty-six per cent of the basic words ought to be recognizably similar if the languages were a single language one thousand years ago. This technique (which goes by the formidable name of "glottochronology" or "lexico-statistic dating") has, for example, indicated that the Eskimo and Aleut were a single language about 2900 years ago and that certain Indian tribes in the Southwest which we know historically as quite distinct constituted a common linguistic community until around 1000 A.D.

Archaeology obviously makes liberal use of natural science principles and methods but it may nonetheless present itself to the reader more as "history" than as "science." "Science," he may say, deals with regularities and with process—not with unique events. The answer is that, in anthropology, historical research is necessary to establish the facts which can then be treated scientifically. For instance, the issue as to whether or not American Indian cultures developed independently of the major inventions and ideas of the Old World does not end as an academic squabble of antiquarians. It bears vitally upon important scientific generalizations as to the nature of man. Did the great ideas basic to civilization just "happen" only once? Or, is the nature of man as a biological organism such that, if he is turned loose in an isolated continent, roughly the same cultural steps will be taken in roughly the same order? We cannot yet answer this question definitively, but only more archaeological (i.e., "historical") work can solve this fundamental scientific question.

Comparative Human Biology

The human family has come a long way from the South African ape-men and from our heavy-browed forerunners of the Lower Paleolithic. However, except for a few apparently minor trends such as those toward the loss of "wisdom" teeth and perhaps the little toe, there is no evidence that evolution has appreciably altered humankind for some thousands of years. The more recent changes have been due to various mixtures between diverse populations, to the effects of movement into new environments, to improved nutrition and medical practices.

The evolutionary process left certain scars upon the species. To the ancient adoption of upright posture[7] is traceable the frequency of various spinal and visceral ailments, for the accompanying mechanical adjustments have not been adequate. Difficulties in birth attend the fact that the heads of human infants have become larger, while the hipbones of women have grown shorter. Some students believe that man is no longer the unspecialized animal that had advantages in the evolutionary struggle[8] but is now overspecialized with respect to head, brain, and locomotion.

Human beings appear to be very variable creatures. They are found in numerous colors and shades with a considerable range of hair form, nose shape, and the like. Height and general physique varies widely both between groups and among individuals within the same group. However, the comparative biologist is not as much impressed by human variation as is the laymen preoccupied with his own species. For an animal who wanders over the whole earth, adapting to almost every existing environment and mating with whomever opportunity affords and fancy dictates, the variabilities are comparatively superficial. In certain features, the gibbons from a single valley in Siam vary as much as all the races of man together. All human populations can and do interbreed with one another and produce fertile offspring. An adopted infant, whatever the "race" of his biological parents, will acquire the language of his foster parents and can learn to ride a canoe, paddle a kayak or pilot a jet plane.

But the fact that the similarities in human biology are vastly more massive than the differences does not mean that the superficial but visible variations have not been socially important. On the whole, human groups have been distrustful or contemptuous of those who

[7] Presumably because this was the most convenient form of locomotion for our large arm-swinging ancestors.

[8] Animals that are too highly adapted to a particular environment can hardly survive when that environment (or other situations faced) changes too radically—compare the enormous reptiles like the dinosaurs, who were suited only to the vast swamps of millions of years ago and who died out when the earth turned into deserts.

looked, dressed, or behaved differently from themselves. And smug nineteenth-century thought in Western Europe seized upon the magic idea of evolution to justify an ordering of both way of life and "race" in a graduated sequence from "savage" to "civilized."

There *are* recognizable physical types of humanity which to some extent correspond to the populations found in distinct areas and, to a much lesser extent, to linguistic and cultural groups. But:

a) These types intergrade. That is, there are individuals who could equally well be classified as "Nordic," on the one hand, or as "Mediterranean" or "Alpine" on the other.

b) They are based upon a limited number of features which have not been shown to be significant as far as the chief cultural capacities and limitations of the groups are concerned. Creative originality, ethical or humane standards of behavior, and the ability to absorb or communicate abstract knowledge are within the potentialities of all the living races of men.

c) Classifications which are based upon different combinations of the small number of features ordinarily utilized do not altogether coincide.

d) These types are not equivalent to the "breeds" of domestic animals, because men for thousands of years have wandered and freely interbred. As a result, the members of practically any human group can be subdivided on the basis of appearance into more than one physical type. In any case outward appearance in the human animal is not a guarantee of hereditary sameness to the extent that it is in animal breeds.

e) The popular (and the older scientific) classifications are based primarily upon such features as head form, stature, skin color. Unfortunately, in most of these cases the heredity mechanisms are complex and mendelian formulas have not been worked out. Hence the distributions of these characteristics in different populations are not amenable to quantitative genetic analysis.

The familiar human "races" must be regarded as common-sense "types," based upon often misleading similarities in outward appearance. They cannot be considered as scientific categories.

This is not to say that all human populations are biologically the same in all significant respects. There appear to be few all-or-none differences, but in the limited area (mainly the blood groups) where we have adequate information it is clear that there are some striking variations. For example, the Basques show a frequency of one blood-group gene which is twice as high as in any other known population and more than twenty-five times as high as in certain groups. African Negroes exhibit a tremendously high incidence of certain serological genes. There is a genetically determined condition of the blood cells known as "sickling" which is widespread among African Negroes and appears to be exclusively confined to Negroes and those who have some Negroid admixture. The genes responsible for thalassemia, hemoglobin c, and for the Henshaw antigen apparently have sharp geographical restrictions. Such genes are not known to be "linked" to other genes influencing temperament, mental ability, and the like. Nevertheless it is a reasonable assumption that such hereditary factors also will eventually be shown to have other than a random distribution among populations. By the same token, it is most unlikely that any single group will be revealed to have a monopoly on "favorable" inheritance.

In terms of mendelian genetics, "races" can be defined as populations which differ markedly in their gene frequencies. Using ten or more genes, for which the frequencies and the hereditary mechanisms are known, the student of blood groups, W. C. Boyd, has tentatively postulated as major human races: Early European, European, African, Asiatic, American Indian, Australian—and perhaps Indian (Hindu). This list does not differ too much from earlier classifications based upon measurements and external features, but has the advantage of resting not upon sometimes illusory appearance but upon characters known to be inherited in specific ways.

Physical anthropology in general is proceeding rapidly from measurement and description to the analysis of process and even to experiment. The physical differences that to some extent differentiate the various groups are brought about by a combination of processes. The only source of new hereditary traits is mutation—the result of chemical changes in genes or structural rearrangements of the chromosomes. But whether or not new inheritable characteristics become widespread in a population and spread to other populations depends upon a variety of factors, of which selection is the most important. Does a new gene give the individual who carries it an advantage in the struggle for survival? Does it increase his fertility directly? Does it give him a physical feature which is favored by the cultural norms of the group so that he can obtain mates more easily and thus be likely to produce more children? Selection (natural, social, and sexual) is the most significant process in the differentiation of populations. The following, however, are also of some importance:

1) "race" mixture due to migrations or other events leading to interbreeding and hence to the alteration of the gene frequencies in a group;
2) "genetic drift" [9] which, particularly in small and isolated breeding populations, may bring about either the complete extinction of certain genes in that group or the fixation of other genes at 100 per cent.

Environmental influences vary in the degree to which they favor the survival of individuals possessing certain genes or combinations of genes. Human culture modifies the operation of natural selection as it works among other animals. Modern science and technology protects those who might not survive if the brute force of nature were alone operative. Even at the primitive level, culture powerfully influences the processes of selection, race mixture, and genetic drift. In some tribes twins are killed at birth, and the old and incapacitated are also done away with. Priests or "medicine men" are required to practice continence over such long periods that they do not produce as many children as other males. In one clan in Madagascar all unusually light-skinned children are killed, while in another clan of this same tribe the unusually dark-skinned are exterminated. Such cultural practices as premarital promiscuity or frequent extremely hot baths may affect fertility. Some peoples are very intolerant of "race mixture"; others accept it readily. Genetic drift takes a sharper form if marriage within a small tribal group or band is rigidly insisted upon or if one must marry one's own cousin.

Contemporary research emphasizes broad relationships rather than

[9] The mathematics are too involved to explain here.

descriptive treatment of separate units of the body—a legacy from the dissection of corpses. The following topics are representative:

specializations of body mass, nose form[10], fat and beard as responses to extreme cold;

climatic selection of individuals of specific physical type;

growth-control mechanisms;

the fertility and life span of lanky and massive individuals;

effects of soil minerals, protein-poor diet, early menopause.

Constitutional anthropology is a subbranch of physical anthropology which concentrates on the individual. It is concerned with the relation between physique and behavior, including susceptibility to various kinds of diseases. Do the differences in size and shape that exist among individuals indicate any temperamental correlates and predispositions toward certain kinds of activity? The best-known approach to these problems is W. H. Sheldon's "somatotypes," which classifies physiques on a three-dimensional scale. The study of constitution is the newest field in biological anthropology and, as usually happens with pioneer work at the frontiers of a science, one of the liveliest. Some students accept Sheldon's descriptive scheme but are most dissatisfied with the interpretations of the psychological and behavioral aspects. Others reject even the classification on the ground that the genetic mechanisms are unknown and that recent work indicates that (a) somatotypes change with age and diet, and (b) that the diagnoses (based on nude photographs) of the relative amounts of bone and muscle are not confirmed by radiological examination of the same individuals.

Almost the only thing that students of constitutional anthropology agree upon today is that "there is something to it." Clinical experience in medicine and anthropological researches using different

---

[10] Is, for example, a high, narrow nose, lined with thin mucous membrane charged with blood, an adaptation which prevents the excessive lowering of body temperature of those breathing the very cold air of far northern lands? Certainly a narrower aperture reduces the volume of cold air admitted to the lungs.

techniques and theories of explanation all converge upon the conclusion that individuals of one type of body build are more prone than those of other types to engage in certain activities and to fall victim to certain illnesses. The most conservative position would be that this is true only for the more extreme forms of each physique type. At this level, there is now fairly satisfactory evidence for a definable relationship between body build and a few physiological and behavioral variables. There are intriguing but as yet inconclusive studies of correlations between body build and mental disorder, ulcers, various kinds of arthritis, acute rheumatic fever, coronary diseases, diabetes, and pernicious anemia.

Human biology sets certain limits for human cultures. The more obvious of these are well known and have often been commented upon. Others remain to be explored. It is suggestive, for example, that the range for the number of kinship terms used in human societies is about the same as the range of the number of sound-classes (roughly but only very roughly represented by letters in alphabets) found in human languages. Every culture differentiates and names certain categories of relatives. In English we call both our mother's and our father's sisters "aunt." In Navaho there are two distinct terms for these relatives. On the other hand, we used to have a kinship term in English "cousin german" (double cousin) for which there is no equivalent in the Navaho system. The point is that each culture uses somewhat different criteria in naming classes of relatives, but all cultures differentiate among roughly twenty and fifty such categories, with about twenty-five as the average number. Approximately the same thing holds for the sound types to which the speakers of each language react as "different." Some Polynesian languages have as few as a dozen distinctive sound classes ("phonemes"); no known language has more than seventy. Does this mean that the average human brain operates effectively only within this range of classificatory units?

Biology supplies the clues for many other aspects of culture. Popular notions of space arise directly from the nature of the human frame (above, below, in front, behind, to this side, to that side—i.e., the six directions found in many cultures). Various dual divisions are based upon the existence of the two sexes; rites of passage, such as those of puberty, crystallize around biological events. Finally, it is plausible, though at present unproven, that the variations in the hereditary make-up of different populations lead to different selections from the objectively open ways of developing and elaborating their cultures. For example, if there is an hereditary predisposition to a high activity level, presumably there will be vigorous attention to achievement, to "doing" as opposed to "being" and "becoming."

But the process goes both ways. Warfare, as culturally defined, plays a part in both selection and fertility. Mutilations and regulations prohibiting or encouraging premarital heterosexual activity do likewise. Biological processes such as vomiting, sneezing, and fainting are produced by somewhat different stimuli in different cultures. Many Americans will vomit if they discover that they have, unknowingly, eaten rattlesnake meat, even though this is—from a strictly biological point of view—nutritious and easily digestible. In other cultures retching will follow upon failure to observe a ceremonial taboo. Cultural beliefs and values play a part in bringing about migrations, relative rates of inbreeding and outbreeding, nutrition level, infant care, preferences for the physical appearance of mates, and other practices that shape, directly or indirectly, the genetic process.

Biological and cultural anthropology are both needed to understand the rise and fall of civilizations. J. L. Angel [11] in his studies of Greece through the centuries shows how the physical environment, biological factors such as hereditary elements and size of population, and cultural practices constitute a complex manifold. Culture growth and human change follow repetitive patterns: heterogeneity and invasion, fusion, and achievement. One of Angel's points deserves special stress because it is a generalization supported by evidence from many parts of the world. Great civilizations appear to arise most often in areas where there is a great deal of both biological and cultural mixture. High cultures seem usually to be "mongrel."

[11] A physical anthropologist who teaches human anatomy at Jefferson Medical College in Philadelphia.

The Ways of Men

Cultural studies investigate repetitive patterns of behavior which are characteristic of groups. Each culture consists of a linked series of man-made patterns and constitutes a selective way of thinking, feeling and reacting. A man, except at the level of reflexive behavior or under conditions of extreme biological stress, does not respond like a machine. He responds to the stimulus situation only as interpreted and defined in terms of conventions he has learned as a member of one social group or another. An Englishman and a Navaho Indian both notice a tree struck by lightning. The Englishman, at most, says to himself "Better stay away from trees during thunderstorms in this country." The Navaho begins to plan a ceremonial designed to protect himself against the dangerous experience of beholding a lightning-struck tree. The "objective" stimulus is the same; the reactions are quite different.

"Culture," a technical term, must not be confused with the more limited concept of ordinary language and of history and literature. To the anthropologist, a cooking pot or a deep freeze is just as much a cultural product as a sonnet or a great picture. The description of a culture may be compared to a map. A map is not a bit of land but rather an abstract representation of a particular area. If a map is accurate and one can read it, one can find one's way around.

Cultural anthropology comprises many topics, among them primitive law, primitive economics, folklore, material culture, comparative music and the plastic and graphic arts. We cannot possibly treat all these interesting and important subjects; we can glance at only a few of the high points on culture change, social organization, religion, culture and personality, cultural relativity.

The major cultural innovations (e.g., writing, metallurgy, and such mathematical ideas as zero and the calculus) appear to have occurred independently in only one or a very few cultures in the whole history of man. The spread of such discoveries then takes place through migrations, conquest, trade, and the activity of religious missionaries—or through the diffusion of ideas by the printed word or otherwise without direct personal contact. Detailed studies of the spread of the alphabet, tobacco use, cultivation of various kinds of food and similar cultural inventions have produced some general principles. New ideas and techniques do not fan out uniformly in all directions and at about the same rate from their center of origin. Rather, diffusion may be compared to a forest fire: things go where the wind blows and where impermeable barriers do not exist. Sometimes the high wind of fashion will lift sparks far over intervening areas. Sometimes the sparks smolder for a long time before they burst into flame. People have to be "ready" for new things. In general, gadgets spread more rapidly than do religious or political ideas. In many cultures women are more conservative than men. There is some evidence that individuals who are most disgruntled or maladjusted in their own societies will accept soonest new religious, political or social beliefs.

Nevertheless, culture growth and change is by no means haphazard. Even the fashions in women's clothes have been shown to be due not solely to the whims of the female and the machinations of Paris designers. In broad sweep the cycles are lawfully patterned in mathematically describable ways.[12] A. L. Kroeber[13] has also convincingly demonstrated that great artists and writers appear in civilizations in "temporary bursts" and that the same sort of bursts in growth tend to characterize nationalistic development as expressed in successful political organization and expansion. Such periods endure for fifty years or for a thousand, though the shorter ones may be regarded as localized "pulses" in larger growths.

Human beings need sometimes to be reminded how much they

[12] The basic dimensions of the clothes of Western women alternate between maxima and minima which average fifty years. In addition to these long trends there are also fairly regular short-term oscillations and well-defined periods of high or low variability of style. For details see "Three Centuries of Women's Dress Fashions" in A. L. Kroeber, *The Nature of Culture*, University of Chicago Press, 1952.
[13] Alfred Louis Kroeber was for many years professor of anthropology and director of the Museum of Anthropology at the University of California in Berkeley. After he became emeritus there, he taught at Harvard and Columbia. He continues to be active in research and writing. He made a field trip as recently as 1952. He has contributed to all branches of anthropology and is generally regarded as the leading anthropologist in the world today.

owe to other human beings of far-off times and places. I am writing (Near Eastern invention) on paper (Chinese invention) in an alphabet which began in the Mt. Sinai peninsula about 1200 B.C. We wear close-fitting garments which developed in cold climates—rather than the loose, flowing robes of the tropics. We eat American Indian corn or Italian vermicelli (which really derives from China via Marco Polo) and drink South American cocoa. The interdependence of humanity is nowhere more dramatically illustrated than by a close study of cultural process.

It is in the field of *social organization* that present cultural anthropology (other than linguistics) is most exact. Some anthropologists map with great precision what goes on in a small group. The observer presses a particular key on a machine whenever a particular person starts to talk. A chart is built up to show which person in a group talks the most, which talks the least, who most often initiates or dominates a conversation, who tends to respond passively. The results often give a picture that is more objective and illuminating than could be obtained by asking the individuals about their relations to one another or from a description of the roles to which they are formally assigned in an organization (such as president and vice-president or lieutenant colonel and captain). These methods and other anthropological techniques are being applied with some success in the study of personnel problems and productivity in business and industry. Anthropologists who go into a factory or a department store try to observe what goes on among the employees with the same detachment that they bring to a primitive tribe. Ignoring any prior opinion they may have as to what motivates workers, they build up from the observation of behavior the regularities that are actually operative. G. P. Murdock[14], among others, has taken a more academic approach to the anthropological study of social organization. From the evidence of changes in social structure, the "social laws of sexual choice," and the adhesions of certain features of social life to one another, he has proved that:

[14] Professor of anthropology at Yale. One of Murdock's greatest achievements was organizing and directing for many years the Human Relations Area Files. This undertaking, now a co-operative task of fifteen universities, has provided a cross-index by topics of the data now available on some hundreds of peoples scattered over the world.

. . . the elements of social organization, in their permutations and combinations, conform to natural laws of their own scarcely less striking than those which characterize the permutations and combinations of atoms in chemistry or of genes in biology.

The principal contribution of anthropology to the study of *religion* has been to show that religion is not normally something apart but rather flows into all areas of life and helps to maintain the adjustment of individuals and the solidarity and survival of societies. Someone has said, "Human beings build their cultures, nervously loquacious, on the edge of an abyss." Religious life not only affords socially approved opportunities for personal expression and prestige but also gives a sense of security in a world which, seen in naturalistic terms, appears to be full of the unpredictable, the capricious, the accidentally tragic. In the face of chance and the unexpected, of wants, death, and destruction, all humans have a fundamental sense of uneasiness. By ritualizing their words and habits, they assure themselves that "reality" too is consistent. They mask the vast role of "luck" in human life by telling each other that such and such a thing happens because of something a supernatural being did or said long ago. In a world full of hazards, myths and rituals affirm that there is rhyme and reason after all. They give the future the appearance of safety by symbolizing the unbroken continuity of present and past.

In both secular and sacred spheres, myths serve as statements of the right way to behave and the reasons therefor. For primitive people they constitute a literature which serves ends from intellectual and moral edification to simple entertainment. Both myths and rituals act as brakes upon the speed of cultural change. They stabilize and sanctify interpersonal relations. Even the "evil" side of religion, such as belief in witchcraft, has its functional significance. Nothing is more intolerable to human beings than to be persistently disturbed without being able to say why in terms that their fellows will understand or without being able to phrase the matter in such a way that some relief or control is considered possible. Witchcraft belief allows one to talk about his anxiety in terms that are acceptable and which imply the possibility of doing something about it. Witchcraft also channels aggression; in many societies it is a substitute for "race prej-

udice" or similar scapegoating. Some cultural systems are more efficient than others in directing aggression into oblique or socially
nondisruptive paths. But among many people witchcraft is the principal answer to the problem that every society faces: how to satisfy hate
and still keep the group solid.

Anthropologists in the field of *culture and personality* attempt to
answer questions of this type:

Does a people's way of bringing up its children make a particular
type of personality unusually common in that society?

How much of any individual's personality is fixed by his biological
constitution and how much depends upon his culture and his own
experience in that way of life?

Is there a connection between the mental illnesses characteristic
of a given group and the social norms that this group enforces with
special severity?

In brief: What makes an Englishman an Englishman? an American an American? a Russian a Russian?

This field has suffered in the last decade or two from being so
fashionable. Many publications have been hasty, overly schematic,
and indeed naïve. History and biology have been neglected to varying degrees by many authors. In some cases there has been a ludicrous
overemphasis upon a few aspects (or even a single aspect) of the
child-training system. Too little notice has been taken of the effects of
the isolation of particular children, or groups of children, from certain segments of the cultures. In short, this anthropological specialty
can be viewed as a promising infant, but a spoiled or overindulged
one.

Nevertheless, there are a few findings that can today be regarded
as established. The first is the regrettably vague one that culture and
personality are indeed interdependent. The second is that the influence of a culture may persist long after the more obvious and exter-
nally observable aspects of that culture have disappeared. Some Chippewa Indians dress and talk and make their living very much as do
the white Americans with whom they go to school and work. Yet
close study of their performance on psychological tests shows that
their way of thinking and reacting is still much influenced by the
aboriginal culture. There are also some negative conclusions. Much

can be explained only historically and in terms of situation. One cannot infer directly from a description of cultural patterns for child training to their consequences in personality formation. Parental attitudes are often more important than methods, though the attitudes are, in part, also cultural products. A few quantitative studies on specialized topics, such as Whiting and Child's *Child Training and Personality*[15], have been completed recently. In general, however, we know little more than we did a generation ago about how culture is "built into" a personality and whether some features of a culture are more crucial than others in forming distinctive personality types. *Cultural relativity* is one of the most influential concepts of modern anthropology. In a vulgarized form it has been taken to mean that behavior which is customary among any people is therefore justified. On this basis, we should have to accept slavery or Nazism as morally acceptable. What anthropologists have wished to point out in this area of their work is the broad spectrum of variability in human values and the necessity for considering all values and items of behavior in their own context. However, it is true that for at least a generation anthropologists concentrated more upon cultural differences than upon the equally factual similarities. It is also clear that insufficient consideration has been given to values as such and to systems of values. If the essence of culture is the selection of certain paths of life from among two or more that are objectively possible, the essence of this selectivity resides in the value system. Man is not only the tool-using animal; he is also the valuing animal, constantly making judgments of "better" and "worse" and behaving in terms of preferences that are by no means altogether reducible to biological needs and to the immediate situation. Human life is a moral life precisely because it is a social life. In human society co-operation and the other necessities of group living are not taken care of by instinct as they are for the social insects. There must be standards.

The broad outlines of all ways of life are and have to be about the same because men always and everywhere are faced with certain unavoidable problems which arise out of the situation "given" by na-

---

[15] Using a rating scale and a correlational technique of statistical analysis, these authors compare child-training practices and their relations to various customs and prevalent ideas of guilt and fear of others in 75 tribes.

ture. Since most of the patterns of all cultures crystallize around the same points, there are significant respects in which each culture is not wholly isolated, self-contained and disparate but rather related to and comparable with all other cultures.

Nor is the similarity between cultures limited to the fact that all cultures have marriage regulations, tools, music, graphic art, forms of shelter, ornaments, grammatical categories, and the like. There are at least some broad resemblances in content, and specifically in value content. Considering the exuberant variation of cultures in most respects, the circumstance that in some particulars almost identical values prevail throughout mankind is most arresting. No culture tolerates indiscriminate lying, stealing, or violence within the group. The essential universality of the incest taboo is well known. No culture places a value upon suffering as an end in itself: as a means to the ends of the society (punishment, discipline, etc.), yes; as a means to the ends of the individual (purification, mystical exaltation, etc.), yes; but of and for itself, never.

We know of no culture in either space or time, including Soviet Russia where the official ideology denies an afterlife, that does not ceremonialize the fact of death. Yet the more superficial conception of cultural relativity would suggest that at least one society would have adopted the simple expedient of disposing of corpses in the way most cultures do dispose of dead animals—i.e., just throwing the body out far enough from habitations so that the odor is not troubling. When one first looks rather carefully at the astonishing variety of cultural detail over the world, one is tempted to conclude that individual human beings have tried almost everything that is physically possible, and that nearly every individual practice has somewhere at some time been institutionalized in some culture. To a considerable degree this generalization is valid—but it is not completely so. In spite of loose talk (based upon an uncritical acceptance of an immature theory of cultural relativity) to the effect that definitions of mental disorder are completely relative to culture, the fact of the matter is that all cultures define as abnormal individuals who are permanently inaccessible to communication or who consistently fail to maintain some degree of control over their impulse life. Social life is impossible without communication, without some measure of order: the behavior of any "normal" individual must be predictable—with a certain range—by his fellows and interpretable by them.

To look freshly at values of the order just discussed is difficult because they are commonplaces. And yet it is precisely because they are *common*places that they are interesting and important. Their vast theoretical significance rests on the fact that, despite all the influences that predispose toward cultural variation (biological variability, differences in physical environments, and the processes of history), all of the very many different cultures known to us have converged upon these universals. It is perfectly true (and for certain types of enquiry important) that the value "thou shalt not kill thy fellow tribesman" is not concretely identical either in idea or feeling for an Australian aborigine and an American Indian. Nevertheless, the central conception is the same, and there is understanding between representatives of different cultures as to the general intent of the prohibition. Some things are inevitable for all men; some habits are essential to survival and to a reasonably orderly life.

The Tongues of Men

There are perhaps only three kinds of activity in which normal adults in all groups take part about equally: sleeping, eating, and talking. Language has inevitably been of great interest to anthropologists, and they have studied it from many different angles. We all know from ordinary experience that a man's speech conveys a good deal of information about him: his level of education and good clues to the social class to which he belongs; often, the region in which he grew up; some hints as to his personality. Indeed, recent collaboration between anthropological linguists and psychiatrists suggests that the patient's speech—and especially his intonation patterns—may give the most sensitive and tangible basis for the diagnosis of certain mental disorders.

Everyone also recognizes in a general sort of way that the language habits of a group are related to or reflect other group habits. The vocabulary of any people holds up a mirror to the rest of their culture, revealing what they have found it important to differentiate and name. The ancient Egyptians had no word for slave and no word for freedom. The political history of the English-speaking peoples has not given rise to such terms as *putsch* or *coup d'état*, and that is why we resort to a German and a French word when we have occasion to refer to events of this type. Even within closely related languages and cultures there are some interesting and suggestive differences. It may be significant, for instance, that the English "stand" for elections, while Americans "run." Over and above vocabulary differences—the presence or absence of words in one language which occur in another—each language has a certain flavor that somehow expresses wider trends in the culture. Thus, a Japanese conversation characteristically defines the relative status of the speakers with great precision but leaves quite ambiguous most of the remaining context.[16]

Once one goes beyond the superficial statement, anthropological linguistics gets immediately technical and a bit forbidding. This is a reflection of the fact that the methods of linguistics are the most distinctive of the behavioral sciences. In fact, linguistics most nearly resembles the physical sciences in rigor and elegance. In this brief section the best we can hope to do is to indicate three reasons for

[16] Because anthropological linguistics has become severely technical, it is now rather forbidding to other students of human behavior. This is a pity since nothing is more human than speech and nothing more revealing of a people's characteristic ways of behaving and thinking. Moreover, the use of language is the one major mode of behavior in which all "normal" adult members of the group participate about equally. Analysis of vocabulary reveals the principal emphases of a culture and also reflects culture history. The clichés of greeting and the bromides of daily small talk mirror standard social situations and often indicate the major tensions. Americans say "How are you getting on?"; Catholic Germans, "May God greet you"; Japanese, "There is respectful earliness." Swedish retains a form of the second personal pronoun "you" for use to inferiors, and lawsuits arise over who is entitled to use this to whom. Linguistic usages that grow up around differentiated terms used toward familiars, equals and superiors highlight the system of social stratification and of interpersonal relations generally. In France husband and wife normally address each other as "tu." But among the old aristocracy they call each other "vous," with the unexpressed understanding that the husband reserved "tu" for his mistress. French Catholics call God "vous," Protestants "tu." Everyone knows that schools, professions, cliques, criminal gangs and summer camps rapidly develop a special slang to symbolize their distinctiveness as a group. "The *linguistic community*" is a significant phrase.

believing that the anthropological study of language will be for the next generation or two in the vanguard of behavioral science.

The first is the simple one that language is the sharpest model of culture generally. Language approaches pure culture: here one sees in complete clarity regular and patterned selection among a limited number of biological possibilities. Infants babble at random almost all the kinds of sounds found in known languages, but by the time they are a few years old they have learned to make and respond to the small number of sound types used in the speech of their elders. An adult finds it difficult, sometimes impossible, to reproduce accurately the sounds of a foreign tongue that he could have mimicked easily as a child. A Hindu confuses the English sound "t" in "top" with the "t" of "stop" not because he lacks the biological equipment to hear this distinction but only because this particular distinction has a different place in the sound system of languages deriving from Sanskrit. And this brings us to a second point where language is a nice paradigm of culture generally. As cultures have organization as well as content, so the sounds of any given language are not a congeries but an organized system. This comes out strikingly in the history of sound change. Once a new principle, say, stress accent or the contrast between voiced and voiceless consonants, is introduced into a language, the principle spreads to every set of similar sounds. What the Spanish linguists call "the empty boxes" get filled in so that symmetry throughout the system is preserved.

Second, language is that aspect of culture where, thus far, order and predictability have been most successfully demonstrated. In the mid-nineteenth century Grimm's Laws (showing the regularity of sound shifts in Germanic and other Indo-European languages) were a dramatic answer to those who claimed that, however fixed in their courses the movements of the planets might be, human beings behaved only according to the caprices of free will or the dictates of God. Since then there have been massive documentations of orderliness in linguistic change—as well as some instances of sporadic change, analogous to the "mutations" known to genetics. In Latin between 450 and 350 B.C. the consonant "s" was changed to "r" *wherever* it came between two vowels. For instances, *genesos*, the possessive of *genus*, became *generis; meliosem* ("better") became *meliorem.* The prediction, on the basis of analysis of sound systems, that ancient Indo-European had laryngeals[17] was confirmed a generation later when Hittite records of 1500 B.C. were uncovered by archaeologists. Another prediction of 1877 about forms in early Greek was verified by an inscription found in 1913. During the eighteenth century in Hausa, an African language, "s" changed to "sh" whenever followed by one of four particular vowels.

The study of sounds on a strictly scientific basis is now possible because linguists have discovered basic elemental units comparable to the atom in physics or to the gene in biology. Every sound system has a number of structure points called "phonemes." These are types or classes of sounds which are treated by the speakers of that language as a unit. Thus in English the sounds "p" in the words *p*in, *sp*in, and ni*p* which we English-speakers react to as if they were identical are, from the standpoint of an acoustic engineer, quite different. The English phoneme "p" makes up not a natural but a conventional or a cultural category.[18] Nature, as reflected in the sound waves recorded by the instruments of a physicist, here reveals three distinct sounds. But where the natural world presents nothing but an indefinite number of contingent varieties the intervention of cultural conventions creates a bundle of distinctive features that have a minimum sameness and are treated as a unit. In one language a sound that is made with the two lips, voiceless, strongly articulated, and with stopped breath is bundled together and contrasted with another sound that is otherwise identical but made with vibration of the vocal cords (voiced). In another language similar sounds are

[17] Sounds produced with a deep simultaneous vibration of the larynx. Such sounds are occasionally made today by speakers of Indo-European languages but only as expressive features.

[18] A "phoneme" is technically defined as the class of all segments and spans containing given features. Take the English word "pin." There are three irreplaceable sound units here. Each occurs in other combinations: the first occurs, for instance, in pip, pill, pocket; the second in pip and pill but not in pocket; the third in tan, run and hen. But these three units cannot be further analyzed by partial resemblances. In the case of "pin" the three phonemes are presented by three letters of our alphabet, but our conventions of writing are not always a trustworthy guide. In "thick" the first phoneme is represented by two letters "th," and the third phoneme by two more letters "ck." The linguist represents the first of these phonemes by a Greek letter, the second by simple "k."

contrasted not on the voiced-voiceless basis but on the force of articulation. The phonemic principle is a specific application of the cultural principle in general: one treats sounds in the conventional system within which they occur; one avoids imposing a pattern from without and seeks instead to discover that which is inherent within an historically derived organization.

Linguistics with its discovery of ultimate significant entities (phonemes and their distinctive features) converges with modern physics which has revealed the granular structure of matter as composed of elementary particles. And in the last decade there has been exciting collaboration between the linguists and the communications engineers. The number of contrasts of distinctive features in the languages studied thus far run about six and eleven. The number of distinctive features needed to describe the number of phonemes would approach the minimum of $\text{Log}_2 n$, where "n" is the number of phonemes in the system. But the students of information theory pointed out that the communication needs of both speakers and hearers would enter into the picture and that therefore the actual number of distinctive features ought to be close to 50 per cent. In languages which have been analyzed this estimate has been roughly borne out. Moreover, in Spanish, where records at four time points have been studied, the number oscillates back and forth over this mean.[19] In other words, the balance between efficiency and redundancy is redressed. If the system gets out of line, the equilibrium is rather quickly restored. From these and other investigations we now know that the view of the older linguists that sound change was regular but "blind" (i.e., due purely to historical accident) is not altogether correct. Sound changes also tend to be "functional." The way sounds are put together represents, among other things, a compromise between the needs of the speaker and of the listener.

Language has been described by the greatest of anthropological linguists[20] as "the mountainous and anonymous work of unconscious generations." These very aspects make the subject peculiarly acces-

[19] For full information see *Psycholinguistics* (Memoir 10, International Journal of American Linguistics, 1954), especially p. 156 ff.

[20] Edward Sapir, Professor of Anthropology and Linguistics at Yale until his death in 1939. See bibliography.

sible to scientific study. For while the behavior of human objects of investigation is ordinarily modified by the investigation itself, linguistic behavior is largely unconscious and automatic and changes perceptibly through time only at a very slow rate. Moreover, linguistics also supplies possible runs of data through periods of time long enough to meet the demands of mathematical statistics. On Indo-European, Semitic, and Sino-Tibetan languages there are available statistical runs of four to five thousand years. The detailed record on such languages is truly "mountainous," and the most complete for any aspect of culture.

The third reason for the central importance at this time of anthropological linguistics is the hypothesis that a language is the key which will unlock the structure of the total culture. One anthropologist, for instance, has asserted that there are remarkable similarities between the languages and the typical social organizations of the American Indians and between language and social organization in the Pacific Islands, the Far East, Negro Africa, and elsewhere. He claims too much on present evidence. Yet other anthropologists believe that there may be important resemblances between certain carefully delimited aspects of linguistic structure and certain carefully delimited aspects of kinship structure. A definitive answer to these questions will probably be obtained only after the very complicated data have been coded and fed into the giant calculating machines now in operation.

Every language is undoubtedly a special way of looking at the world and interpreting experience. B. L. Whorf[21] has argued that concealed in each different grammar are a whole set of unconscious assumptions that channel perception and inference. Certainly any language is a logical relational system and not just a collection of words. Subject and predicate forms, contrary-to-fact conditions, transitive and passive verbs, and the like, all imply a metaphysic. Logic is concerned with the patterning of certain cultural forms, and different languages are built upon different philosophical principles. West-

[21] One of the more interesting of recent American intellectuals. Trained in natural science at Massachusetts Institute of Technology, he earned his living as a top executive of the Hartford Fire Insurance Company but taught linguistics at Yale in his spare moments and published extensively in learned journals. His brothers are Richard Whorf, the actor, and John Whorf, the water-colorist.

ern European languages make tense (the relation of before, present, and past) central in their verbs, whereas other languages make "aspect" (the type of activity) crucial, and still others are primarily epistemological—i.e., the verb must above all things state the kind of information on which the assertion is founded.

Whorf pointed out that the language of the Hopi Indians gets along nicely without tenses. In the Hopi view time disappears and space is altered so that the Hopi do not conceive of the homogeneous and instantaneous timeless space of our supposed intuition or of classical Newtonian mechanics.[22] Whorf insists that various grand generalizations of the Western world, such as time, velocity, and matter, are not essential to the construction of a consistent picture of the universe. A Chinese scholar has suggested that the emphasis in the Chinese language upon "how" rather than "what" has led to the neglect of epistemology in China and little original development in science. A number of writers have related Western science to the nature of the Greek language and specifically to the facility for the creation of nouns in that language.

The extent to which language is the shaper of ideas rather than merely a reproducing instrument for voicing them is an intensely arguable question but enormously interesting. Much experiment and other factual testing remain before we can say whether linguistic patterns inescapably limit sensory perceptions. Nevertheless language

[22] To give concrete illustrations: in the Hopi Indian language one cannot use cardinal numbers as imaginary plurals. One can speak of "ten men" because ten men can actually be seen together. One cannot speak of "ten days." English "they stayed ten days" can be expressed in Hopi only as "they stayed until the eleventh day" or "they left after the tenth day." Actually, in this respect the Hopi language is more operational in expression. Likewise, in Hopi there are no *nouns* corresponding to English adverbs in grammatical form. Therefore one cannot objectify or personify the seasons as in English poetry. "Summer is hot," or "this summer" become in Hopi "summer is when heat occurs" and "summer now" or "summer recently." In the language spoken by the Trobriand Islanders of Melanesia causation cannot be expressed—only propinquity in time or space. In selecting verbs in Western European languages we must refer to past, present or future (and to varying combinations of these basic notions). Other languages which dispense with tenses are fussy in insisting that each verb form must indicate whether the information in the assertion is derived from direct sense observation, from inference on the basis of sense experience, from a myth, from hearsay, from knowledge of habitual or customary behavior on the part of an individual or a group.

does at least influence how we talk about what we perceive: how we categorize our perceptions and reason from them. Language is both a key and a fetter to thought. At present it appears that different languages have some influence upon the thought processes of their speakers, but that language both determines and is determined by the total experience of the people who use it.

The Uses of Anthropology

The direct practical bearing of archaeology and of historical anthropology generally is limited. One could point to the role of archaeology in public adult education through popular articles and through the participation of archaeologists on the staffs of our museums and national parks and monuments. The historical study of human evolution is useful to physicians and dentists because the evolutionary history of limbs, jaws and teeth makes clear certain causal elements in present difficulties. However, the main contribution of historical anthropology is indirect. To the trained eye the past gleams beneath the surface of the present. The business of the anthropological historians is to reveal the less obvious features hidden from careless eyes in the contemporary situation. Anthropological history, because it is comparative, serves better than does the history of any single people or period to give enlightening perspective. Only in this light can we hope to understand the vast processes of world history: the relative importance of invention and discovery as opposed to copying and to the spread of new things; the limitations and stimulations imposed by the natural environment; comparison of the significance of outstanding individuals contrasted with massive but impersonal historical trends; the whole problem of the growth, flourishing and decay of civilizations.

Anthropological linguistics is applied more immediately. The methods now used by the United States government to teach military and civilian personnel to speak languages of non-Western type are largely the product of the experiences of anthropologists in their field work. Linguistic analysis has served in the deciphering of secret codes. The study of exotic languages has had important implications for modern logic and for taking account of the extent to which Western science is bound by the nature of Western languages. All grammars are ways of classifying relations between things and events. Relationships that are paid attention to in all languages may be presumed to constitute the subject matter of universal logic: the logical problems that are inevitably posed to human beings by virtue of the nature of their nervous systems and their situation in the physical world. Conversely, an unfamiliar category in a primitive language may suggest a logical problem heretofore neglected by the logicians of Western civilization.

Physical anthropology has many technical, though intellectually trivial, applications, most of which arise from the careful studies made by physical anthropologists of the size and shape of the human animal: the utilization of anthropologists in the identification of war dead; in the design of railway seats, gas masks, seating and seat-desk arrangements designed for growing school children, gadgets adapted to body size and capacity in aviation and in industry, and other equipment; in the systematic planning of the sizing of clothing for the armed forces and for mass commercial manufacturers. More interesting scientifically are the contributions of physical anthropology to medicine and to dentistry. Growth studies of the bones and of the development of posture and investigations of the evolutionary aspects of postural adaptatation have been useful to orthopedic surgeons even to the extent of improving the quality of artificial limbs. Growth studies, particularly those having to do with "racial" and environmental conditioning factors, have aided pediatrics. Extended knowledge of the range of variation in human pigmentation and of the "racial" response to radiation has contributed to dermatology. Obstetricians have been helped by information on female pelvic types, growth changes in the pelvic bones, sex differences, and long series of comparative pelvic measurements. Constitutional anthropology has aided in selecting personnel and in establishing performance standards in aviation and other aspects of military medicine. Evolutionary and growth studies of the teeth and jaws have contributed to the ability of dentists to treat and prevent malformations of the jaws and teeth. Analyses of dental variability among "races" and among groups having different diet and tooth-use patterns have added to the science of dental medicine.

The practical side of cultural anthropology has many facets. In part, as in the case of physical anthropology, they are primarily technical. Anthropologists act as information gatherers and "trouble shooters" in the problems of administering and generally dealing with colonial, minority or dependent peoples. To illustrate: an American Indian tribe that was poverty stricken further complicated its economic problems by destroying the dwelling and all the personal property of a deceased person. An anthropologist persuaded them to cease this practice by suggesting an extension of "fumigation" procedures already established in their religion. The objective advocated by U. S. government officials was achieved, but achieved within the framework of the native culture. The British were having serious trouble with a people on the West Coast of Africa. It took an anthropologist to point out that the uprisings occurred because some British were taking back to England as "curios" certain wooden stools which the Ashanti regarded as embodying the guardian spirits of their people.

Often the primary role of the anthropologist is that of a "go-between." He interprets the people of different culture to the administrators and, in turn, interprets the administrators to the administered, thus improving communication and minimizing needless friction. One of the great lessons of applied anthropology thus far is that no amount of knowledge of the culture of one group will take us very far. There must be an equally technical analysis of the other group involved in the interaction. To get along with the French we must understand ourselves as well as the French.

Industrial anthropology has been mentioned. The applications of cultural anthropology in medicine are expanding rapidly. Anthropologists study the social structure of hospitals (doctors, nurses, orderlies, patients and visitors) with somewhat the same methods that they have developed in work with primitive tribes. Cultural and subcultural factors in disease susceptibility and in doctor-patient relationships are investigated. The largest number of anthropologists employed outside the world of colleges and museums is, however, in the government and in international agencies. First and foremost, these anthropologists work as area specialists in intelligence, psychological warfare, and communications groups. Effective communication of any kind with foreign groups requires a systematic analysis of their way of life, of their habitual, taken-for-granted manner of feeling, thinking and reacting. It also requires something more than a "common sense" understanding of how human beings generally learn, or are changed, through communication.

A generation hence educated citizens are likely to accept the fact that there is a science of human behavior. They will assume that anthropology must play a part, along with the other sciences and with economics and history, in the field of international relations. Anthropological field work has already established that the objective superiority of a technological process or a food or a public health practice does not automatically win its acceptance abroad. The implications for the Point IV program, medical and other projects of foundations and religious groups are obvious.

At present, however, there is not uniform enthusiasm for the turning of anthropology from the natives toward international relations, industry and the study of American and "modern" cultures generally. Enthusiasts for this development feel that only a science which sees institutions and values in cross-cultural perspective can usefully be applied to the problems of the mid-twentieth century. Those who are troubled by anthropology's new look doubt the applicability of anthropological field methods to complex, dynamic modern civilizations; they question the relevance of principles derived for the most part from the examination of small, "static" societies.

As usual, there is much to be said on both sides. Some anthropologists are undoubtedly moving a little hastily into the contemporary field. They are insufficiently critical of their discipline and of their own work. One can point to a few irresponsible pronouncements suggesting that anthropology has *the* answer rather than a useful but partial and limited contribution to *some* contemporary problems. There are quarters in Washington and even in the business world where anthropology is oversold, where in effect it is regarded as the newer magic, where anthropologists are being asked questions which the present generation cannot hope to answer. To the extent that anthropologists encourage or even countenance such overestimation, the profession will pay. The present demand for consultants and for workers on research of immediate relevance threatens the normal structure of the profession. Too many young men are going immediately into the applied field without the seasoning of further field work, teaching and reading. Too many older men "consult" so much that they fail to keep up their basic research. There is no doubt that the detachment upon which anthropologists, rightly or wrongly, have prided themselves, is challenged.

On the other hand, the great bulk of anthropological publication remains descriptive, detailed, rigorous within the limits of the accepted theoretical framework. Against the few messianically tinged books of too easy generalization that have caught the public eye, one can name hundreds of solid monographs produced in the same time-period. Perhaps it is also fair to ask whether the same standards of criticism have been applied to these works as to comparable popular books from other fields. When the anthropologist writes of Yap or of Dahomey, he may be found tiresomely esoteric or idly amusing, but at any rate he is safe. When he writes of American social classes or of sexual behavior or of Soviet-American relations, he can no longer be ignored or reserved for cocktail-party talk. He should, to be sure, be held to the level of workmanship that he presumably adhered to in describing Yap, or at least required to avow publicly the thinness of his data. Yet there are grounds for suspecting that the emotional heat of many critiques was generated less by righteous indignation at careless scholarship and logic than by fury against the raising of certain personal and cultural issues comfortably buried in the unconscious. One must also, I think, make careful discount for polemics engendered by the rivalries of vested interest. Some sociologists do not like anthropological poachers at all. Some literary people feel that the depiction (other than that made possible with the aid of brass instruments) of the ebb and flow of human feeling in the social scene is the inalienable property of the novelist and the poet.

One of the war cries of the Thomases who doubt modern anthropology is the relative lack of numbers, of tables showing ranges of variation, of statistical manipulations. In part, this dissatisfaction is justified. Cultural anthropologists have often been cavalier on the problems of representativeness and of validation. In part, however, these objections arise from a misunderstanding of the nature of "proof" in the cultural realm. What is significant in cultural phenomena is often not distance or intensity or other measurable quantities, but rather position in a pattern under a given set of conditions. The pertinent variation is alternation from one configuration to another, rather than movement in terms of measurable positions.

In the present-day world the constancies and variations between peoples, and the reasons for them, are a matter of the most intense practical as well as intellectual interest. Yet anthropological knowledge and the anthropological viewpoint can be disturbing. They seem to open the way to a complete and chaotic relativism. This interpretation is not warranted by the empirical data of anthropology, but it must be admitted that anthropologists have insufficiently emphasized the order and similarities in human cultures. In part, resistance to anthropology is an aspect of a much wider process: a fear of the freedom of the open society, a frightened retreat from the frustrating heterogeneity of the twentieth century.

Anthropology is also sometimes reproached by philosophers, theologians and moralists for exalting the irrational and nonrational aspects of human conduct. It is true that anthropology grants to the varieties of human custom the same kind of amnesty which the psychiatrist gives to erotic dreams. But no moral judgments are involved. Rather, these phenomena are deemed to have meaning and hence to be worth study. Anthropology, however, has never been "vitalist" in tone, advocating a surrender to the forces of chaos and unreason. On the contrary, like all sciences, anthropology is the study of discoverable regularities; it seeks to extend the areas which reason can understand and perhaps to some extent control. In the contemporary world where varied races and cultures are in uncomfortably close contact, it is a primary intellectual function of anthropology to supply, on a smaller scale and in a scientific manner, the perspective which philosophy has traditionally attempted to give us in a cosmic and unscientific manner.

PSYCHOANALYSIS

ERICH FROMM

Erich Fromm

Erich Fromm was born in Frankfurt, Germany, in 1900. After studying sociology, psychology and philosophy at the University of Frankfurt, he proceeded to Heidelberg where he got his doctorate in philosophy in 1922. He continued his studies at the University of Munich and it was in this city that he was first trained as a psychoanalyst. Further training followed at Frankfurt and at the Berlin Psychoanalytic Institute, from which he graduated in 1931. The same year saw the publication of his first book, The Evolution of the Dogma of Christ.

Fromm's career as a lecturer began in the period 1929-1932 when he gave courses at the Psychoanalytic Institute in Frankfurt and at the Institute for Social Research at Frankfurt University. In 1934 he came to the United States and has since lectured at Columbia University, Yale, the New School of Social Research, Bennington College and the William Alanson White Institute of Psychiatry, where he also served as Chairman of Faculty. Since 1951 Dr. Fromm has spent part of each year in Mexico, holding a professorship at the National University and training psychiatrists in psychoanalysis.

Fromm has been brilliantly successful at attracting large audiences for the most pressing issues of psychology, psychiatry and sociology. His books include Escape from Freedom, published in 1941; Man for Himself, 1947; Psychoanalysis and Religion, 1950; and The Forgotten Language, 1951. One of his main themes is the effect of *modern social and political circumstances upon the individual. In Escape from Freedom, for example, he portrayed with unusual sensitivity what it is within man that not only permits him to tolerate, but even causes him to welcome, the yoke of authoritarianism. Man for Himself examines the psychological basis of ethics, how man's nature shapes his moral beliefs and values. The forces in Western industrial society that lead to mental illness and how these forces can be counteracted is the subject of Fromm's The Sane Society, published in 1955. In the following essay he explains with admirable clarity the fundamental ideas of psychoanalysis and their development in theory and practice by various schools since Freud.*

PSYCHOANALYSIS

ERICH FROMM

Medieval culture was a system based on traditional beliefs, in which the world seemed closed and hence certain and secure. The earth, and man on her, were the center of the universe. Everything was ordered by the laws of God, which had been revealed to man. There seemed to be nothing new to discover, no blank space to fill in. But about 1500 this secure and closed world burst wide open. Man was thrown out of his central place from which the whole universe seemed well ordered and known. Everything around him, and he himself, became a problem, a question, something to be discovered. The first crack in the shell of serenity was Copernicus' discovery that the sun is the center of our planetary system. This has led to a knowledge of the skies in which the sun is only one amongst billions of suns, in a galaxy which is but one amongst billions of galaxies. Copernicus began a train of insights which culminated 500 years later in the theories of Einstein and others as to the nature of space, energy and matter. Not only do our senses deceive us about the relative position of sun and earth, they deceive us even more thoroughly—so contemporary physicists teach us—about the physical environment which surrounds and supports us.

The new discoveries about nature began earlier, and went further, than those about man, but the latter followed the same principle of trying to arrive at the *forces behind observable phenomena* in the fields of man's biological, social and psychological development.

In essence, this new principle was that not sensory experience nor common sense nor tradition is a guarantee of the truth; that to grasp reality—outside of man and within him—we must know the nature and direction of forces which are not directly visible, but which can be inferred from the visible phenomena they produce. Darwin hurt man's vanity by showing how he had developed, under a law of natural selection, from distant animal origins. Marx showed that man's social systems, and even his thought and culture, are determined by social forces which operate behind his back, as it were. Freud completed the process by showing that the conscious thoughts man has about himself and others are only a small part of what goes on within him. What is more important, he showed that most of the acknowledged thoughts are products of fears and desires which are not acknowledged. Freud taught man to be objective and to be humble; to be skeptical toward his conscious thoughts; to probe for the truth hidden in his unconscious, rather than to be satisfied with what he *consciously* believes to be true. Freud's discoveries are part and parcel of the progress made toward objective thought in the last 500 years, toward seeing the world, nature, our fellow men and ourselves as they are, not as we want them to be.

Psychoanalysis is a *psychological theory,* as well as a *method of therapy,* for mental disturbances (psychoneuroses). Although the theory and the therapy are closely related, they must be dealt with separately, because, if for no other reason, the theory is important to any student of human nature, while the therapy is of great concern only to those who train themselves to cure mental sickness or to those who suffer from it.

Nineteenth-century psychology was mainly occupied with describing and classifying various processes in the conscious mind (perception, memory, etc.). Freud broke from this pattern by setting himself the goal of answering questions which until then had been dealt with mainly by philosophers and novelists: what makes man act, think and feel as he does? What are the forces underlying and determining his behavior? What law can be observed in the operation of the human mind?

1. Psychoanalytic Theory

The fundamental discovery of Freud—a discovery which will probably influence thought about man as Copernicus' discovery continues to influence man's thought about the universe—is his concept of the *unconscious*. Although Spinoza, almost 300 years earlier, had stated that we know our desires, but do not know the reasons for our desires (and hence live under the illusion of choosing freely), Freud succeeded in showing more widely and more concretely what the statement implied. He demonstrated that none of us is aware of more than a small sector of our mental personality (the conscious) while the bulk of what goes on within us evades our awareness, is unconscious, repressed.

Two simple examples may help to clarify the point. A man who is constantly bragging, boasting, belittling others is perhaps aware of himself as a masterful, superior person. What he is not aware of is that in reality all these feelings of power and superiority are only compensations for the very opposite. Deep down he feels weak, helpless, childish, and at the very moment when he tells us "look here what a great guy I am," he is really praying "do not let them find out that I feel like a helpless child." If we were to investigate further, we might find that this man feels like a helpless child because he has never overcome a deep fixation to his mother, a passive attachment which, normal for the child, is weakening for the man and should long since have been severed. His aim is probably still to be nursed, cared for, protected, admired by mother, and just because of his attachment, he feels like a child and hence weak and inferior. He may, in a more extreme case, have acquired the habit of compulsive drinking; only when under the influence of liquor can he overcome the feeling of powerlessness and at the same time the drinking is a substitute for his wish to be nursed and indulged by mother. The deeper one searches into the unconscious, the more links one uncovers in the chain of behavior.

In the other example of unconscious motivation a young student, brilliant, intelligent, conscientious, gets so frightened before an examination that he is almost paralyzed and jeopardizes his whole career. He is particularly frightened when the examiner is a teacher whom he does not like. Otherwise, the young man shows no signs of fear, has no feeling of inferiority, and is always poised and sure of himself in his relationship to older people or contemporaries. If one seeks the reasons of his examination fear, one finds at first an intense rage against the examiners, and especially the ones whom he does not like. Behind that rage is a feeling that it is an unbearable humiliation that he should be forced to submit to authorities who can decide about his career. Without going into the history of this intense rebelliousness against authority, it may be said that his anxiety, of which he was conscious, replaced and covered up what he was not aware of—a deadly rage which he had to repress because to show and express it would have made his position untenable. Here, as in the first example, a person is aware of his feeling, but not aware of what causes it. Freud compares the relationship between the conscious and the unconscious to an iceberg: the small part of it which is visible is the conscious; the bulk of it, which is submerged beneath the water, is the unconscious. He proved empirically the truth and significance of an earlier statement by Nietzsche: " 'I did that,' says my memory. 'I could not have done that,' says my pride, and remains inexorable. Eventually—the memory yields."

Closely related to the concept of the unconscious is the concept of *resistance*. We do not want to know that which we have repressed, because it conflicts too much with our own ideals and standards, with the picture which we have, or which we want others to have, of ourselves. We do everything to make sure that what is repressed does not come to light. We deny it, we get angry with someone who touches upon it, we get tired and sleepy when mention is made of it, or we hide it by rationalizations.

The concept of *rationalization* is one of the most important discoveries in Freud's theoretical system. All of us rationalize when we attempt to justify an action, thought or feeling as motivated by reason, conscience, practical necessity, instead of admitting that it is motivated by irrational desires. The process of rationalization is well known to anyone who ever tried to quit smoking. In order to explain to himself why he wants to smoke just that one cigarette, he discovers that it is because he feels so good, or because he feels so bad, or because everyone else is smoking, or that he is not so weak as to have to give up smoking, or that there are so few pleasures in life otherwise, or . . . or. . . . There is hardly an end to the number of rationalizations in this, as in so many other similar situations in life.

To give one more illustration, it is the rationalizaton of a destructive or sadistic person that he beats his children, or tells people painful and hurtful things, in plain response to duty. He sees himself obedient to noble impulses, when in reality he is driven by the desire to hurt or to destroy.

The unconscious, operating thus in the dark, is not immediately accessible to conscious investigation. We have to infer it from accumulated data, as the theoretical physicist often infers forces which in themselves cannot be observed directly. However, in certain situations unconscious forces can be observed directly. These situations are all alike in that they are states of dissociation, ones in which the conscious mind is not active, or not properly functioning. The only normal state in which this dissociation occurs is *sleep*. Sleeping, we shed our consciousness and withdraw our watchful attention from the outside world. In this condition, we think and feel things which are quite contrary to our conscious, daytime thoughts. Somebody, for instance, may have hurt our feelings during the daytime, but we may not have been aware of feeling hurt, much less of feeling angry. The following night, however, we may dream that the person who had hurt us committed a crime, was caught by the police, and has been executed.

In most cultures dreams have been taken seriously as meaningful expressions of our mind. But by the time of Freud, this attitude had generally changed in Europe, and dreams were believed to be silly and meaningless phenomena. One of Freud's greatest achievements was to show that dreams express feelings and ideas which we dare not be aware of in waking life, sometimes with utter frankness, but most of the time hidden and distorted even in the privacy of our sleep life. Freud assumed that dreams are always the fulfillment of unconscious wishes which we do not dare to recognize in waking life. (This author, like some others, believes that dreams are not always or necessarily expressions of inadmissible desires; that often we are more wise, more human, more decent when we are alone with ourselves in the state of sleep than we appear to be in the market place of daily living.)

Another state of dissociation in which the unconscious can be observed directly is *hypnosis*. In a state of deep trance, a grown-up person may feel and act like a child of ten, five or two, provided the appropriate suggestion is given to him. This experiment of "age regression" shows that all previous stages of our life are still alive within us; that in the specific condition of hypnotic trance they again take hold of our feelings, only to be completely forgotten when we return to daylight thinking. Many other experiments with hypnosis give a striking proof that the unconscious is pursuing its hidden course "behind the back" of consciousness. Thus, for example, Dr. Mitchell Gold [1] in his studies on hypnosis showed how emotional responses are elicited by specific factors or constellations in the environment. The subject, under hypnosis, is told that she is accused of something and that she feels anxious and guilty; at the same time, the hypnotist shows her his raised finger. At the mention of being accused, the subject shows all signs of terror and anxiety, which leave her when she is assured that the accusation was false. After three or four repetitions of this little drama, she reacts with the same signs of terror when only the finger is raised, no mention being made of an accusation. In other words, a conditioned reflex has been established and the raised finger, which was at first neutral, became a conditioned stimulus. After she has emerged from the hypnotic trance, and is aware of nothing that has taken place, she refuses to look at the hypnotist's raised finger, and turns her head away until the finger is lowered. In her unconscious she is still afraid of the accusation, symbolized by the finger, and yet, consciously, all she feels is an inexplicable aversion to the finger.

In cases of *insanity*, ideas and feelings which are repressed in a normal person are accepted as real. The paranoid person may be convinced that people are plotting against him, or he may be convinced that he is a Roman emperor. Similar suspicions or grandiose ideas would be repressed by the nonpsychotic individual and he might be aware of no more than a magniloquent daydream or a nagging anxiety that people do not like him. His thinking is controlled by an

[1] Research Supervisor of the Scientific Personality Research Corp., New York.

awareness of reality, and the irrational phantasies can never appear to him as if they were real. To the psychotic person reality appears as it appears to all of us when we are asleep. We give up most of our reality awareness in sleep and do not doubt the reality of our dream experience. But when we wake, the unreality of the dream strikes us so forcefully that we often cannot even remember its content. Dreams are transitory states of insanity, or insanity may be said to be dreaming while being awake.

Another situation in which unconscious feelings are expressed directly is the state of mind caused by various *drugs*, the most frequent being intoxication by alcohol. The drunken person has suspended most of his critical judgment, and when he transforms himself into a boastful megalomaniac, or into an aggressive attacker, he gives himself over to forces so repressed in his sober state that he may have no hint of their existence.

The theoretical as well as the practical problem which confronted Freud was to find a way in which a person who is neither psychotic, drunk nor asleep could discover what was *in* him, yet *outside his awareness*. To become conscious of what is unconscious seems a paradox; it was part of Freud's genius that he solved the riddle. He began by using hypnotic methods, but gave these up after a while in favor of the study of dreams—the "royal road to the unconscious"— and of a method he called *free association*. On the face of it, this latter process is simple. A person is told to say just what comes to his mind, disregarding all conventional rules of what is proper, intelligent, polite, etc. The psychologically trained listener can discover in these random associations connections of which the subject is not aware. He may thus detect thoughts and feelings which are unconscious. A simple example will illustrate the point: thought (a) deals with a friend toward whom the patient feels consciously very friendly, although in fact he felt jealous on hearing the night before of his friend's promotion; association (b), apparently without connection, deals with an incident the patient read about in the morning's paper: a man was killed by a rival; association (c) recalls the patient's life in school, when he felt very unhappy at having been demoted from first to second place. Though the patient is not consciously aware of a connection among these three associations, it is not difficult for an objective observer to find the thread. As in the dream, the repressed material of free association is often censored and distorted. At the point when the free association might bring out significant repressed material, the patient may begin to talk about trivial things, feel sleepy, get discouraged, angry or what not. He does not realize that all these reactions are so many attempts to get away from the repressed material.

In addition to dream interpretation and free association, Freud discovered a third method for getting a glimpse of unconscious strivings; this was the study of *transference*. Freud noticed that his patients often developed ideas about him and reactions to him which were not founded at all on reality. One patient might see him as an all-powerful or all-wise man; another as a weak and timid man; a third as a sinister ogre. As in the states of dissociation mentioned above, these feelings were experienced as being quite real, and it was difficult for the patient to convince himself that they were not. Further study showed that these particular feelings were not accidental; that the patient had had similar experiences with a significant person of his early childhood—father, mother, brother, etc.; that unconsciously he was still experiencing other people in terms of these early feelings, seeing them, not objectively, but as if they were those same important childhood figures. He *transferred* his experience, as it were, from the past to the present.

This concept of transference cannot be understood without reference to another of Freud's discoveries: the *importance of the first years of childhood*, especially the relationships with parents and siblings, on the character development of the child. While Freud never thought that the newborn child is like a blank sheet of paper on which the environment simply writes its text, and while he was convinced that each child is born with certain constitutionally given qualities, he nevertheless could show the tremendous influence of early childhood experiences on all later development. The phenomenon of transference demonstrated that the adult retains the experiences of early childhood, often to such an extent that he is not able to see the world objectively.

So far I have given a brief summary of the most important of Freud's findings which are accepted by all psychoanalytic theories based on Freud's discoveries. However, there is a great deal of controversy about the content of what is so strongly repressed and so influential in man's life. Freud himself believed that the most powerful and most repressed strivings are sexual (the energy of the sexual drive he called "libido"). He assumed that from birth on the individual is endowed with sexual strivings, but that the nature of the strivings undergoes a definite development from birth until puberty. At birth the libido is mainly centered around the mouth, and its aim is to be nursed. Later, the passive wish to be nursed is transformed into the more active drive to bite, and to possess with the mouth. The stage after this "oral libido" is the "anal libido," connected with the functions of elimination and resulting in various psychic tendencies like parsimony, overcleanliness, overorderliness (or their opposites). After this, the libido for the first time centers upon the genitals, and pleasure is connected with genital excitement. Following this stage, which occurs around the age of five or six, Freud assumed the existence of a so-called "latency period," which lasts until puberty, and during which no further change occurs in sexual development. With puberty the libido gains its full development and seeks its satisfaction normally in the sexual union with a member of the other sex.

This development, according to Freud, is not as simple and easy as it may sound. The main complication is that, when the phallic level has been reached, the little boy becomes closely attached to his mother, but at the same time finds himself confronted by his father, an invincible rival who forces him to resign, and eventually to suppress, his sexual wishes. (Little girls experience a parallel development.) Under the name of the "Oedipus complex," Freud described the development in which the little boy hates his father, but then becomes afraid of him and, instead of hating him, identifies himself with the father. Freud believed that in a normal development the incestuous attachment to the mother is overcome, while in all cases of mental sickness the unsolved Oedipus complex is the center of the pathological picture.

Freud attempted to explain character trends in terms of his libido theory. To him, the forces which we find underlying a person's character are in the last analysis sublimations of, or reaction formations against, the libidinous strivings, especially the pregenital ones. Thus,

Freud assumed that a dependent, receptive person was stalled, as it were, on the oral-receptive level of libido development; an aggressive, exploitative person, on the oral-sadistic level; a stingy, overorderly, pedantic person, on the anal level of libido development.

In spite of a certain dogmatism, Freud was never a man to be easily satisfied by his own theories, nor one to shut himself off from new observations of facts. Perhaps the First World War brought to a climax Freud's awareness that he had not paid sufficient attention to the role of destructiveness and hostility among the motivations within man. Until then he had thought that hostility was a secondary factor, a reaction to sexual jealousy and rivalry; now he began to believe that it had a much deeper source. The development of his idea led him eventually to assume that there was in man an innate drive for destruction which was just as powerful as *eros*. Eventually he saw in the sexual instinct one manifestation of a drive for life, the aim of which is to unite living matter, while he saw in destructiveness and hostility one manifestation of the drive for death, the aim of which is to return to the original state of inorganic matter. Thus sexual desire and hostility became only the two most visible expressions of the two forces battling within man, one directed toward life, the other toward death. In this theory Freud attempted to connect psychoanalysis with general biological and philosophical concepts, and thus laid the foundation for the more philosophical treatment of psychoanalytic data.

Freud applied his theoretical concepts not only to the individual, but also to the study of society and culture. He believed that primitive man lived out his instinctual desires without too much frustration by society, but that because of this there was a great deal of mutual hostility, and thus a great deal of insecurity, in life. Progress in civilization was essentially an increasing repression of man's instinctual desires. These repressions resulted in sublimation, that is, the transformation of the libido into culturally valuable aims which have no direct connection with the original instinctual aims. Culture, according to Freud, is thus an effect of sublimation. But many people lack the capacity for sublimation which is required by the rigid rules and taboos of many societies; the conflict between their instinctual forces and the social requirements for repression produces neuroses.

Freud's theory on the development of culture is accordingly rather pessimistic. The more man develops culturally, the more he must frustrate his instinctual desires, and as his civilization increases, so does his proneness to mental sickness.

According to his libido theory, Freud assumes that religion, art, philosophy, political systems and so on, are all outcomes in one way or another of libidinal forces, and unsolved libidinal conflicts. He thus becomes a critic of religion, in which he sees mainly the expression of the child's dependence on an all-powerful father. Nevertheless, it would be quite wrong to assume that ethical ideals play only a minor role in Freud's concepts; like the philosophical leaders of the eighteenth century enlightenment period, he believes in truth and freedom as the aims toward which man must strive for a satisfactory solution to life.

It was almost unavoidable that Freud's theories would make him into a social critic (or perhaps only a social critic could have arrived at such theories). While he was convinced that a certain amount of sexual repression was necessary for the development of culture, he protested against the degree of repression which was characteristic of the nineteenth century. He believed that the strictness of the moral code of the Victorian age went beyond its legitimate cultural function and created more neurosis and mental suffering than was warranted. He also saw that the degree of sexual repression customary in his culture tended to cripple the free development of man, and to hobble his reason, thus preventing him from emerging from the state of childhood to that of maturity.

But in spite of the fact that Freud was a social critic, and in many ways a spiritual companion of the enlightenment philosophers of the eighteenth century, he was very different from them in his pessimism about the future of man. Since he did not see the destructiveness of man as a trait produced by the cultural and social conditions of his age, but as an innate trait, he assumed that no social or spiritual change could eradicate it: thus, wars and civil wars, suicide and murder, are inevitable. Man to him was competitive and hostile by nature, and resembled the being characterized by Hobbes in the words: *Homo homini lupus.* The position was not too different from that of the classical economists who saw competitiveness-aggressiveness as elements of human nature, rather than as traits produced by the social order in which they lived.

2. Psychoanalytic Therapy

Psychoanalysis as a therapy is an application of its theory to the problems of mental sickness. It must not be thought from this, however, that Freud first developed his theory, and then applied it. The theory itself developed from his treatment of mentally sick patients, and theory and practice constantly complemented each other. In the first years of psychoanalytic therapy, the patients who came to Freud or other psychoanalysts, mostly suffered from definite *neurotic symptoms*, such as inordinate anxiety, morbid fears, psychosomatic reactions to certain purely psychic stimuli, or obsessive and compulsive thoughts and rituals. Freud assumed that the symptoms resulted from "the injuring of the instinctual impulses through repression," that they were an indication of, and substitution for, an unachieved instinctual gratification. In order to cure a symptom, the patient must become aware of the unconscious instinctual wishes. Being aware of them, he can then find a more mature and effective solution to the conflict between instinct and the organized and conscious part of the self—or the id and the ego as he called these two—than the one found in the formation of the symptom.

In the course of the years, the type of patients who came for psychoanalytic help changed considerably. More and more frequently, these people displayed, not any of the circumscribed symptoms mentioned above, but what is often called a *neurotic character*. Such people find it difficult to work, to have satisfactory relationships with other human beings, especially in their marriage; they are overanxious, overambitious, or on the other hand suffer from lack of self-confidence and from feelings of inferiority. It became increasingly clear to Freud that these characterological defects were also produced by forces unconscious to the person, and that character itself could be changed if the patient gained insight into the unconscious forces which had assumed control of his life. In fact, he came to see what while specific symptoms are the more dramatic and, in an obvious sense, the more painful expressions of unconscious conflicts, the neurotic character is what really matters; and these symptoms will be only superficially eliminated unless the whole character in which they are rooted is changed.

So far we have spoken only of the form of mental disturbance commonly called neurosis. A much more severe type of mental illness is known as psychosis. The neurotic person has retained a grasp of reality at least to the extent that he can function in society. He may bend reality, but he does not rend it. The psychotic person has so completely withdrawn from the outer world that the only reality he knows is that within himself. He hardly responds to events or people and thus Freud thought him incapable of the kind of relatedness to the analyst which was necessary for the analytic cure. However, a number of pioneering psychoanalysts have begun to break through this barrier. The psychoanalytic treatment of schizophrenia was first inaugurated by Harry Stack Sullivan at the Sheppard and Enoch Pratt Hospital, then by Bullard and Frieda Fromm-Reichmann at Chestnut Lodge, and by the Menningers at their clinic. In more recent years psychotherapy of psychoses has been taught and practiced at the Henry Phipps Clinic at Johns Hopkins, at the psychiatric departments of Yale and Harvard Universities, at the Austen Riggs Center and other medical schools and private hospitals, and by a number of individual analysts, both in the United States and abroad.

The method of psychoanalytic cure is implied in what has been said about psychoanalytic theory. It is based upon the analysis of free associations, dreams, transference, and resistance. Its aim is to arrive at an insight into the desires and ideas which motivate the patient but of which he is not conscious. The essence of psychoanalytic therapy is to help the patient to recognize his own inner reality, to remove the veils of rationalization, to gain strength by developing his reason and objectivity. The method which Freud discovered is indeed an application of the ancient precept "know thyself" to the cure of mental illness. It must be emphasized particularly that psychoanalysis has nothing to do with persuasion and giving advice to the patient; it is the exact opposite of such methods. It rests upon the belief that the patient must make his decisions for himself, and that the function of the analyst is only that of helping and stimulating him to gain increased insight into the forces which motivate his behavior.

These general principles are common to all schools of psychoanalysis, but ideas about the particular *contents* of the unconscious depend on the various theoretical expectations held by the different psychoanalytic schools.

As to some practical aspects of psychoanalytic treatment, it must be said that it is rather lengthy, lasting from one year, to two, three or four, or in exceptional cases even longer. In this respect it hardly differs from the length of treatment in any number of chronic illnesses. However, in recent years increasing efforts have been made to shorten the length of the treatment. Unfortunately, psychoanalysis is also expensive, as are all other treatments which require considerable medical assistance. The fees for analysis are normally somewhat lower than those a specialist in other fields would charge for an equivalent amount of time, yet they are high enough to make analytical treatment exceedingly difficult for people below the middle-class income level. Analysis has been extended—as yet to only a small extent —by various psychoanalytic institutes which have set up low-cost clinics. Of course, the demand always exceeds the time available for patients in these clinics.

The therapeutic success of psychoanalysis cannot easily be reduced to statistics. Success depends partly on the severity of the mental disturbance, and very often people come to the analyst only after all other treatment has failed. It depends also on the skill and experience of the individual analyst. And, perhaps even more than other medical statistics, "cure," "improvement," and "negative outcome" are somewhat subjective criteria. The most that can be said today is that psychoanalysis is the only method of cure which promises any help in many cases of mental sickness. Secondly, that a large number of even severe cases of mental sickness are cured by analysis, while many others are not. Thirdly, that unless the analyst makes serious professional mistakes, treatment rarely harms the patient, even if it does not help.

Analysts go through a rigid course of training, which lasts four years or more, and the center of which is their own analysis, and the supervision of their own analytic work by a teacher. By undergoing psychoanalysis, the analyst learns the method of free association and dream interpretation from the inside. Furthermore, he convinces himself of the presence of unconscious strivings by the discoveries he makes about himself in his own analysis. This also alerts him to his own blind spots and to irrational strivings which would diminish his ability to help his patients.

Originally, the psychoanalysts in each country were organized in societies which were part of an international organization under the leadership of Freud. These societies were responsible for the institutes which gave the above-mentioned training to candidates. In recent years, psychoanalytic associations and training institutes have been founded on premises which differ more or less from Freud's teachings. Also, some universities have instituted psychoanalytic training as part of the university curriculum (for instance, Columbia University, the National University of Mexico, and others). Freud himself thought that the practice of psychoanalysis should not be restricted to physicians, but should be exercised by students in other fields of the science of man. His view was accepted in all psychoanalytic institutes except those of the United States, but in the last few years a change has taken place in the United States too. Universities have trained psychologists in the handling of psychic difficulties, and some psychoanalytic institutes have admitted clinical psychologists to psychoanalytic training.

3. Further Developments in Psychoanalysis

Freud laid new foundations for our knowledge of man; but although a genius, Freud was naturally a son of his time, and as with all other scientific discoveries it is to be expected that the generations standing on Freud's shoulders will modify his theory in many details.

Even during Freud's lifetime some of his closest disciples suggested new theories which, like most later developments, had in common a questioning of Freud's assumption of the primary role of sexual strivings. Unfortunately, most of these theoretical deviations led to personal antagonisms, and to the foundation of mutually hostile schools.

The most important deviation from Freud's theory was developed by Carl J. Jung in Switzerland. Jung changed the concept of libido from that of *sexual* energy to *general* psychic energy; he saw in mythology and religion expressions of profound human wisdom, rather than of infantile phantasies; he studied the connection between the great myths of various cultures, and the dreams and neurotic manifestations of individuals, and made many brilliant contributions to the understanding of the unconscious as well as to that of religion and mythology.

Alfred Adler, another of Freud's early disciples, also split from the original thought because he did not share Freud's belief in the supremacy of the sexual instinct. But being less philosophical and more practical-minded than Jung, he put most of his attention on what might be called the tactics and strategy of life. He discovered the psychological significance of organic defects, and explained many character traits as compensations for such early organic inferiorities. He believed the main source of human striving to be the striving for power, by which he meant essentially social recognition and prestige.

The last of Freud's disciples to leave his school was Otto Rank. Less systematic than Jung, yet like him interested in problems of culture, art and philosophy, he developed a number of brilliant theories. At one time he thought he had found a basic cause for neurotic development in the anxiety occurring during birth (birth trauma). Later, he developed interesting ideas about the connection between artistic creation and neurotic-symptom formation. The neurotic person refuses the pretense of role playing, which in Rank's view is characteristic of the average man, but at the same time he is unable to be creative like the artist.

Another, and one of the oldest and closest of the disciples of Freud, Sandor Ferenczi, never broke with him and the official school, although he developed toward the end of his life ideas which differed from Freud's, and which were never accepted by the latter. In contrast to Freud's idea that the analyst should be an objective observer, quite detached from the patient emotionally, Ferenczi insisted that love is not only the necessary leaven in all living, but that it is especially necessary in the healing work of the therapist.

In the last twenty years, certain changes have been taking place both within and without the Freudian school. Within, developments are mainly centered upon greater study of the ego development (Hartman, Kris, Wälder and others); the application of psychoanalysis to anthropology (Geza Rohheim and Abram Kardiner); psychosomatic diseases, and brief psychotherapy (Franz Alexander and his associates), and the psychoanalytic study of psychoses already mentioned. A tendency which differs markedly from that of most Freudian psychoanalysts is to be found in the Southern German and Swiss school of psychoanalysis (Gustav Bally and others). Common to the thinking of this group is an emphasis on the philosophical and anthropological problems of human existence, and on a conviction that the full analytic understanding of man must deal with these problems. In Japan a group of psychoanalysts (Dr. Kenji Ohtsuki) which fundamentally accepts Freud's theory tries to adapt it by introducing specifically Asiatic philosophic concepts.

Somewhat more deviant from Freud's theory are those often called neo-Freudian (Harry Stack Sullivan, Karen Horney and Erich Fromm). Although they have certain features in common (emphasis on social and cultural factors and a critical attitude to the theory of the primacy of the sexual instinct) they nevertheless differ considerably among themselves. Horney's theories are more remote from Freud's than the two others; in some respects they constitute a fruitful and constructive continuation of Adler's thinking.

Without ignoring the significance of childhood experience Horney judges it less important, both for understanding and for therapy, than the events of the present. She places much emphasis on the conflict between various "neurotic trends," and on the role of anxiety in keeping these trends going. In trying to adjust himself to his environment, the child, and later the adult, can move towards people, against them, or away from them, and Horney gives a brilliant description of what happens when these three forms of approach to the world are intermingled, and if none of them is brought to its full fruition. To move "towards people," in the sense of becoming unduly dependent on them, leads to helplessness, "against people" to hostility, "away from people" to isolation—withdrawal.

Sullivan, who started his research with a profound new insight into the nature of schizophrenia, proposed later that, not the fulfillment of sexual desires, but a need for security and the avoidance of intense anxiety and the feeling of aloneness, were the central cravings of man. He considered the need for security, for intimacy and the satisfaction of lustful striving (sexuality) the motivating powers in man's psychic structure. Thus Sullivan does not put emphasis on sexual libido alone, but on the total organism as a psychobiological unit, and on the various forms of relatedness to the outside world which this organism can choose. It is characteristic of his viewpoint that he defined psychiatry and psychoanalysis as the study of "interpersonal relations." Sullivan's work is characterized by extraordinary respect for the mentally sick person, especially those suffering from schizophrenia. To have transmitted this respect to his many students is not of the minor achievements of this brilliantly gifted man. Like Freud, he saw in the earlier years of the child the root of his later development. He made one of the most minute and imaginative studies of the experiences of early childhood, and particularly the relationships between the child and significant persons around him. It must be noted that Sullivan had a keen interest in the application of psychoanalytic knowledge to problems of anthropology, sociology and politics. Although he did not write any larger study on these subjects, his influence on students in the social sciences was fruitful and extensive.

Fromm believes that while man's physiological needs become imperative motivations of action if not satisfied, they are not the basic inner forces which determine man's actions, feelings and thoughts. Only by considering the specific conditions of human existence, and its inherent contradictions, can we understand the basic forces and passions in man. Man is a "freak of nature"; lacking the instinctive equipment which regulates the life of all animals, but gifted instead with reason, imagination, and self-awareness, life becomes for him a problem which must be solved. He has to relate himself to others, to find a new rootedness to replace those roots in nature which other animals have; he must acquire a sense of identity (self) and a system of orientation and an object of devotion. Mental health is identical with the development of a *productive orientation,* the ability to grasp the world in the realm of feeling by *love,* in the realm of thought by critical and imaginative *reason,* and in the realm of action by *creative work* and *art.* The norms taught by all great humanist, religious and philosophical teachers are at the same time the goals which man must strive to attain in order to be sane. Fromm has emphasized the role of the socioeconomic structure on the character development of the individual. According to him, each society creates a personality type which "strives to *want* to do what it *has* to do, and thus to transform the general psychic energy into energy useful for the particular purposes of a given society." But these social needs can be, and often are, in conflict with needs stemming from the nature of man, and its inherent need for love, human solidarity and the development of reason. Insofar as a given society does not satisfy these human needs, it will produce a "socially patterned defect" common to all its members.

Among the group of neo-Freudians, Fromm has put most emphasis on the criticism of society and its effect of stultifying and paralyzing man, not because contemporary society forces him to repress his sexual desires, but because it inhibits his faculty for critical thought, and tends to transform him into an automaton, into a marketing personality who loses the capacity for genuine and profound feeling and thought, and whose sense of identity depends on conformity.

SCIENCE AS FORESIGHT

JACOB BRONOWSKI

about

Jacob Bronowski

Jacob Bronowski was born in 1908 in Poland, but lived in Germany as a child during the First World War. From there he went to England in 1920, where he has lived ever since. He was trained as a mathematician, being a wrangler in the University of Cambridge (the name given there to a student in the highest class of honors in mathematics) and gaining his M.A. and Ph.D. in 1933. In the following years, he published numerous papers in algebraic geometry and topology, and more recently in mathematical statistics. From 1934 to 1942 he was Senior Lecturer in Mathematics at University College, Hull. He left university teaching in 1942 for wartime research, became head of a number of statistical units dealing with the statistical and economic effects of bombing, and was a pioneer in the development of operational research methods. At the end of the war he was Scientific Deputy to the British Chiefs of Staff Mission to Japan in 1945 and wrote the classical British Report "The Effects of the Atomic Bombs at Hiroshima and Nagasaki." For a time he served at UNESCO as head of the Projects Division, and from 1947 to 1950 engaged in applying statistical research to the economics of industry. He is now Director of the Central Research Establishment of the National Coal Board, from which post he was granted leave of absence in 1953 to visit the United States as Carnegie Visiting Professor at the Massachusetts Institute of Technology.

His boyhood problem of learning English as a new language at the age of twelve gave Bronowski an abiding interest in the literature of England and America. He has written two widely-known and much admired books on literature: The Poet's Defence *(1939) and* William Blake: A Man Without a Mask *(1944). He is well known for radio talks and dramas, including* Journey to Japan *and* The Face of Violence; *the latter won the Italia prize for the best dramatic work broadcast throughout Europe during 1950 and 1951 and has recently been published in book form with an introductory essay which analyzes the modern impulse, in life and in literature, toward violence and crime. Bronowski has done solid mathematical work; in recent years its emphasis has changed from pure mathematics to statistics as he has grown more interested in the nature of probability. A subject to which he has devoted a good deal of thought and on which he has written some first-rate papers is the nature of scientific thinking and what logical and mechanical systems and machines can do to help explain it. He has concerned himself with the logic of experiment and with a broad range of philosophical problems bearing on the anatomy of research and scientific method.*

The combination of scientific and literary interests has bade Bronowski a leader in the modern movement of Scientific Humanism in England. His book The Common Sense of Science *reinterprets the development of scientific ideas in a way which makes them meaningful to scientists and nonscientists at the same time. It is a gracefully written, lucid and penetrating essay. He is now working on a sequel to it, based on a series of lectures he gave at the University of Oxford in 1951, which looks broadly at the place and responsibility of the thinker (scientific, literary and social) in the modern world, under the title* The Draught of Hemlock. *His courses on the Philosophy and History of Science in the School of Humanities at M.I.T. were concerned with the similar problem of making the concepts of science part of the developing culture of the modern world. His three public lectures on this theme are about to be published under the general title* Science and Human Values.

Bronowski is married and has four children. He lives with his family at Cheltenham. For hobbies he plays chess and squash rackets ("I like watching all professional sport," he writes); he enjoys reading old and modern poetry, but no novels. "I detest detective stories and science fiction and all purely constructive or ingenious writing—I want writing to have human character and a philosophy, two things which I find moving in the theater more often than elsewhere." Although he claims to be not very knowledgeable about music, his taste being confined to modern music, he is writing an opera (called My Brother Died) *with a young English composer, Peter Racine Fricker. With all this, nine-tenths of his reading and thinking remains in science and the philosophy of science. The essay which follows is an exceptional achievement as to scope, clarity and readability. Bronowski manages in less than 15,000 words to impart to the reader a clear understanding of a sprawling but fascinating subject whose topics include computers and logical machines, the theory of games and information theory, cybernetics, the logic of experiment, the nature of human thinking and the light cast upon it by the study of automata. He has asked me to acknowledge the helpful advice he has had from Mr. D. G. A. Thomas, particularly in the preparation of the diagrams.*

SCIENCE AS FORESIGHT

JACOB BRONOWSKI

1. Introduction

Man is plainly distinguished from other animals by his control of his environment. An animal can perhaps make a shelter, migrate, or learn to change some of its habits; beyond this, it can do little to counter the rigors of its world, and must fit into them much as it finds them. By contrast, man has remade his world. He takes his climate with him; he has invaded the sea and the air, has changed his speed and his skin and his senses to his own design, and lengthened his life several times over. We marvel at the stick insect and the crocodile bird because they are so ingeniously adapted to their environments. But the example of man shows that the most successful adaptation in evolution is intelligent flexibility. By this one gift, the human population has come to dominate the world, from a total of some tens of thousands in prehistory to two and a half billions today.

Man has changed the world by acting as (what Benjamin Franklin called him) a tool-using and tool-making animal. The obvious tools for this purpose are those which shape things and those which move things. To rearrange or, better, to reorganize matter by these means is our main skill and work. Even the African negro uses the knife for one and the bow for the other; and so other races use the plough and the wheel, the lack of which has kept the African more primitive than the cultures of Europe and Asia.

385

But the tools which shape and those which move, the power tools, are not the only world-changers. The Egyptians, who had the plough, also studied the flooding of the Nile, and made themselves great by coupling the two skills. Knowledge can be a means to control nature as power can. The study of astronomy in navigation was as helpful as the wheel and the sail in building the trade of Europe in the Middle Ages.

There is thus another set of human tools, the tools of information and control. In ancient astronomy, the cross-staff and the astrolabe were such tools. Today the telescope, the camera, the spectroscope, the photoelectric cell and the automatic scanner, and many others, are extensions of these. Every laboratory is cluttered with such instruments, which enlarge our "intelligence" in both meanings—the military meaning, and the everyday one.

Machines, like animals, have in fact evolved in two directions: the one toward muscle or strength, and the other toward brain or fore-sight. It happens that in the last two hundred years, since the Industrial Revolution bred first water-driven and then steam-driven machines in England, we have been preoccupied with the power-hungry machines. Technology during these years has been goaded by the search for power—electricity, chemicals, and now nuclear fuels. As a result, the machine of intelligence has usually been thought a laboratory instrument only. But this is to overlook some of our most important inventions. The basis of modern life is the clock; and it was for improvements in the clockwork (then for the purpose of finding one's longitude at sea) that the British government offered (and tried to avoid paying) perhaps the largest cash prize in the history of science, in the eighteenth century. Since then the automatic timer, the switch and the fuse, the telegraph, the Morse Code, the telephone, the type-writer, the tape recorder, have grown as necessary to modern industry as the dynamo and the internal-combustion engine. Edison founded his career on his patents in a typical instrument of intelligence, the stock ticker.

In short, the machine of power and that of intelligence are complementary. Much of man's power derives from his discovery of fire; but as much derives from the discovery of speech and writing, which make it possible to hand on experience from generation to generation, almost as Lamarck once thought evolution might act. Early machines were largely such devices of knowledge and control—the clock, the quadrant, the printing press, Leonardo's wind vane and his elegant machine for controlling the cutting of teeth on a file. (Leonardo did not understand the demands for power which other machines make; this is why his flying machines were merely a dream.) Then for the two great industrial centuries from about 1750, the drive was for power (rather than control) to shape nature—until the nucleus gave us all we are likely to need. And as physics has now given us power from the nucleus at the center of the atom, so it has given us a new source of control and intelligence on the outskirts of the atom, from the electron. It is characteristic that the two machines whose names became catchwords at the end of the war were "nuclear pile" and "electronic brain."

I have been lumping together three kinds of power tools: generators of power, such as the nuclear pile; converters of power, such as the electric motor; and users of power, such as the trip hammer. It is not relevant to this essay to distinguish among them, since they all contribute to the reshaping of the world by physical strength. It is, however, important that I distinguish between the different kinds of control mechanisms and processes which can be used, and which form the subject of this essay.

We can use knowledge to help us control our relations to our environment, because it gives us foresight. That is, experience encourages us to believe that the future follows the past in a repeatable pattern; and knowledge helps us to isolate and to forecast this pattern. The subject we are studying is therefore foresight. We take the first step to this by accumulating observations; but I shall not discuss instruments of observation, because they provide only the raw material for foresight. For example, I am not interested in the automatic voting machine or the census taker, as such.

But once these data, the votes and the census record, have been taken, they allow us to make predictions about future votes and censuses. Now the forecasting machine enters for the first time; and I shall begin with the giant calculators, to show how such a machine digests its information and then projects it forward into a new setting, an election or a census.

Machines of this kind, I shall show, are distinguished by nothing but their speed. In type, they remain purely deductive machines, and even if their forecast is wrong time and time again, they have no capacity for changing its basis. They cannot learn from their own mistakes.

It is therefore appropriate to go next to machines which do have a mechanism for adaptation and learning. These machines, which change not only their answers but their approach to a problem as a result of their own findings, form an interesting analogue to the human brain.

Once we are talking about mechanisms for adapting behavior, we enter the field of the strategy of foresight. There is now no longer just one way to get to our goal, the control of a situation; we have to find how to shift our procedure with the results we achieve. We are here entering the theory of strategy and of automatic controls of the subtlest kind.

The more we press into such problems, the more we find that underlying them is a deeper problem: to grasp the right arrangement of the facts on which we proceed. This is the theory of communication and information. And I apply it finally to the nature of human and scientific enquiry in general—not only how we foresee the movement of the world, but more deeply how we understand it.

In this way, we begin from the machines which are poor copies (and copiers) of the essential steps in human logic and foresight; and we use them step by step to teach us something of what the mind can do better, in deduction, in comparison, and finally in imagination, until we see of what the mind's meaning itself is made. Our procedure in this essay is to learn by constantly pushing forward, beyond the field which each machine or process can explore, in turn, into the more complex actions of which it falls short.

2. Deductive Machines

I have made the point that there are two kinds of human tools or machines: those which are, as it were, extensions of the hand, and those which are extensions of the brain. (In man himself, these two functions are related, and there is fossil evidence that the enlargement of the brain followed, in human evolution, the development of the hand.)

This essay is concerned with extensions of the brain, and what they have to teach us about the brain. I therefore begin with the simplest of all aids to the brain, and what not long ago would have been thought the dullest: the calculating machine.

i) *Analogue Machines*

There are many devices which will serve to simplify special calculations. The engineer's slide rule (which depends on Napier's invention of logarithms just after 1600) simplifies multiplication and division, and this and other slide rules can be made to solve other special problems. Or we can build machines which take advantage of some natural relation, say the law of electric conduction discovered by Georg Simon Ohm,

$$\text{current} = \text{potential difference} / \text{resistance},$$

in order to carry out multiplication and division.

Devices of this kind—of which Diagram 1 is a practical example—use the analogy between our problem and some natural process and are therefore called analogue machines. They are compact and cheap to build for small problems, but they have two drawbacks. They are rather inflexible in use, so that they cannot easily be put to new problems; and in a sequence of steps they tend to accumulate their errors, so that their accuracy is limited.

For these reasons, the analogue machines are neither as useful nor, inherently, as interesting as machines which keep close to the basic procedures of arithmetic. I shall confine myself now to the latter, which use the ordinary numbers or digits to work with, and are therefore called digital machines or, as I prefer to call them, arithmetical machines.

ii) *The Arithmetical Machine*

The processes of arithmetic are all rooted in counting, and all arithmetical machines are really counters. The simplest digital machine is therefore the clock, which fundamentally counts notches or impulses

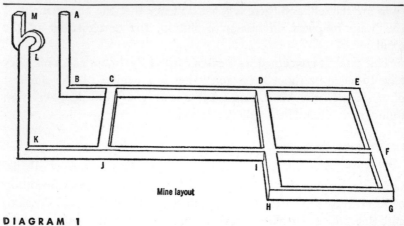

Mine layout

DIAGRAM 1

An Analogue Machine

The pressure drop along a mine airway is proportional to the square of the airflow. The potential difference along an electric resistance, however, is directly proportional to the current flowing. Hence an ordinary electric network is not an analogue to a mine layout.

But if each element in the network is a filament which is heated by the current flowing through it, its resistance will itself change in proportion to the current; and therefore the potential difference now becomes proportional to the square of the current. Hence problems on the ventilation of mines can be (and are) solved on an electric network of the kind shown here, in which the air resistances are simulated by heated filaments. The distribution of pressures in the airways is given by the potential differences in the network, and the airflows by the electric currents flowing.

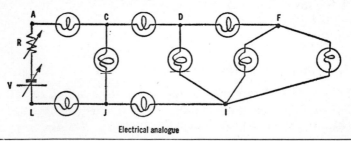

Electrical analogue

(assumed to be regular) and registers its count on dials. (By contrast, the egg timer and the water clock are analogue machines.) Elaborate clocks which go on to register the date, the day of the week and the phases of the moon show this principle of counting very clearly.

This principle was first built into an adding machine by the French mathematical (and religious) prodigy, Blaise Pascal, in 1642, when he was 19. His machine adds (for it still exists and works) as machines have done ever since, by turning a toothed wheel so many notches; the wheels are geared so that ten notches on one wheel shift the next wheel forward a single notch. The cash register, the mileage counter on an automobile, the automatic record on a Geiger counter, and a thousand such devices, still use Pascal's mechanism.

In 1673 another philosopher and mathematician, Gottfried Wilhelm Leibniz, fitted to Pascal's machine the device which multiplies a number by adding it over and over again. A machine which can add can, of course, also subtract, by going in reverse; and usually a machine which can multiply can also divide. (Diagram 6, however, shows that this is not always so simple as it sounds.) Thus the Pascal-Leibniz machine was able to carry out all the familiar steps in arithmetic. In essence, the calculating machine for nearly 300 years remained as these two great men made it, and as we see it (somewhat electrified) in banks and accounting houses.

iii) *The Problem of Speed*

The large electronic machines have now replaced the toothed wheel by a tube or a circuit. This has not changed the principle of the arithmetical machine; it has merely changed its speed. As Diagram 2 shows, a tube or a circuit is still a device for counting; it simply counts much faster than a notched wheel. The difference is one of scale, just as the difference between chemical and nuclear energy is one of scale.

In the case of energy, the scale is set by comparative distances: the distances between the parts of the nucleus are about a million times smaller than the distance between atoms, and therefore the fission of the nucleus releases about a million times more energy than does a reaction which breaks chemical bonds between atoms.

In the case of counters, the scale is set by comparative speeds. The

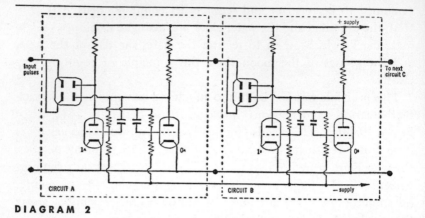

DIAGRAM 2

The Circuit as a Counter

The left-hand circuit A shown here counts 0 or 1; when it reaches 2, it carries it forward to the right-hand circuit B, which counts 0 or 1 *pairs*. When the right-hand circuit reaches 2 pairs (that is, 4), it carries it forward to the next circuit C on the right, which is not shown; and so on.

As the diagram shows, each circuit contains a pair of tubes; at any moment, only one tube of the pair (0 or 1) is conducting. The current is transferred from one tube of a pair to the other when a pulse is received from the preceding circuit on the left. The table below gives the number of pulses which have been counted, and the tubes which are conducting, at each count. The correspondence between numbers and tubes is particularly simple when the numbers are written in the binary notation explained in Diagram 7, and a column has been added on the right to show this.

Number Counted	Tubes Conducting	Number in Binary Notation
0	$0_B 0_A$ (initial condition)	0
1	$0_B 1_A$	1
2	$1_B 0_A$ (pulse has been carried to circuit B)	10
3	$1_B 1_A$	11
4	$1_C 0_B 0_A$ (pulse has been carried to circuit C)	100

tube or the circuit uses electrons to transmit its impulses, and they move at a speed comparable with the speed of light. The notched wheel uses mechanical pressures, and they are transmitted at a speed comparable with the speed of sound. Since light travels about a million times faster than sound, the tube or the circuit counts about a million times faster than does the notched wheel.

When a machine works as fast as this, it sets a new problem: How are we to keep up with it? This is the problem which has transformed the new machines and given them their unexpected interest.

An electronic machine can multiply two numbers, each the size of the National Budget, in less than a thousandth of a second, and adds them in a tenth of this time. Nothing has been gained by these fabulous speeds if the operator has now to spend minutes in comparing the answer with some other result, and in arranging the machine to go on with the next step. He might as well have done the addition and multiplication too on an ordinary accounting machine; it would only have added a few seconds to his total time.

The electronic machine is quick at arithmetic; and if we are to take advantage of this speed, we must make it as quick at the other logical processes which go into solving a complete problem. When the machine has reached an answer at one stage, it must be able to link this to some other part of the calculation and to continue of itself. That is, it must be able to store and to follow a sequence of instructions which has been given in advance, some of which are conditional instructions—say, to choose the larger of two numbers which it has found, and to work on with this. It must be able to store, compare and use its own answers at each step.

When a machine can work to a well-planned, orderly and repetitive program like this, its output is hair raising. A dozen machines are now chugging away, on both sides of the Atlantic, on calculations of atomic structure, of the nuclear processes by which matter was or is built up, of aeronautics and gunnery, and of large-scale statistics. The speed of the machine in digesting detailed statistics has now been shown in several elections, and the presidential election of 1952 will serve as an example. In that election, President Eisenhower won a spectacular and unforeseen number of electoral seats. Nevertheless when, forty minutes after the poll closed, UNIVAC made a forecast based on the first two million votes, it differed from the correct final distribution of electoral seats by less than one per cent. I ought to add that the experts in social assessment of course disbelieved the answer and hastily shushed the machine. The distrust of exact calculation is deep-seated, and continues to keep it out of national statistics and economics.

iv) *A New Arithmetic*

The electronic machines are remarkable for their speed and therefore for the amount of work they can do in a manageable time. They do this not by their complexity but by their simplicity. Like the human brain, they achieve complexity only by the repetition of simple elements—tubes or circuits, where the brain repeats the same unit cells. Their strength, in fact, is repetition; we tax their logical apparatus least, and make the most of their arithmetical speed, by breaking down a problem into very simple steps, which are taken over and over again. Diagram 3 is a hypothetical but illuminating example of how a mathematical process (squaring a number) might be broken down for some machines (into primitive and repeated additions). Diagram 4 shows the instructions which the machine would receive for this purpose.

No mathematician will square a number as Diagram 3 does because the labor of simple repetition will take him many hours, and expose him to the constant danger of making mistakes, from tedium or inattention if for no other reason. But the machine is inured to tedium and inattention, and fairly safe from error; and simplicity and repetition are what it is best at.

Thus the large machines run counter, in many ways, to the trend of mathematics. Mathematicians have always looked for short cuts, devices to avoid tedious work, and contractions of processes. In a sense, all mathematics is the discovery of short cuts (algebraic geometry, the integral calculus, and complex functions are examples), and the avoidance of repetitive methods such as trial-and-error and step-by-step approximation. But the machine asks us to go back on all this and to seek instead for precisely the opposite: for ways to break the problem into small, repetitive parts, over and over again, and step by step. (For this reason, the machines have been used from the out-

DIAGRAM 3

Machine Procedures are Simple and Repetitive

A mathematician asked to square the number 8,921 does it by multiplication:

$$\begin{array}{r} 8{,}921 \\ 8{,}921 \\ \hline 71{,}368{,}000 \\ 8{,}028{,}900 \\ 178{,}420 \\ 8{,}921 \\ \hline 79{,}584{,}241 \\ \hline\hline \end{array}$$

A machine might find it more convenient on occasion, (say, when compiling a table of squares for permanent record) to use the simple repetitive device of adding the odd numbers, as follows:—

$$\begin{array}{r} 1 = 1 = 1 \times 1, \\ 1 + 3 = 4 = 2 \times 2, \\ 1 + 3 + 5 = 9 = 3 \times 3, \\ 1 + 3 + 5 + 7 = 16 = 4 \times 4, \\ \cdots\cdots\cdots\cdots\cdots\cdots \\ 1 + 3 + 5 + 7 + 9 + 11 + 13 + 15 + 17 + 19 = 100 = 10 \times 10, \\ \cdots\cdots\cdots\cdots\cdots\cdots \end{array}$$

and so on until the machine reaches

$$1 + 3 + 5 + 7 + \cdots\cdots\cdots$$
$$\cdots\cdots\cdots + 17{,}841 = 79{,}584{,}241 = 8{,}921 \times 8{,}921.$$

DIAGRAM 4 ――――――――――――――――――   ――――――――――――――――

Programming a Machine to Carry out a Simple Repetitive Procedure

Below are given the formal instructions to a machine to carry out the procedure for squaring a number by the method of Diagram 3. These instructions will be understood more easily if the procedure is first sketched in general terms. It consists of three kinds of steps:

(i) The odd numbers are built up one after another (in Store 2), beginning with the number 1, by adding the number 2 over and over again.

(ii) A count is kept (in Store 3) of how often this remains to be done, in order not to overshoot.

Meanwhile, the steps shown in Diagram 3 are carried on, namely,

(iii) The odd numbers obtained (in Store 2) are added up, as they are obtained, in Store 5, where the answer will be reached after the right number of steps (controlled by (ii) above).

Once the general method is understood, it is clear that the machine need be able to do only three things:

A. Read the number in one Store and add it to another Store;

B. Read the number in one Store and subtract it from another Store; and

C. Inspect one Store and stop the calculation when zero is reached there.

For the control of the machine, orders are read in sequence from a tape, and it greatly increases the capabilities of the machine if several Tape Readers can be used at will. It is therefore convenient to have a further order,

D. Change from one Tape Reader to another.

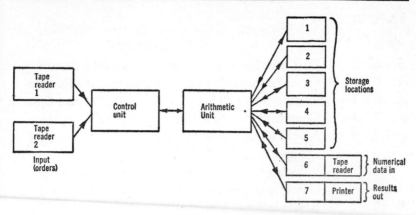

Here is a functional diagram of such a machine.

The orders for this machine are given in three parts:

Part 1	*Part 2*	*Part 3*
A. Add	Store from which number is to be obtained.	Store into which number is to be added (or subtracted).
B. Subtract		
C. Inspect	Store which is to be inspected.	Not needed (Zero).
D. Change source of order.	Input tape which is to be used.	Not needed (Zero).

Three tapes are used: Tape I for the numerical data, and Tapes II and III for orders. The orders have been split between Tapes II and III because it is convenient to put orders which are repeated many times during the calculation (subroutines) on a separate tape. The subroutine Tape III is often a closed loop, as here.

Only three numbers are needed on the data Tape I: they are 2, 1 and 8,921 (the last is the number to be squared). The groups of numbers required on the other tapes are shown below. The program has been designed so that Tape II is used only once; Tape III is used 8,921 times. The machine starts by reading Tape II.

DIAGRAM 4 *continued* _____

TAPE II

Order	What Happens
A. 6. 1	First number (2) on Tape I added into Store 1.
A. 6. 2	Second number (1) on Tape I added into Store 2.
A. 6. 3	Third number (8,921) on Tape I added into Store 3.
A. 2. 4	Contents of Store 2 added into Store 4.
D. III. 0	Source of next and subsequent orders transferred to Tape Reader III. When Tape Reader III is operating, Tape II is stationary, and hence when control returns to Tape Reader II, the next order is read.
A. 5. 7	Result in Store 5 printed.

TAPE III. (which comes into operation after the fifth order on Tape II.)

Order	What Happens
A. 2. 5	Contents of Store 2 added to Store 5.
A. 1. 2	Contents of Store 1 added to Store 2.
B. 4. 3	Contents of Store 4 subtracted from Store 3.
C. 3. 0	Contents of Store 3 inspected. If zero, the next order is carried out; if not, the next order is omitted and the next but one carried out.
D. II. 0	Source of next and subsequent orders transferred to Tape II (which resumes operation with the sixth order).
A. 2. 5	(This is a return to the first order on Tape III, which is a closed loop.)

This is a hypothetical program, designed only to show the general principles on which a complicated operation is broken up into many simple steps for a machine. Few machines, in fact, would need to go to so much trouble in order to square a single number (because most machines, unlike that assumed in this example, are able to multiply directly). But notice that the program given here does have one advantage: it finds the squares of all numbers smaller than 8,921 on the way to finding the square of 8,921. This program could therefore be used to record for future use a table of the squares of

DIAGRAM 4 *continued* ————————————————————————

all these numbers. (To do this, it is only necessary to add a single order to Tape III: the order A. 5. 7 after the fifth order on that tape.) The preparation of permanent tables of this kind is a useful application of large machines.

---

set for calculations which naturally go from one result to the next, like those which make gunnery and other tables, or those which explore point after point in a field of flow as in aeronautics.) And as Diagram 6 shows, stepwise approximation and trial-and-error are daily and powerful tools in the arithmetic of the machines. Most deeply, the machine demands that its work be reduced to the simplest, basic processes; and to plan a program for these machines is to work in a new and, as it were, perverse arithmetic.

v) A New Political Arithmetick

The great but essentially simple power of the machine in calculation brings with it also a new way of looking at its (and our) problems. Many problems in economics, social science and national planning are at bottom problems of statistical accounting. (For this reason these subjects were called by their inventors in the seventeenth century, political arithmetick, a graphic name which I am glad to see revived.) But the actual labor of accounting, the arithmetic of examining all possible relations and interactions between the entries, has hitherto been unmanageable. Therefore these social subjects have, like the physical sciences, looked for short cuts in general principles. They have not been successful, largely I think because the subjects have lacked the experimental data from which laws in the physical sciences are crystallized. There are of course social and economic data in plenty, but they are unwieldy and uncontrolled, and no one has been able to isolate more than the barest trends from them. (When they have tried to do more in extracting some mathematical model from the chaos of markets and policies, as Professor Colin Clark has bravely tried, they have been as wide of the mark as was his forecast of an economic blizzard in 1954 based on the experience of 1949.)

The new machines offer us the chance of handling massive social and economic data without any preconceptions at all. In this way, even the limited variations in national statistics can become the basis of an experimental approach, but one different from the physical sciences. In the physical sciences, the variables are in the main under our control, and it has therefore been possible to evolve an experimental technique of simplification, for example by varying one condition at a time. Social and economic results cannot be handled in this way; they must be explored for their hidden interactions and correlations as they stand, without the assumption (which physics has held for 600 years since William of Ockham) that laws shall be simple. By making this possible, the fast machines open the prospect of a new intellectual approach to the aims of statistics, and beyond that a new empirical approach to national planning. Where calculation in the past has been so crude, there has been an excuse for the planner's preference for his own (optimistic) hunches, and his appeal to imponderables; he could hardly be more wildly out than Professor Colin Clark or the professional weather forecasters. But the administrator's "imponderables" means at bottom the integrated impression made in his mind by the complex of individually small shifts and nuances in the data, which have not been separately analyzed. Today there is no reason why they should not be analyzed and given their proper, ponderable weight. Thus the new machines may found a new social and economic science, which need no longer shirk the arithmetic in political arithmetick. Its relation to current economic rules of thumb may be, roughly, that of UNIVAC to a traditional tag such as "As Maine goes. . . ." Indeed, the work of correlation which underlies the election forecasts of UNIVAC is a first example of the new methods.

vi) *The Logic of the Machines*

Let us turn back to take a last look at the workings of the new machines. I have remarked that these are forced on us by the speed of the machines; to take advantage of its speed, a fast machine must store, use and compare its instructions and its own answers. (This was foreseen in the design of a fast mechanical machine about 1835 by Charles Babbage, who detested piecemeal calculation and organ-grinders.) How in fact is this done?

The instructions must be both permanent and rapidly scrutinized; they are therefore usually punched as holes in a paper tape—essentially the device for storing information which Dr. H. Hollerith invented in 1891 when the U.S. census became unwieldy. Diagram 5 shows a machine tape of instructions (for taking square roots). It makes for speed if all that the machine need note and obey as it senses the tape is "hole" or "no hole," that is, a simple choice of "on" or "off," "yes" or "no." For this reason, most machines code both their orders and their arithmetic in a system which has only two symbols, "yes" and "no"—which are usually written simply as "1" and "0." Diagram 7 shows how this arithmetic works.

This system makes numbers a great deal longer than in everyday writing (over three times as long) and involves the "translation" of ordinary numbers into and out of it. Nevertheless, as Diagram 2 illustrates, the simplicity of so instructing and running a machine, and of making tubes and circuits for it, is usually held to outweigh this disadvantage.

The instruction tape works the machine much as would the fingers of an operator pressing the keys of an ordinary accounting machine. But instead of registering each answer on a display panel, the electronic machine holds it on a magnetized drum or tape, or some other dynamic record—that is, a record which recalls its contents at regular intervals. Meanwhile, the instructions send the machine on its next step, while the last answer remains stored on the revolving drum or record. When this answer is wanted, in order to compare or combine it with that found at another step, the machine follows instructions which tell it to pick it up from the magnetic drum again. The operations of the machine are accordingly geared to the speed of the drum or other dynamic "memory."

In this way, successive steps in a long calculation follow one another without outside interference, until the machine finally reaches a result which is to be permanently recorded. This it usually puts on a magnetic tape, and thence types.

There is nothing recondite in these machines. Their steps are logical, and they are possible because deductive logic can be formalized and therefore mechanized. Yet, direct and understandable as their mechanics are, they open an arresting query. The machine stores,

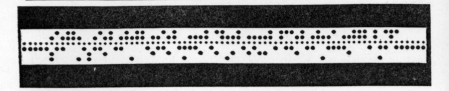

DIAGRAM 5

Program Tape

This example shows how the instructions to a machine are set out as punched holes in a tape. (This particular tape carries the instructions for taking a square root—the reverse process to that illustrated in Diagrams 3 and 4.)

DIAGRAM 6

Step-by-Step Approximation

Repeated approximation is a powerful tool in a calculating machine. For example, some machines have no separate mechanism for long division. Instead they use the fact that

If

$$y_0, \ y_1, \ y_2, \ \cdots\cdots \ y_n, \ y_{n+1}, \ \cdots\cdots$$

is a sequence of numbers such that

$$y_{n+1} = y_n \, (2 - a \, y_n),$$

then the numbers y of the sequence rapidly approximate to $1/a$ (provided the first number y_0 is chosen reasonably).

As an example, let us find by this procedure $\frac{355}{113}$ — a famous approximation to π known to the Chinese in the fifth century and rediscovered in Europe in the sixteenth century. We begin by finding

DIAGRAM 6 *continued* ─────────────────────

$\frac{1}{113}$, taking as first number in the sequence $y_0 = 0.01$. We find

y_n	$a\,y_n$	$2-a\,y_n$	$y_{n+1}=y_n(2-a\,y_n)$
$y_0 = 0.01$	1.13	0.87	0.0087
$y_1 = 0.0087$	0.9831	1.0169	0.00884703
$y_2 = 0.00884703$	0.99971439	1.00028561	0.008849556800
$y_3 = 0.008849556800$			

Seven-figure accuracy has been obtained after only three repetitions, and gives (on multiplying by 355) $\pi = 3.1415927$. A fourth repetition would give eleven-figure accuracy, which however is out of place here, since $\frac{355}{113}$ is no longer a good approximation to π beyond the sixth decimal place.

───────────────────────────────

DIAGRAM 7

Binary Notation

The notation is most simply explained by examples. Thus, the number 5 is rearranged, in binary notation, as $4 + 1$, that is
$$(1 \times 4) + (0 \times 2) + 1$$
and is written as
$$1\,0\,1.$$
The number 8 is rearranged as
$$(1 \times 8) + (0 \times 4) + (0 \times 2) + 0$$
and written as
$$1\,0\,0\,0.$$
The number which we write every day as 19 is rearranged as $16 + 2 + 1$, that is
$$(1 \times 16) + (0 \times 8) + (0 \times 4) + (1 \times 2) + 1$$
and written as
$$1\,0\,0\,1\,1.$$

DIAGRAM 7 *continued* _____

We are accustomed to build up a number from units, tens, hundreds, thousands and so on; instead, the binary notation builds it up from units, pairs, fours, eights, sixteens and so on.

One reason why the binary notation is convenient for machines is that it has very simple addition and multiplication tables: namely

$$0 + 0 = 0, \qquad 1 + 0 = 1, \qquad 1 + 1 = 10,$$
$$0 \times 0 = 0, \qquad 1 \times 0 = 0, \qquad 1 \times 1 = 1,$$

and nothing more.

_____

uses and compares its instructions and its own answers. These are the parallels to what in a human mind would be called a program of work, a memory, and the exercise of choice. They have made it tempting to call these machines "electronic brains." But does it make sense to call what the machines do "thinking"?

Plainly the machines are not original thinkers. They follow instructions, and they break down if they meet a choice which has not been foreseen. But these are not in themselves inhuman attributes: to follow instructions and to break down in face of the unforeseen are both sadly human. The machine carries through a sequence of logical steps; it is today becoming more and more a logical machine rather than a mere calculating machine. If by thought we mean logical reasoning, then the machine can think as well as we can. We are prejudiced against it only because, like other prodigies, it was taught by its maker instead of by a schoolmaster.

That is: the essence of deductive logic is that it can be formalized; it can therefore be incorporated in a machine; and the machine can then deduce or reason from given data as well as we can. In this branch of reasoning, the machine is potentially our equal. If we want to claim more for our brains, we must turn to a larger field than deductive reasoning.

3. Adaptive Machines

The obvious shortcoming of the purely deductive machine is that it cannot learn. It cannot gain from its experience, because it cannot change its own method. Its procedure is inflexible, and the machine cannot itself adapt it to changes.

In this sense, the deductive machine, although it may control a whole assembly line or an automatic factory, imitates only the instinctive behavior of animals—the wonderfully complex but (in the main) fixed sequence of actions of a gall wasp or a burying beetle. Before, therefore, we can begin to look in the machine for a model of intelligent procedure, it must include at the least some sign that it can modify its own course in order to reach its goal in changing circumstances.

i) *Goal-Seeking Strategy*

I have used the word "goal," which brings into the discussion the breath of an oddly sporting air. This is not, as might be thought, inappropriate. It is in fact not an accident that creatures of rigidly fixed behavior, such as the ants (some of which finished their evolution fifty million years ago, and have not changed either their anatomy or their organization since) do not play games. There are students of animal behavior who regard play, in the fox cub, the young bear, or man, as essentially a training in choice, and the natural mark of a growing freedom of behavior.

Games of sport as we play them differ from our real life in this: that the purpose or goal of the contestants is simple and precisely defined, and the ways in which they may gain their goal equally are simple and limited. This is true, whether the game is an exercise of muscle or, in human beings, of mind, all the way from rowing and football to billiards and chess—and to war. They are goal-seeking activities with rules.

For this reason, games are natural models for all purposeful activities, in which we can study with great clarity the strategy for reaching our aims in the competition of life. I shall therefore often illustrate the working of machines and of planning with precise examples from games, rather than vague generalizations from economics and the stock market. I am in this essay looking at all thinking as foresight, that is as the search for strategies which anticipate future events or moves; and as our language shows, in words like "goal," "competition," and "moves," games are compact fields (itself a game-word) for this.

ii) *Unlimited Foresight*

I said that the deductive machines which I discussed in the last chapter cannot modify their own strategy, and must therefore proceed as it were only by instinct. This may seem unfair to any machine which has provision in it for choosing between two courses of action, by some criterion of purpose. Let me illustrate it by examples; first, an extreme and impractical example.

Think of a machine into which we have wired the rules of chess. We could set it to work on a given position, and let it grind out in turn every possible consequence of every move, reaching always either mate, stalemate or the endless repetition of the same moves. In this way, we could (in theory) ensure that the machine made no move which was not sure to win (if the initial position could be won). I have said "in theory" and that this is an impractical example, and so it is, in a position of any prolonged complexity—certainly in the opening position of a game of chess. But I ought to add that an electronic machine has been programed to do just this for two moves, in order to solve two-move chess problems, as it were by brute force.

In the game of draughts or checkers, the accumulated practice of players, as recorded in books, has over the years acted like such a machine, and has produced so complete a knowledge of the game that virtually nothing remains to be found. There is really no reason for playing checkers except human fallibility. Collective experience has been a checkers machine which has analyzed every move to the end. We could therefore put this into a simpler machine: a mechanical reference book which consults itself after each move by its opponent, and in reply plays (without analysis) the move which book-analysis has shown to be best. A noughts-and-crosses machine has in fact been built which plays just like this, automatically.

This "fossilization of experience" can take another form. There is a charming game which has the merit that it needs no apparatus except a box of matches, and is yet an intellectual tussle between two players—if they do not know its theory. Diagram 8 gives the rules of this game of Nim and a characteristic position.

As in the game of chess, we could wire a machine to grind out every possible consequence of every move in Nim. If this machine were faced with the position in Diagram 8, I have no doubt that, after a deliberation running to hours or days, it would make the winning move (there is only one).

A knowledgeable human player will make the same move in a matter of minutes; and will make it, not by analyzing all the consequences of this position, but because he has already analyzed all the consequences of all positions. That is, he knows the *theory* of the game; for as Diagram 8 shows, the only demerit of this attractive game is that its theory is fully known.

Here, then, the simpler course would be to build the theory into the machine, rather than the laborious capacity to analyze. (The way the theory rests on sub-piles of 16, 8, 4, 2 and 1 matches makes it particularly convenient to put into an electronic machine.) In fact, at the Festival of Britain in 1951, a machine was built in this way, to play Nim automatically; and Professor Norbert Wiener and I played a memorable session on it, against one another and against the machine. In an intellectual sense, no doubt we knew the theory better than the machine; but the machine won, because its wiring (its "instincts") never made a mistake in applying the theory.

In summary: a machine can be conceived to have unlimited foresight and to grind out a game to the bitter end. Such a machine, however, is impracticable unless the game offers few alternatives. And in such cases, it is easier to make the machine into a form either of memory or of instinct, which plays the right move because the right move is known from practice or theory, and has been built into the machine with no nonsense.

iii) *Experience in Machines*

I have shown that a machine can be arranged to prefer one move to another, and to respond to the moves which its opponent in a game of strategy makes, and still it is doing no more than follow a

DIAGRAM 8 ————————————————————————————————

The Game of Nim

The contents of a box of matches are stacked in several piles, at random. The game is between two players who move in turn. A move consists in picking up a number of matches from one pile; the player can pick them from whichever pile he chooses, and he can take as many matches as he likes (including the entire pile); but he must take all his matches on one move from one pile only—and he must take at least one match. The player who clears the table (that is, who picks up the last match or pile of matches) wins.

Consider a characteristic position—say when there are three piles left on the table consisting of 5, 8 and 19 matches. What should the player do who has the move?

He should think of each pile as made of sub-piles of 16, 8, 4, 2, and 1 matches, precisely as in the binary system explained in Diagram 7. Thus he thinks of the three piles on the table as

$$(1 \times 4) + (0 \times 2) + 1 = 1\,0\,1,$$
$$(1 \times 8) + (0 \times 4) + (0 \times 2) + 0 = 1\,0\,0\,0,$$
$$(1 \times 16) + (0 \times 8) + (0 \times 4) + (1 \times 2) + 1 = 1\,0\,0\,1\,1.$$

He should now pick up enough matches from one pile to leave an even number of each kind of sub-pile on the table. This is done by arranging that there is left an even number of 1's in each column on the right, above. Therefore, in this case, he must reduce the third pile to

$$(1 \times 8) + (1 \times 4) + (0 \times 2) + 1 = 1\,1\,0\,1,$$

which means leaving thirteen matches in the third pile. The player who is to move therefore takes six matches from the third pile. In this way, he obtains a stranglehold which his opponent cannot break, and which he renews each time it is his turn to move again.

rigid routine. It is still working entirely by calculation, and when it does this the machine might as well follow either the "reference book" or the theory of right moves which its designer could work out and build into it. In other words, the logical machine was "born" with all its procedures already ready-made; and while we admire such infant prodigies (who, characteristically, among human beings are usually remarkable only at chess, mathematics, music or languages) we do not rank them with those whose achievement is a response to their individual experience of life: with William Shakespeare, Thomas Jefferson or Johann Wolfgang Goethe.

Nor are we satisfied with ready-made responses to stimuli. Many machines exist which adjust themselves to outside stimuli: the thermostat does so in a small way (as Diagram 9 shows), and the automatic pilot in a large. These machines "sense" the outside temperature or wind, feed this information back into their mechanism, and automatically move to counter the outside change—to raise the temperature, or keep the aircraft on an even keel. But there is nothing in this feeding back and subsequent response which distinguishes these from the machines which make a move in response to a move of mine. The thermostat and the automatic pilot feed back information on their environment and respond to it, continuously instead of from time to time: that is their only difference. They still carry out no more than reflex actions.

We are looking for a machine (by which, of course, we mean essentially a process) which is genuinely modified by its experience: which accumulates experience, and uses it to change its procedure permanently, as a growing child does. We are looking for a machine that learns, in the sense of changing its own strategy.

There are several ways in which animals learn; of these, the most convenient to put into a machine is trial-and-error. Suppose, for example, we go back to our ideal chess-playing machine. We cannot really make this machine blindly follow to the end every conceivable sequence of moves. But we can make it pick out some moves to try and follow their possible consequences for five or six moves. Suppose that we let the machine play in this tentative way, with limited foresight, and give it a mechanism for deciding on a reasonable move on these restricted findings. Against a human player, this machine

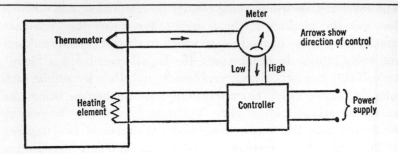

DIAGRAM 9

Feedback

In this thermostat, the thermometer measures the temperature which is to be controlled, and feeds back its finding to the meter and controller. If the meter shows the temperature to be below that which has been set, the controller steps up the power sent to the heating element and so raises the temperature. If the meter shows the temperature to be too high, the controller cuts down the power sent to the heating element and so lowers the temperature.

The system is self-correcting, but fails if there is excessive or grave dislocation. For example, if the wires between the meter and the controller are accidentally crossed over, the system runs away.

DIAGRAM 10

An Ultrastable System

The system is the same as that shown in Diagram 9, with one addition: a relay has been added which (by means of a switch) reverses the connection between the meter and the controller if the meter reading remains persistently too high or too low. This system will therefore correct itself even if the wires between the meter and the controller have been crossed over.

DIAGRAM 10 *continued*

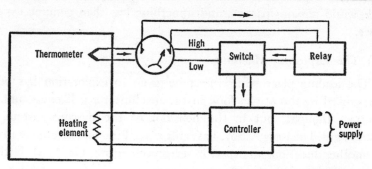

The relay could be designed to do more than simply trip the switch. For example, it could be made to explore different time lags and different control ratios between the meter and the controller. In an ordinary thermostat (as shown in Diagram 9), if the controller follows the meter too closely, the temperature constantly oscillates between too high and too low, and the system is no longer stable. Here, however, the relay would correct this: it makes the system ultrastable.

---

will often lose. But suppose we now put into the machine also a memory which counts its wins and losses, relates them to the moves chosen, and then steers the machine away from moves which lose repeatedly. By these means, the machine would learn in time (a long time) to keep away from losing lines and to choose winning lines. It would learn *habits*, not mere responses.

They would not be habits of perfection; as in the human player, they would be the empirical result of playing with people. Indeed, if the machine played constantly against bad players, it would learn some very poor habits—just as playing chess or tennis against inferior players teaches a human player bad habits, which are punished when he meets a good player.

In this way, we can visualize a machine which truly learns from experience. In its simplest form, of course, the learning procedure by trial-and-error is no more than the acquisition of a conditioned reflex. The machine learns to "associate" a stimulus, namely an opponent's move, with a result, namely win or loss. But our chess-learning machine adds to this an active element of exploration. For without deliberate exploration, what we or the machine get from the outside world remains passive, and something less than genuine experience.

iv) *The Exploring Machine*

The leading place which must be given to exploration has been recognized by those who look in the machine for a likeness, not to abstract thought, but to the behavior of the nervous system. A neurologist, Dr. Ross Ashby, has built a machine on these lines (and, in another direction, an expert in servomechanisms, Dr. A. M. Uttley, has studied the theory of similar processes). In this machine, exploration is the task not of one fixed process, but of many small elements of enquiry and decision. The machine has a large number of connections and internal paths, each with a simple "off or on," "yes or no" response. The task for the machine is to adapt itself to an "environment," that is to settle down under assigned conditions in a way which is stable. By this we mean, in the first place, that the machine shall change its state slightly when the environment changes slightly, and return when the environment returns.

The thermostat and the automatic pilot are stable in this sense, as Diagram 9 shows; and so far, Dr. Ashby's machine may seem to do no more than they do, except that it finds its own stable states. When the conditions for the machine are set, it runs through many possible adjustments and connections quickly, in a random sequence, its elements blinking "off or on" decisively at each attempt until it reaches a stable state. Its random connections have joined up to find and hold a path which remains stable under small changes in the environment.

But the machine does not stop there. It also explores large changes in its (external or internal) environment, under which its first state may no longer be stable; and it will then run through its connections to find a new stable state. Thus the machine has the ability to reach and hold states which are stable in a much wider sense. The thermostat and the automatic pilot cannot follow excessive and gross changes; but Dr. Ashby's machine is ultrastable and can find a new stable state even after wrong wiring or injury. Diagram 10 shows, in its simplest form, the principle which makes this possible. In the actual machine it is achieved, as it may be in the nervous system, by having many small units or paths (cells in the brain, nerves in the body) whose connections are not rigid, but are run through on a system of probabilities, and so maintain a constant internal exploration.

v) *Adaptation and Logic*

Let me summarize the ideas of this chapter. Its central question is, What is there in good thinking which is not logical deduction? A logical machine, such as UNIVAC, cannot improvise; it cannot, of itself, learn to change. That is, it cannot look ahead and adapt its processes to its goal. These are the deeper components of the exploring mind. Can a machine be made to show such adaptation?

In order that a machine may adapt itself to a changing environment or task, it must do two things. It must explore the different actions open to it. And it must feed back into itself the results of its efforts, so that it may choose the most successful. The second of these skills is not peculiar to adaptive machines; in essence, it exists in a logical machine, if the latter can follow alternative strategies. Many simple machines keep themselves adjusted to change by such feeding back: I have quoted the thermostat and the automatic pilot. In short, those are only reflex actions; they bear no semblance to thinking.

If the machine is to do more than, as it were, jump when it is pinched, it must give the largest place to exploration. It must have many choices built into it at each of its steps. It need not be made to test them all, or to follow to the end the consequences of those it tries: neither a man nor a machine would ever make a move at chess if this were demanded. On the contrary, there must be built into the machine a mechanism which makes it take chances. For, above all, the machine must not haver. It should be built up of units which take decisive steps, off or on, yes or no, with no crisis of indecision.

It has been shown that such machines can be designed to adapt themselves to change, and their behavior will remain internally stable. More, they can do what no machine has done before: they can adapt themselves to injury. I have seen Dr. Ross Ashby remove the wiring from his odd machine, leave out some and connect the rest at random. The machine balked, but it worked; after a few minutes, the machine pointer was again following the environment pointer.

Such machines imitate animal behavior: instinct, reflex and adaptation. They remind us that we once learned some anatomy from the pulley and the lever, and that we now have something to learn about nerves and brain from the electric switch.

It may seem perverse to ask of machines, What is thought? The question seems to turn nature upside down, as Jonathan Swift tried to turn it upside down in that terrible close to *Gulliver's Travels* in which only the animals are noble and logical, and the men are brutalized by desire and irrationality. Yet Swift was trying to analyze the complex countercurrents of the human character; and our question also is an attempt to see two facets of the mind. Pascal, who invented the first calculating machine, called man "a reed, but a thinking reed"; and put into that phrase Swift's contradiction, that man is ennobled above his weakness only by his mind. But as Pascal also remarked, the mind is not a calculating machine. We do not think only in logic; and man does not become irrational when his thought moves outside deductive logic.

There is an activity of thought in the mind, an imaginative activity, which explores and puts together unforeseen likenesses. So far as we can now see, it is not imitated either by the logical machine or by the adaptive machine. But their conjunction has taken us two steps toward it; and we must now prepare to take the third step.

4. Strategy and Its Safeguards

I began with situations (in a game, or an economic or strategic problem) in which the choice before us was clear cut. There were several alternatives, the consequence of each of which was (in theory) exactly foreseeable. One (or some) of these alternatives had more advantageous consequences than all the rest. The right strategy was therefore a matter of calculation, followed by the choice of the alternative which calculation had proved to be best.

Since then, we have by degrees moved into situations which are not so starkly black and white. The reach of calculation has become shorter, and we have had to venture beyond its limits and to take chances. Words like "chance" and "random" have begun to appear in my description of the machines themselves; in situations of such limited foresight, the machine or procedure can neither explore nor decide infallibly.

But to stop there would be to encourage a very dubious belief, the belief that "chance" and "probability" are words only for our present ignorance. It is certainly true that we have to introduce the idea of "chance" at the point where our foresight meets a check, and exact calculation can advance no further. But we must not suppose that this breakdown is our fault, and that a more penetrating eye might see to the end, and a more patient machine might calculate beyond probability to certainty. This was indeed believed by scientists in the last century, almost as an article of faith; and they looked on science as a continuous refinement of calculations which, at any given time, were limited only by practical and temporary blocks. But the present century has shown that this belief is out of keeping with some known facts (in atomic physics, for example, and more remotely in mathematical logic). We must believe that probability is not a fiction which will shrink from generation to generation until it vanishes, but is in places an irremovable element in the formulation of scientific laws.

i) *Games Based on Chance*

It would therefore be wrong to let our analysis rest at machines whose reach or foresight is limited simply by practical difficulties— the difficulty, in practice, of calculating the exact run of a set of billiard balls, or of seeing fully more than five or six moves ahead in a game of chess. For we also face, in life and in science, situations in which decision by calculation, in the classical manner, is not merely difficult but is essentially impossible; and where, nevertheless, decisions have to be made.

The obvious examples are games of chance—obvious, and by no means negligible. The theory of probability, and with it all actuarial and insurance work, as well as much genetics and atomic physics, spring from the inquiry of gamblers. Galileo first solved a problem on the fall of dice for an Italian nobleman; and a French noble, the Chevalier de Méré, put to Pascal a more difficult question on gamblers' stakes which set mathematicians thinking about probability.

Suppose, then, we begin with a game based on the simplest

chance: a game in which you toss a silver dollar, and I call "heads" or "tails." I want to make this a fair game, and since I believe that I am free to call "heads" or "tails" as I choose, I will leave you equally free to control the fall of the dollar, by any sleight of hand you have. You can therefore make your dollar come down "heads" or "tails," as you choose. Then what is your best strategy, and what is mine?

Your best strategy is *not* to use the choice you have, but let the dollar fall as it chooses, with no influence from you. For suppose you make your throws follow some system; suppose you throw more "heads" than "tails," or now and again throw runs of "heads" and runs of "tails." By analyzing the sequence of "heads" and "tails" you throw, I shall discover your system, and shall call more "heads" myself, or (in the second case) call "heads" and "tails" in runs; and I shall then win.

In the same way, if I initially have any bias in my calling (and most people have), you will detect it and exploit it, and I shall lose. That is, my best strategy also is to call at random and not in any orderly way. In fact, if I am wise, I will keep a dollar of my own behind my back and call according to its (undetectable) whims, rather than risk my own more transparent ones.

This may seem a trifling example and the strategy self-evident. Yet, in fact, it contains many hidden assumptions, and the strategy depends on these. For instance, you and I have naturally assumed that when I call right, I win, and always win a dollar; and if I call wrong, you win a dollar. If we vary these conditions (for instance, if we give bonuses for runs of right or wrong calls), our strategies will have to be changed.

Let me illustrate this. Suppose I still get a dollar when I call right; but when I call wrong, I pay a dollar and a half if my call was "heads," and only 50 cents if I called "tails." This does not look like a very different game, and may even strike you as fair. But it is not fair; this is a game at which (with average luck) I can win money. By what strategy?

It is of course obvious that my strategy should be to call "tails" more often than "heads," since this reduces my risk of loss. How much more often? The answer is that my best strategy is, in any eight calls, to call on the average five "tails" and three "heads." If you cautiously toss all "tails," then my eight calls will give me a profit of 50 cents; and if you boldly toss all "heads," I still make a profit of 50 cents. So it does not matter what mixture of "heads" and "tails" you choose to throw, and in what proportions, I will (except for bad luck) average 50 cents profit on any eight calls.

I said that I must call five "tails" and three "heads" *on the average;* and this is important. I must still be scrupulous not to have any order or system in my calling; you must never know what I am going to call next. I must call "heads" and "tails" by chance, only arranging that the chances now are not equal but are three to five. For example, I must not call steadily in groups of eight calls, in such a way that there are exactly five "tails" and three "heads" in each group. For if I did this, you would always know what my eighth call was to be (and sometimes the seventh, sixth, fifth, and even fourth as well); and since this knowledge would allow you at the least to win 50 cents on the eighth call, the game would turn from a win for me into a win for you.

ii) *Larger Choices*

We need not confine the choice of calls or moves, or of strategies, to two. In principle, any game (most simply between two players) in which the loser pays the winner, has a best strategy of this mixed kind. If the game is so dull as to be fair, this strategy at least assures its user (with average luck) that he will not lose.

As an example, Diagram 11 shows a simple form of the Finger Game. This is an elegant and difficult game which does not even require a box of matches, and it is recommended to all. As Diagram 11 shows, the best strategy is unexpected, and hardly likely to be guessed by an unmathematical player.

iii) *Minimax Strategy*

The reasoning which lies behind these mixed strategies is straightforward. I scrutinize each of my lines of play or strategies and every possible mixture of them. Against each I write the *maximum* loss which you might inflict on me, if you knew in advance that this was to be my general strategy. Then I choose that mixture which *minimizes my possible maximum loss.* This is the best strategy for me;

DIAGRAM 11

The Finger Game

The two players move simultaneously. Each shows either one or two fingers, and at the same time guesses whether his opponent is showing one or two fingers. If both players guess right, or both guess wrong, no one pays. If only one player guesses right, he wins from the other as many dollars as the two players together showed fingers.

Thus each player has the choice of four courses:

    (a) to show 1 finger   and call 1,
    (b) to show 1 finger   and call 2,
    (c) to show 2 fingers   and call 1,
    (d) to show 2 fingers   and call 2.

If his call is right and his opponent's wrong, then course (a) will win two dollars, courses (b) and (c) will win three dollars, and course (d) will win four dollars.

The game is fair, but a player who knows the right strategy will (with average luck) win against one who does not. The right strategy is to ignore courses (a) and (d), and to play courses (b) and (c) in the ratio of 7:5. That is, the right strategy is,

in any 12 calls,
    show 1 finger   and call 2
on the average 7 times, and
    show 2 fingers   and call 1
on the average 5 times.

This strategy is unlikely to be guessed by a gambler who plays hunches.

---

and if the game happens to be biased in my favor, my loss on this strategy will actually be fictitious—it will be a gain.

This principle, of minimizing my maximum loss, or minimax, has wide application. (There is a parallel principle of maximizing my minimum gain, which is called similarly the maximin principle; but the two principles differ only formally.) It is useful in warlike, economic and even, in a sense, moral situations. It can be applied to all those problems of traffic control, production, provisioning and organization which are usually called (linear) program problems. At bottom, the principle is a principle of insurance, designed to minimize over-all risk where (and this is essential to our thought) it is impossible to foresee which of a number of alternative risks we may meet.

iv) *Scale of Values*

Yet the minimization of risk is itself a very limited approach to life; you might think it an old maid's approach. Why play "heads" and "tails" at a dollar a toss at all if I am instantly going to retreat into a safety play which will ensure me a cautious 50 cents average every eight throws? This question is not foolish, but it does not go to the root of the matter. If I am playing to win money, and every cent equally is money to me, then the minimax strategy I have given is incontrovertibly the best. If you find it deficient, that is because there is in your mind some other reason for our playing, some value which is not measured in equal cents. If this is so, it is no use our calculating in cents; we ought to look at the possible wins and losses of the game again, in terms of the values which really underlie our interest. We ought to attach a special pleasure value to wins against the odds, if that is what we feel; or if small sums do not interest us, we ought to write them off in an appropriate scale. Provided the losses of one of us still become the gains of the other, we can revalue the game, and find the best strategy on this scale of values. It will be a minimax strategy, but so far as is possible, it will yield the satisfactions which really underlie our game—occasional long-shot wins, or big gains, or whatever we really think we play for.

In short, when we criticize the result of a minimax policy, our dissatisfaction is not with the arithmetic or even, at bottom, with the principle; it is with the scale of values on which we marked the wins and losses. You cannot in the end get sensible answers, even in economics, unless you consider the meaning of the values which are to be exchanged: for example, whether the marginal dollar really means as much to you as the first dollar you earned. No theory of science, and no theory of life, is complete until it has looked at the underlying units with which we are working.

5. Organization and Information

I have for some time been using words like "chance" and "random," and have contrasted them with the ideas of a "system" and "order." This contrast is central to much of modern thought, in science and outside it, and I want to look at it closely.

i) *Signal and Noise*

Suppose that you are on the lookout for some definite signal or instruction—let us say that you are driving along a highway, and you are looking for a signpost which will tell you where to turn off it. This signal usually has a certain strength; that is, at dusk, when you drive home, you can usually see the signpost when it is two hundred yards away. At this distance, you are in no danger of missing the signpost. You do run this danger, progressively, as the strength of the signal drops, that is, as the early evening light grows fainter. (If the signal strength becomes too weak, you will have to increase it by adding to the light reflected from the signpost; you must turn on your headlights.)

This may seem to be the only danger: that the signal will be too weak to be *seen* in time. But the first time that there is fog about, you realize that there is a second danger: the danger that the signal does not make sense, because the signpost is not *recognizable* in time. Because of the fog, you may have left for home in good daylight, in which the signpost would otherwise be visible for miles. The light is now scattered by the fog, but even so, there is as much at two hundred yards from any object as there usually is at dusk. Yet you cannot see the signpost at two hundred yards, because the irregular scattered light blurs the outline of things and loses them in the general haze.

The orderly or systematic shape that you are looking for, the signpost or signal, has been swamped by the random scattered light. The absolute strength of the signal is still great enough, but its strength *relative to the background* of disorderly scattered light is no longer enough to distinguish signal from background.

The situation is not improved by adding to the total light, because this amplifies the background as well as the signal, and does not improve their relative strength. You do not, in fact, see better in a fog by turning on your headlights; you see worse. To see better in a fog, you should cut down the total light which reaches you; you should wear dark glasses. Drivers of automobiles often think this incredible, because it diminishes the light which can reach them from the signpost they are looking for. It does; but it also cuts down the scattered light, and in doing so it can improve the receiver's response to the ratio of signal to background, and make the signpost distinguishable.

The state of affairs which I have been describing is universal. Light is scattered more in a fog, but it is scattered always. (Since blue light scatters more than red, the sky looks blue; as John Tyndall said, "we live *in* the sky, not under it.") There is a random background to everything we do, and whatever sense we are using. When we listen to talk, to the radio, on the telephone, we have to filter what is meaningful, the signal from the background noise. Indeed, this is so general an example that all background scatter is often called "noise," and the relative signal strength to background scatter is simply called the signal-to-noise ratio.

And this distinction, between signal and noise or background, between the systematic and the randomly scattered, between the steady trend and the fluctuating variations, underlies all our actions and, with them, our machines and devices.

ii) *The Noisy Line*

In the presence of irregular noise, a signal can never be read without ambiguity: even if it happens to have reached us with no distortion, as it were through a gap in the noise, we do not know this at the time. Nor can we grow certain of the signal by having it confirmed; for however often it is repeated, there remains the lingering doubt that noise has by chance played the same trick each time, and again turned into "yes" a signal which was meant to say "no."

We cannot be certain of the signal, by repetition or other means; and yet, we can be *certain enough*. This is an important idea in science as in practical life. We accept a signal for what it intends and act on the instruction it carries, at something short of certainty. The shortfall is a measure of the risk we take, and must take, if we are to act at all. If the action is critical, we can reduce the risk by stipulating a greater confirmation, and therefore a smaller shortfall. But some shortfall we must fix on and accept. Even a thermostat or an automatic pilot will not work if we ask it to reach perfect equilibrium; for then its oscillations, as it hunts for perfection, will always take it into an unstable tremor. To be stable, the machine must have some roughness or tolerance: it must accept as equilibrium all states which fall short of it by not more than some chosen margin.

What is true of a single signal is true of a sequence or message. Consider a sequence of symbols sent over a telegraph line in one minute, or punched along one foot of tape; and suppose that this sequence carries an amount of instruction or information I. The message, however, suffers some distortion: there is noise on the line, or the tape reader makes occasional errors. As a result, an amount of information i is lost, and only

$$I - i$$

is effective. This effective amount $I - i$ can sometimes be increased (per minute or foot) by choosing a better system of arranging or coding the message; thus the possible systems will determine a

$$\text{maximum of } (I - i),$$

which is the absolute capacity of the noisy line per minute, or of the tape reader per foot of tape.

But this capacity,

$$\text{maximum of } (I - i),$$

can only be approached; it cannot in general be reached. For what do we mean when we say that the amount of information i has been lost? We mean that a man who knew both the message and the errors would have to provide an amount of information i in order to correct the errors. But he would have to provide it directly, as it were in person; he could not send it along the same line, or through the same tape reader, without further loss.

Once again, in the presence of noise, we cannot expect to reach the absolute capacity of the line, without errors. All that we can do is to make the average number of errors (per minute or foot) smaller than some acceptable tolerance.

iii) *Redundancy*

One way of reducing the surviving errors is to repeat the signal. So telegraph companies usually repeat numbers and names; and the sender himself repeats critical words, for (as he would explain) he does not, repeat not, want to risk a misunderstanding. In the same way, the instruction tape shown in Diagram 5 uses for its basic symbols not single holes but pairs of holes. The machine stops if it meets a single hole, and this is a safeguard against errors made in punching the tape.

Repeating a signal is appropriate when, as in these cases, it largely stands apart from the rest of the message. More often, the symbols or parts that make up a message are linked among themselves. This linking makes the symbols partly redundant and thereby provides a check on the accuracy of the message as it is received.

For this reason, every code has some overlap or redundancy. That is, its symbols do not all add their full weight of instruction, and instead they add confirmation. The letter "u" after "q" in English is entirely redundant; the letter "h" after "w" often is; and so are many doubled letters. We could write most words (as Bernard Shaw wanted us to do) unmistakably with fewer letters, and most sentences in fewer words. But what we would gain in paper we should lose in internal confirmation.

Redundancy is itself a loss of information: we are packing less into a minute or a foot than we could with the same symbols. We try to make this voluntary loss match (on the average) the loss imposed by the expected noise. We can in fact approach the absolute capacity of a line, to any tolerance we fix, by putting our messages in a code whose redundancies are appropriate to the form of noise. The redundancies then show up, and allow us to correct, all but an acceptable proportion of the errors. That is: redundancy gives the code a structure or skeleton, which resists the distortion of its individual symbols.

iv) *Information in a System*

When we say that a message carries information, we mean that it gives instruction; for example, it may be punched on a tape and tell a machine what to do. (In the same way, some philosophers hold that the meaning of a word or phrase must be defined as its use—the instructions which it gives and the contexts in which it does so.) Therefore the information lies not in this message or that, but in the whole system or code of instructions. The information lies in the totality of messages which the system can form.

In some sense, then, the information in the system or code can be measured by the number of messages which it can form (say, per foot of tape). It is convenient to count this number not directly, but in multiples of two. That is, we say that the information is increased by one unit when the system is made able to form twice as many different messages (per foot of tape). The reason for choosing this scale (a logarithmic scale) can be seen by looking at Diagram 2. The counter shown there is in effect a simple device for forming messages, in a code of 0's and 1's (or dots and dashes). When it has two circuits or units, it can form four messages; when a third circuit is added, it can form eight; and each unit which is added doubles the number of messages again.

The number of possible messages is a measure of information, in this way, when all are formed equally often. But most systems use some symbols and form some messages more often than others; and allowance must be made for this. We ought to count, not the totality of messages, but the totality of choices open to us among them.

v) *Information and Entropy*

How does any one message contribute to the total of information? Not by its length and not by its ingenuity, but by its *scarcity*. A message which occurs again and again is expected; it tells us little that we did not anticipate, and like the words "the" and "which," it adds little that is specific to the instruction. By contrast, a message which occurs seldom, such as an SOS, tells us something unexpected and new and is highly specific in its call for action.

If the relative frequency of these two messages is p_1 and p_2, their scarcity is $1/p_1$ and $1/p_2$; so that, on the logarithmic scale which we have proposed, their information contents are $\log 1/p_1$ and $\log 1/p_2$ (where the logarithms are calculated to the base 2). In any foot of tape, however, there will be (on the average) p_1 messages of the first kind for every p_2 messages of the second. Hence the information contributed by the two kinds of message is

$$p_1 \log 1/p_1 + p_2 \log 1/p_2.$$

Similarly, if there are n possible messages in all, whose relative frequencies are

$$p_1, p_2, \ldots, p_j, \ldots, p_n,$$

we measure the information I in the code or system (per average foot) by

$$p_1 \log 1/p_1 + p_2 \log 1/p_2 + \ldots + p_j \log 1/p_j + \ldots + p_n \log 1/p_n.$$

This formula agrees with the measure we proposed when the messages were all equally frequent. For example, for the counter shown in Diagram 2, there are four equally frequent messages; that is,

$$p_1 = p_2 = p_3 = p_4 = \tfrac{1}{4},$$

so that

$$\log 1/p_1 = \log 1/p_2 = \log 1/p_3 = \log 1/p_4 = 2,$$

and the amount of information

$$p_1, \log 1/p_1 + p_2 \log 1/p_2 + p_3 \log 1/p_3 + p_4 \log 1/p_4$$

is 2 units.

The formula for the amount of information I is precisely that for the *entropy* of a physical system which can occupy n possible states (with the relative frequencies given). The more nearly equal are the frequencies, the larger is the information or entropy, and the smaller the redundancy; and (in a physical system) the less useful energy can be drawn from the system. Thus entropy is, in a sense, the opposite of available energy—as I remarked at the outset that information is the complement to energy. For example, the Second Law of Thermodynamics states that the entropy of a closed physical system always increases; and this means that in any self-contained part of the universe, the available energy is running down.

vi) *Organization in a Code*

I have not given these formulae because they have an interest in themselves; they have not, and even their practical usefulness is small. Their real interest derives from the quantities which occur in them and from the way these are put together.

The quantities are frequencies, and they bring home to us that the organization of a code is statistical. This was clear when the redundancies of the code were designed to combat irregular noise. But even in the absence of noise, the code (to approach the capacity of the line) must be statistically appropriate; it must match the relative frequencies of the instructions which will be sent. The everyday messages must be short and the rare messages long, so that the information in each foot or minute remains as near its average as possible.

For this reason, expressive codes move away from a mass of special symbols (some with a small, some with a large content) toward a few simple symbols which carry information by their arrangement. This is the progress of written language from hieroglyphics or ideograms to letters, and from letters to Morse's code of dots and dashes. The writing of numbers first in Roman numerals, then in an "alphabet" of ten digits, and then only with the symbols "1" and "0," shows the same movement.

That is, the information rests in the arrangement. What we measure essentially is the organization of the messages—not the meaning of individual symbols, but the structure of the whole. This is the most important thought in the theory of information. In whatever way we seek or exchange information about the world, we do not seize its underlying units themselves: what we learn is always about their organization. When in science, or in life, we analyze experience into parts, the meaning that we reach for lies not in the parts but in the structures which they form.

6. The Logic of Science

I closed my description of machines by saying that they mimic two gifts of the mind, deduction and exploration; but that, so far as we can see, there remains a third gift still to be understood. Since then, I have been laying out the tools for this understanding. It is time that we come to grips with it.

i) *Insight and Foresight*

When we watch a subtle act of anticipation, on the football field or in the design of an experiment, what strikes us is its individuality. It is neither a deduction nor a habit but something more unexpected than either; it belongs, in an exact way, to the man and the situation. The man has grasped the situation, has seen into it and solved it, by an act that goes to its heart.

That is our feeling, and it plainly appreciates something important. Men do not act only in ways which have already been used. They invent; they make a new interpretation of events. And the methods which they invent are based on their interpretation.

All living things act to anticipate the future; this is what chiefly distinguishes them from lifeless things. But not all methods of foresight are the same. Man has evolved a foresight based on the *interpretation* of events. He seeks to anticipate the future, not merely by responding to the present, but by understanding it. This is his characteristic method, the method of foresight based on insight; and he uses it systematically in science.

ii) *Likeness*

We are all aware of this special approach to foresight, which makes the difference between a stampede and a gale warning, between a homing pigeon and a guided missile. We know what we mean when we say that someone proceeds by seeing into and understanding events. Yet how does he proceed? What tools has he for looking below the bare happening, to reveal something which seems more universal?

Man has only one means to discovery, and that is to find *likenesses* between things. To him, two trees are like two shouts and like two parents, and on this likeness he has built all mathematics. A lizard is like a bat and like a man, and on such likenesses he has built the theory of evolution and all biology. A gas behaves like a jostle of billiard balls, and on this and on kindred likenesses rests much of our atomic picture of matter.

In looking for intelligibility in the world, we look for unity; and we find this (in the arts as well as in science) in its unexpected likenesses. This indeed is man's creative gift, to find or make a likeness where none was seen before—a likeness between mass and energy, a link between time and space, an echo of all our fears in the passion of Othello.

So, when we say that we can explain a process, we mean that we have mapped it in the likeness of another process which we know to work. We say that a metal crystal stretches because its layers slide over one another like cards in a pack, and then that some polyester yarns stretch and harden like a metal crystal. That is, we take from the world round us a few models of structure and process (the particle, the wave, and so on), and when we research into nature, we try to fit her with these models.

iii) *Analysis into Units*

Yet one powerful procedure in research, we know, is to break down complex events into simpler parts. Are we not looking for the understanding of nature in these? When we probe below the surface of things, are we not trying, step by step, to reach to her ultimate and fundamental constituents?

We do indeed find it helpful to work piecemeal. We take a sequence of events or an assembly to pieces: we look for the steps in a chemical reaction, we carve up the study of an animal into organs and cells and smaller units within a cell. This is our atomic approach, which tries always to see in the variety of nature different assemblies from a few basic units. Our search is for simplicity, in that the distinct units shall be few, and all units of one kind identical.

And what distinguishes one assembly of these units from another? the elephant from the giraffe, or the right-handed molecule of sugar from the left-handed? The difference is in the organization of the units into the whole; the difference is in the structure. And the likenesses for which we look also are likenesses of structure.

This is the true purpose of the analytic method in science: to shift our gaze from the thing or event to its structure. We understand a process, we explain it, when we lay bare in it a structure which is like one which we have met elsewhere.

iv) *Finding the Units*

This method at once recalls my description of the theory of information: the different assemblies are, as it were, different messages constructed from the same alphabet of units. And the analogy would be convenient, but for one defect, which is critical. In science, we do not know the units in which the "messages" are written. We have to find them.

Leibniz long ago described the procedure of science as like the solving of a cryptogram; and this is a deep and an exact remark. In a scientific research, we have to do the opposite to transmitting information, so that we have to turn the theory of information backward. Instead of sending messages in a known code, we receive messages in an unknown code. The aim of science is to break the code of nature.

This is evident in any practical example. One of the characteristics of science is that it tries to put its descriptions of nature in a mathematical form. Mathematical formulae, of course, display the arrangement of coded messages most clearly. Thus when Isaac Newton in 1687 formally set out the laws of motion, he was (in the language which I have been using) writing the basic messages of which all mechanics is a rearrangement. And such a message as

$$F = m \times f$$

(applied force equals mass times the resulting acceleration) does not arrive from nature ready-made. On the contrary, it has to be puzzled out from an apparently meaningless multiplicity of everyday observations and experiments, and the puzzle is to find the units which matter within these. Newton's genius was precisely this, that he disentangled the units and showed that the observations made sense if they were expressed in them. He set out what was happening in terms of force and mass and acceleration, and for this purpose he and those who had come just before him (particularly Galileo, who died in the year 1642 in which Newton was born) had to invent such concepts as force and mass.

What is mass? Newton did not really define it, and even now, when the general theory of relativity has healed a great duality (between inertial mass and gravitational mass, that is roughly between mass and weight), we are still remote from understanding the nature of mass. What is force? The theory of relativity has undermined the concept of force altogether, but even before this, its standing had been uncertain. And in fact, the concepts of mass and force were never independent, but defined one another indirectly by the formula I have just written, in which only the acceleration f is fairly directly measurable.

In short, mass and force are not in any definable sense real entities, discovered by turning a microscope on nature, and there seen manifestly to cause her behavior. They are concepts whose isolation makes the behavior of nature orderly. In discovering these concepts, Galileo and Newton were not making a statement of fact. They were finding units of a code, an alphabet in which mechanics could be written coherently and consistently. The formula I have written is one of its basic messages, and what is important in it is not the fact but the discovery of the code.

v) *The Implication of a Code*

We can see the same thought at work, the search for the key to a cryptogram, wherever a science has had to go forward to frame a new concept. John Dalton worked in the same way when, in 1808, he proposed that chemical action is a linking of atoms with atoms. So did Louis Pasteur when, in 1848, he related some chemical differences to the right-handed or left-handed structure of crystals. Such discoveries as the benzene ring, the electron, and insulin, all followed the same thought. Diagram 12 shows in outline a characteristic progression of decoding in science, and the new concepts implied at each step.

DIAGRAM 12 _____

Scientific Theories as Decoding

The action of what was then called oil of vitriol on common salt was known to Dr. Johann Rudolf Glauber in 1648. But only in the last century did this and other chemical reactions fall into place, and become a connected system of messages, by being written out in their elements:

$$H_2SO_4 + 2NaCl \rightarrow Na_2SO_4 + 2HCl.$$

The units or symbols in this code are the (concepts of the) atoms of the 92 natural elements.

Next, chemists began to ask why S is so often coupled with O_4, and why the letter H moves about in so many of these messages. This is the familiar step in decoding which counts the frequencies of letters and groups. Here it leads to the theory of valency and the concept of chemical bonds.

By analyzing in the same way sentences in which physicists record their experiments, we group these bonds round new concepts: the physical atoms. At this stage, each atom has a nucleus round which are arranged electrons in shells. Thus the symbols H and O and S are being further broken up, each into an unknown nucleus and a characteristic (atomic) number of electrons.

Since 1932, the nucleus in turn has been analyzed into unit concepts —the proton and the neutron. Thus all atomic and nuclear reactions are written (in their essential skeletons) in a four-symbol code: e^- for the ordinary electron, e^+ for the positive electron, p^+ for the proton and n for the neutron. When letters H, O and so on are still retained for the elements and their isotopes, it is merely as familiar and useful contractions.

For example, one of the two processes by which hydrogen is fused

DIAGRAM 12 *continued* ─────────────────────────

to form helium in the sun, in three steps, is written (in its essential skeleton),

$$p^+ + p^+ \rightarrow (p^+n) + e^+,$$
$$(p^+n) + p^+ \rightarrow (p^+p^+n),$$
$$(p^+p^+n) + (p^+p^+n) \rightarrow (p^+p^+nn) + p^+ + p^+;$$

in which (p^+n) is a heavy isotope of the hydrogen nucleus, and (p^+p^+n) and (p^+p^+nn) are two isotopes of helium.

So, step by step, the concepts or units in the code of nature grow fewer, and her meaning is carried by their arrangement.

───

vi) *The Use of Experiments*

Plainly it is stimulating to think of the discovery of new scientific concepts thus, as the unraveling of a coded puzzle. But we naturally ask, how do we set about it? What procedure have we which will ensure that we find the code?

The answer is, none. As in all cryptography, there is no process which is certain to break the code. But as in all cryptography, there are systematic methods which are likely to help. In science, there is one most powerful method: we can add to the stock of coded messages on which we have to work, by doing further experiments. This method is seldom open to the cryptographer, and never to the historian; they have to take the messages they have, and be thankful.

The sciences, however, do not have to make do with the observations of nature as they come. They are able to ask questions of nature, to which she replies in the same code. That is, they can do experiments, and add the new results to the observations they already have. They can do this even in so inaccessible a subject as astronomy, if they think out their experiments on earth appropriately. Christian Doppler in 1842 learned from the whistle of a locomotive that a receding star should also change the pitch or wave length of its light. And today the big nuclear accelerators (and the big calculating machines) are used to see whether our theories of the evolution of the stars fit and hold together.

For the strength of the scientist is that he can choose the experiments he makes. Like a cryptographer who has captured an enemy agent, he can send searching signals which are designed to evoke simple and decisive answers. This is the function of the well-planned experiment: to isolate one possible concept from the rest, and thus to get results which establish decisively that one unit or symbol enters in the messages of nature in a specific way.

Experiments, then, are questions which we put to nature in order to add to the stock of messages from which we must decipher her code. But since we can choose the questions, we can design them to get particularly simple replies, which make the task of decoding less haphazard. This is why the experimental sciences have been so much more successful in finding unifying concepts and results than have other human speculations.

vii) *The Test of Induction*

The theory of information is like the logic of deduction: it begins from accepted general principles, and can then go forward step by step, with no false starts and returns. But the discovery of scientific concepts turns the processes of information backwards, as induction turns deduction backwards; and like induction, it is not unique. It is in fact an extension of induction.

Induction is the process of generalizing from our known and limited experience, and framing wider rules for the future than we have been able to test fully. At its simplest, then, an induction is a habit or an adaptation—the habit of expecting tomorrow's weather to be like today's, the adaptation to the unwritten conventions of community life. All our conscious acts are based on such inductions, uncertain but indispensable; and most justifications of induction are content with such piecemeal habits.

But the striking feature of your behavior or mine is that it is not piecemeal: it is of a piece, it makes a coherent personality, it is linked and organized within. It is based on concepts of nature and of conduct which have been formed not only by habit but by interpretation. Induction in animals may be nothing but habit, which anticipates the future mechanically as a copy of the past. But human beings base their foresight on understanding, that is (we now see) on forming concepts and joining them into structures which are simple models of the world.

In intelligent human behavior, therefore, the test of induction is not simply whether it accords with past experience. Many alternative ways of expecting the future will do that; induction is never unique. How are we to choose among these alternatives, each of which will equally fit what has happened in the past?

In my view, we choose the alternative which best organizes our total experience. Let me put this precisely, and for this purpose let me return to scientific rather than everyday behavior. We have, then, a collection of facts or experiments, by which I mean processes with known results. We think of each of these as a message which goes forward in time, from left to right, saying what we start with and what then happens. These messages are in an unknown code. We propose a code and examine the messages. Some of them now are implied by the remainder and say nothing new; we discard these. The rest form a system of basic messages assembled from the code symbols. We can measure the information content of these messages as

$$p_1 \log 1/p_1 + p_2 \log 1/p_2 + \ldots + p_j \log 1/p_j + \ldots + p_n \log 1/p_n,$$

as we learned to do for any messages made up of known symbols. The total content of information of the system of basic messages in this code can therefore be calculated.

Then if we have a choice of codes which otherwise accord equally well with our experience, we prefer the code which gives the highest content of information. We have, in fact, one object in looking for concepts in nature: to unify her, make her orderly and, in this sense, meaningful. Therefore the concepts or code symbols which we prefer are those which make our experience more orderly and connected than others. We try to maximize the meaning that we can find in nature.

viii) *Conclusion*

I have taken a wide survey of man's intelligent activity, specifically as it is displayed in the methods of science. It may seem odd to have done this by looking at machines and at games of strategy. My reason is that these mechanisms embody most clearly the formal procedures we know for looking toward the future.

The first of these procedures is that of deductive logic. It is seen in all calculating machines, which are today largely logical machines. They can give us new courage in tackling problems which are too complex for isolation and experiment, say in economics and social science. And their approach there is interesting, because it does not begin by making a simplified model of the process. It accepts all the data, and searches them for all correlations.

These logical machines can be made to run a chemical factory, to choose the winning move in a chess problem, to translate a simple text, to put together a reasonable debate or sonnet. This kind of machine has always fascinated men, long before it rode into the comic strips. When Charles Babbage in the 1830s was building his pioneer machine, complete with automatic instructions and memory (a hundred years before his time), the paleontologist Thomas Hawkins wrote that his friend John Clark had in mind another

> extraordinary machine which he was constructing:—one that makes Latin verses—no two alike—for ever, all of them quite grammatical and of pure sense.

Machines of this kind can be enlarged to explore alternative courses, to feed back the results of their actions, and accordingly to correct themselves. They can even be made to learn from this process, by incorporating the correction permanently into their program of action. But in doing so, the machine becomes more and more an adaptive rather than a deductive mechanism—a biological rather than a physical model, whose procession is more like that of evolution than like, say, a planetarium. This kind of machine is best made of many unit elements and circuits, with random connections, and with single on or off, yes or no decisions based on chance. It is particularly suited to exploring a changing environment and will of itself find adaptations which, while stable in the largest sense, respond delicately to small changes.

These two kinds of machine display two kinds of foresight. There remains, in my view, a third kind, which is characteristically human. This is the wish to base foresight on insight. It seeks to understand nature by looking for unifying and simplifying concepts. I have shown that, on this view, the processes of nature can be pictured as messages written in a code whose unit-symbols are unknown to us, and which are the concepts we seek. We can help our search by experiments which are planned to evoke decisive answers from nature. But there is no automatic procedure for breaking a code and no assurance that our way of deciphering it is unique. On the contrary, the displacement of one scientific theory by another shows that it is not. Nature is more intricately organized and cross-linked than our theories, so that each model or likeness that we try scores some striking successes and then falls short. All that we can do, at any state of our factual knowledge, is to prefer that code which makes what we know most orderly. That is, we choose those concepts which organize the messages of nature most coherently. We achieve this, in my view, by maximizing their content of information or meaning. This is the test for the inductions by which we try to generalize from our particular experience and to gain a basis for foresight.

Charles Darwin said sadly at the end of his life that

> my mind seems to have become a kind of machine for grinding general laws out of large collections of facts.

Darwin was too modest. If such a machine can indeed be made, we do not know how to make it. Indeed, we do not know anything like it, except a man. For the discovery of laws is a complex induction like the solving of a cryptogram which, so far as we know, a machine procedure can help but cannot complete. It depends on an imaginative act, seeing the structure of the solution in a likeness, and seizing a likeness where none was expected. This is the third gift of the mind.

Bibliography

ANTHROPOLOGY

GENERAL

1. Kroeber, A. L. *Anthropology*. New York: Harcourt, Brace, 1948.
   Not a textbook, but a treatise. Insofar as it can be done between the covers of a single book and by one man, Kroeber has synthesized the total theoretical and substantive content of anthropology.

2. Kroeber, A. L. (Editor). *Anthropology Today*. Chicago: University of Chicago Press, 1953.
   Fifty specialists survey the state of existing knowledge in most, but not all, of the principal fields. Many of the chapters are highly technical, but this is an authoritative compendium of present anthropological knowledge.

3. Beals, R. L. and Hoijer, H. *An Introduction to Anthropology*. New York: Macmillan, 1953.
   A reliable textbook.

4. Kluckhohn C. *Mirror for Man*. New York: McGraw Hill, 1949.
   A popular presentation of all branches of anthropology as they relate to contemporary intellectual and practical issues.

ARCHAEOLOGY

5. Howells, William, *Back of History*. New York: Doubleday and Company, 1954.
   Skillfully combines archaeology and physical and cultural anthropology, but the emphasis is archaeological. Unfortunately lacks a bibliography.

6. Coon, Carleton S. *The Story of Man*. New York: Alfred Knopf, 1954.

The best up-to-date and popular biography of mankind. A wider sweep than Howells' and richer in ideas.

7.   Childe, V. Gordon. *Social Evolution*. London: Watts and Company, 1951.

This book, by a foremost archaeologist, summarizes some of the main findings on Old World archaeology and relates them to the evolution of economy and social organization. Childe is a stimulating writer.

8.   Oakley, K. P. *Man the Tool-Maker*. London: British Museum, 1949.

Simple but careful discussion of the antiquity of man, the Paleolithic, and early technology.

9.   Clark, J. G. D. *Prehistoric Europe: The Economic Base*. New York: Philosophical Library, 1952.

A thoughtful and quite comprehensive volume.

10.   Brew, J. O. *Archaeology of Alkali Ridge, Southeastern Utah*. Papers of the Peabody Museum of Harvard University, 1946.

One of the best monographic studies of North American archaeology with incisive treatment of method and theory.

PHYSICAL ANTHROPOLOGY

11.   Hooton, E. A. *Up from the Ape*. New York: Macmillan, 1946.

A good general book on human evolution.

12.   Demerec, M. (Editor). *The Origin and Evolution of Man*. Cold Spring Harbor Symposia on Quantitative Biology, vol. 25, 1951.

Somewhat technical but authoritative papers by 37 European and American anthropologists and biologists. The best single source available on many aspects of biological anthropology.

13.   Boyd, W. C. *Genetics and the Races of Man*. Boston: Little, Brown and Co., 1950.

Racial anthropology from the standpoint of an immunologist and geneticist. Good material on methods, especially quantitative.

14.   La Barre, Weston. *The Human Animal*. Chicago: University of Chicago Press, 1954.

An introduction to human biology from the standpoint of a cultural anthropologist. Not altogether successful, it nevertheless provides what is otherwise lacking: a readable account of the intertwining of biology and culture.

CULTURAL ANTHROPOLOGY

15.   Kroeber, A. L. *Configurations of Culture Growth*. Berkeley: University of California Press, 1944.

The outstanding anthropological study of the great civilizations of the world. More modest in scope and in conclusions than Spengler, Sorokin and Toynbee, it is also better poised and more genuinely scientific.

16. Benedict, Ruth. *Patterns of Culture*. Boston: Houghton Mifflin, 1934.

A classical and readable introduction to cultural anthropology for the layman.

17. Firth, Raymond. *Elements of Social Organization*. London: Watts and Company, 1951.

A nontechnical treatment with excellent material on economics and art.

18. Linton, Ralph. *The Tree of Culture*. New York: Alfred A. Knopf, 1955.

A stimulating treatment of the culture history of the major areas of the world. Rich in picturesque detail, bold interpretation, and pleasant to read.

19. Howells, W. W. *The Heathens: Primitive Man and His Religions*. New York: Doubleday and Company, 1948.

A good book on primitive religion.

20. Redfield, Robert. *The Primitive World and Its Transformations*. Ithaca, New York: Cornell University Press, 1953.

A broad but pointed survey of some of the principal issues in cultural anthropology with particular stress upon values.

21. Honigmann, John. *Culture and Personality*. New York: Harper and Brothers, 1954.

A clear synthesis of this new and controversial field. Bibliography will lead the reader to the most important sources, whether books or articles in learned journals.

22. Barnett, H. G. *Innovation, The Basis of Cultural Change*. New York: McGraw Hill, 1953.

A profound study of the anthropological and psychological facts and principles relating to the acceptance or rejection of new things and practices.

23. Evans-Pritchard, E. E. *The Nuer*. Oxford: Oxford University Press, 1940.

The recommendation of a single tribal monograph is invidious. However, no reading list would be complete without at least one such basic work. This study of an African people is outstanding for its soundness of documentation, originality and readability.

24. Dyk, Walter. *Son of Old Man Hat*. New York: Harcourt, Brace, 1938.

It is also essential to get at least one full-bodied picture of the individual in his culture. This Navaho Indian autobiography has vividness and immediacy.

ANTHROPOLOGICAL LINGUISTICS

25. Sapir, Edward. *Language.* New York: Harcourt, Brace, 1921.

> This little book is dated in some technical respects, but its succinctness and the felicity of its style make it enduring. Both students and laymen will find it a pleasure to read.

26. Mandelbaum, David (Ed). *Selected Writings of Edward Sapir.* Berkeley: University of California Press, 1949.

> About one-half of this book consists of well-known papers on language by the greatest of anthropologicalinguists. The remainder of the volume deals with culture—with a psychological and literary emphasis.

27. Bloomfield, Leonard. *Language.* New York: Henry Holt, 1933.

> A standard and admirable textbook, although it lacks some important contributions of the past two decades. Behavioristic in standpoint.

MATHEMATICS AND LOGIC

1. Ball, W. W. Rouse. *Mathematical Recreations and Essays.* 11th edition. New York: Macmillan, 1939.

> Packed with information but arranged more as a handbook than for continuous reading. Indispensable for anyone interested in puzzles.

2. Bell, E. T. *Men of Mathematics.* New York: Simon and Schuster, 1937.

> A most enjoyable collection of biographical sketches of the leading mathematicians from Zeno to Poincaré.

3. Cohen, Morris, and Nagel, Ernest. *Introduction to Logic and Scientific Method.* New York: Harcourt, Brace, 1934.

> An admirable textbook requiring no previous training in mathematics and logic. It presents an excellent survey of logic, scientific method, probability and related topics and is thoroughly readable.

4. Hogben, Lancelot T. *Mathematics for the Million.* New York: W. W. Norton, 3rd edition, 1951.

> Not mathematics for the millions but a lively and stimulating survey for anyone prepared to use pad and pencil on the hard parts.

5. Hardy, G. H. *A Mathematician's Apology.* Cambridge: Cambridge University Press, 1941.

> A delightful volume of reminiscences by the late G. H. Hardy, one of the world's great mathematicians. He examines the nature of mathematics, explains why it is worth studying and explores the traits of mind of persons attracted to the subject. There is no other book quite like this one.

6. Jourdain, P. E. B. *The Nature of Mathematics*. London: T. C. and E. C. Jack, 1912, and New York: Dodge Publishing Company, 1912.

> A book of 90 pages, this is one of the best primers of mathematics ever published. Jourdain was a talented mathematician and logician. He had wit, a clear style and a genuine feeling for popularization. (Out of print but included in a new anthology of mathematical literature edited by James R. Newman and to be published in 1956 by Simon and Schuster.)

7. Kasner, Edward and Newman, James R. *Mathematics and the Imagination*. New York: Simon and Schuster, 1940.

> The only popular survey primarily concerned with the higher branches of mathematics, such as topology, theory of infinite classes, probability, non-Euclidean geometry, the calculus, and the foundations of mathematics.

8. Kline, Morris. *Mathematics in Western Culture*. New York: Oxford University Press, 1953.

> An exceptionally readable account of the contributions of mathematics to Western life and thought from the ancient Greeks to the present. Professor Kline is an interesting writer and a brilliant explainer of difficult mathematical ideas.

9. Titchmarsh, E. C. *Mathematics for the General Reader*. London: Hutchinson's University Library, 1950.

> A lucid, unhurried survey of the science of number, from arithmetic to algebra, trigonometry and the calculus. Rewarding even for the reader who is unable to follow every argument.

10. Smith, David Eugene and Ginsburg, Jekuthiel. *Numbers and Numerals*. New York: Teachers College, Columbia University, 1937.

> An authoritative, well-written, attractively illustrated pamphlet which tells the story of numbers, how they came into use, what the first crude numerals or number symbols meant "in the days when the world was young."

11. Sutton, O. G. *Mathematics in Action*. New York: Thomas Y. Crowell Company, 1955.

> The director of the British meteorological office, a foremost mathematician, presents a clear account of how mathematics is applied to various sciences: physics, astronomy, ballistics, aerodynamics, weather forecasting, astronomy, etc. It is a feat to cover this enormous field in two hundred-odd pages, but Sutton not only succeeds in accomplishing it but in explaining the rudiments of higher mathematics to readers without special training.

12. Tarski, Alfred. *Introduction to Logic*. New York: Oxford University Press, 1941.

> The best elementary book in English on symbolic logic. If Whittaker's essay has whetted the reader's appetite for more information on the subject he

is fortunate to be able to follow up with two such good books as Cohen and Nagel and this more specialized volume.

13. Whitehead, Alfred North. *Introduction to Mathematics*. New York: Oxford University Press, revised edition, 1948.

Whitehead's book has to a certain extent been superseded by other popularizations; but it is still worth reading and the flavor of Whitehead's personality confers distinction on every page.

14. Moroney, M. J. *Facts from Figures*. London: Penguin Books, 1951.

An able introduction to statistics for the serious reader. One can learn a great deal from Moroney's book, but one must be prepared to follow its mathematical reasoning which, though taught from the ground up in these pages, is not always easy.

15. Tippett, L. H. C. *Statistics*. New York: Oxford University Press, 1943.

This book in the Home University Library series affords a fine introduction to statistical reasoning, without the use of equations or symbols. Recommended for itself or as a less strenuous companion to Moroney.

ASTRONOMY AND COSMOLOGY

1. Hoyle, Fred. *The Nature of the Universe*. New York: Harper and Brothers, 1950.

A brief description of the modern view of astronomical subjects. Very easy to follow.

2. McCrea, W. H. *Physics of the Sun and Stars*. New York: Longmans, Green and Co., Inc., 1951.

An excellent introduction. Thorough, but almost wholly nonmathematical.

3. Johnson, Martin. *Astronomy of Stellar Energy and Decay*. London: Faber and Faber Limited, 1950.

An outline of facts and theories about the life history of the stars written with a fine appreciation of the problems involved. The book is divided into two parts, one for the general reader, one for the more advanced student.

4. Gamow, George. *The Birth and Death of the Sun*. New York: Viking Press, 1945. (Also in an inexpensive reprint in the New American Library series.) Also, *The Creation of the Universe*. New York: Viking Press, 1952.

These two books deal informally and agreeably with modern problems of astronomy. The first volume is primarily devoted to stellar evolution and is in a few places already out of date. The second is an absorbing presentation of relativistic cosmology.

5. Lemaître, Georges. *The Primeval Atom.* New York: D. Van Nostrand Company, Inc., 1950.

> The classic nonmathematical description of Canon Lemaître's hypothesis of the origin of the universe. A book of charm and fascination.

6. Payne-Gaposchkin, Cecilia. *Stars in the Making.* Cambridge: Harvard University Press, 1952.

> The Phillips Astronomer at Harvard presents a popular study of all the observational clues to the problem of stellar evolution. Dr. Gaposchkin is an admirable writer.

7. ———. *Introduction to Astronomy.* New York: Prentice-Hall, Inc., 1954.

> A superior primer of astronomy: up-to-date, authoritative, rich in historical and biographical details.

8. Struve, Otto. *Stellar Evolution.* Princeton: Princeton University Press, 1950.

> A penetrating but rather advanced study.

9. Menzel, Donald H. *Our Sun.* Philadelphia: Blakiston, 1949.

> An unencumbered discussion of surface phenomena on the sun (a subject not discussed in Dr. Bondi's essay), with a chapter on the interior of the sun.

10. Shapley, Harlow. *Galaxies.* Philadelphia: Blakiston, 1943.

> Dr. Shapley, one of the foremost living astronomers, is a lively writer. Here he gives a satisfying account of observational cosmology.

11. Hubble, Edwin. *The Realm of the Nebulae.* New Haven: Yale University Press, 1936.

> For the scientifically minded general reader, a skillful description of what is known about the nebulae. This book is slightly more technical and a little longer than Shapley's.

12. Bondi, Hermann. *Cosmology.* Cambridge: Cambridge University Press, 1952.

> Bondi's beautifully succinct description of modern cosmologies is difficult in parts, but the thoughtful reader need not stay away.

13. Whitrow, G. J. *The Structure of the Universe.* New York: Hutchinson's University Library, 1949.

> The emphasis of this interesting book is on the more philosophical problems of cosmology and on the historical aspects.

14. Eddington, Sir Arthur Stanley. *The Expanding Universe.* Cambridge: Cambridge University Press, 1933.

> This popular masterpiece is now slightly out of date but it is enormously readable and still worth reading. Both this book and Whitrow's were written

before the publication of the steady-state theory; these two, and Bondi's book, before the recent redetermination of the distances of the galaxies.

PHYSICS

1. Hecht, Selig. *Explaining the Atom*. (Revised and expanded by Eugene Rabinowitch.) New York: The Viking Press, 1954.

By far the best popular book on atomic energy, explaining with exceptional clarity the main features of atomic structure and behavior, the mechanics of fission and fusion, the future of atomic power. The late Selig Hecht was a brilliant biophysicist who felt deeply the social responsibilities of the scientist.

2. Eddington, Sir Arthur Stanley. *Space, Time and Gravitation*. Cambridge: Cambridge University Press, 1920.

Dated with respect to developments of nuclear physics and other advances of the last quarter century, this book by a leading 20th-century physicist and a master of popularization remains one of the classic accounts of relativity theory and how the new physics differs from the old. An enthralling volume, but not easy.

3. Taylor, Lloyd William. *Physics: The Pioneer Science*. New York: Houghton Mifflin, 1941.

An attractive text for a "liberalized course in general physics" at the first college level; rich in historical and biographical material.

4. Lemon, Harvey Brace. *From Galileo to the Nuclear Age*. Chicago: The University of Chicago Press, 1946.

A clear, entertaining introduction to physics. Fine illustrations.

5. Crowther, J. G. *British Scientists of the Twentieth Century*. London: Routledge and Kegan Paul Ltd., 1952.

Essays describing the lives and achievements of four of the foremost contributors to modern physics: J. J. Thomson, Lord Rutherford, Sir James Jeans, Sir Arthur Eddington. A thoughtful, interesting book by the leading British science journalist.

6. Einstein, Albert and Infeld, Leopold. *The Evolution of Physics*. New York: Simon and Schuster, 1938.

An able, popular account of the growth of ideas in physics, from the mechanical view of the universe to field theory, relativity and quanta. Not always easy to follow but worth the effort.

7. Frisch, Otto Robert. *Meet the Atoms*. New York: A. A. Wyn, 1947.

Dr. Frisch, a pioneer of nuclear research, provides a lively, well-paced, informal guide to the essential ideas of modern physics.

8. Durell, C. V. *Readable Relativity*. London: G. Bell and Sons Ltd., 1938.

> This book is an extraordinary achievement. Step by step, leaving behind no unanswered questions, Durell, using only the simplest algebra, explains the entire formidable apparatus of relativity, both the special and the general theory. If you remember any high-school algebra and want to gain an inkling of the mathematical reasoning underlying the most celebrated of modern scientific concepts, you will find this book an exciting intellectual adventure.

9. Dampier, Sir William Cecil. *A History of Science*. Cambridge: Cambridge University Press, 4th edition, revised and enlarged, 1949.

> The standard modern one-volume survey, wholly accessible to the thoughtful general reader. Dampier's history covers fully the evolution of physics—as well as the other sciences—and is particularly valuable in exhibiting the relations between science, philosophy and religion.

10. Sedgwick, W. T. and Tyler, H. W. (Revised by Tyler, H. W. and Bigelow, R. P.) *A Short History of Science*. New York: The Macmillan Company, 1939.

> Somewhat more elementary than Dampier's book and skimpy on the science of the 20th century, but a straightforward, readable history with many excellent illustrations.

11. Cajori, Florian. *A History of Physics*. New York: The Macmillan Company, revised edition, 1929.

> An authoritative work, succinct and not too difficult.

12. Millikan, Robert Andrews. *Electrons (+ and —), Protons, Photons, Neutrons, Mesotrons and Cosmic Rays*. Chicago: The University of Chicago Press, revised edition, 1947.

> A noted American scientist describes the development of atomic theory during the last 50 years. Interestingly written, comprehensive, accessible, in large part, to a wide audience.

13. Needham, Joseph and Pagel, William. *Background to Modern Science*. Cambridge: Cambridge University Press, 1938.

> Ten leading scientists explain in popular style the work that led to the scientific advances of recent times. Recommended especially for the essays on physics by Lord Rutherford, crystal physics by W. L. Bragg, atomic theory by F. W. Aston, astronomy by Sir Arthur Eddington.

CHEMISTRY

HISTORICAL AND CULTURAL

1. Read, J. *Humor and Humanism in Chemistry*. London: Bell, 1947.

A richly illustrated work of the historical type, with the underlying theme that "the study of chemistry, if approached befittingly, may reasonably take rank beside the humanities as a broadly educative, cultural and humanizing influence. . . ."

2.　————. *Prelude to Chemistry*. New York: Macmillan, 1937.

A work dealing with alchemy in its multifarious aspects, containing much original matter, and copiously illustrated.

3.　Partington, J. R. *A Short History of Chemistry*. London: Macmillan, 2nd edition, 1948.

A concise and authoritative account, well documented and containing many illustrations.

4.　Findlay, A., *Chemistry in the Service of Man*. London: Longmans, Green, 1947.

"Some account of what the science of chemistry, both in its general principles and in its industrial application has accomplished for the material well-being and uplifting of mankind." With illustrations.

5.　Jaffe, Bernard. *Crucibles: The Story of Chemistry, From Ancient Alchemy to Nuclear Fission*. New York: Simon and Schuster, Inc., revised edition, 1948.

A fine popular account of the growth of chemical knowledge told through the lives of the leading chemists from the 15th century to the present period.

6.　Friend, J. Newton. *Man and the Chemical Elements*. New York: Charles Scribner's Sons, 1953.

The story of the discovery of the various chemical elements: how they were sought out, by whom, the uses to which they have been put. A clear account with many diverting historical sidelights.

INORGANIC CHEMISTRY

7.　Findlay, A. *General and Inorganic Chemistry*. London: Methuen, 1953.

A volume in the Home Study Series, planned to provide new interpretations of modern knowledge for the layman.

PHYSICAL CHEMISTRY

8.　Goddard, F. W. and James E. J. F. *The Elements of Physical Chemistry*. London: Longmans, Green, 1954.

A clear, simple introduction to the subject.

ORGANIC CHEMISTRY

9. Read, J. *A Direct Entry to Organic Chemistry*. London: Methuen, 1948.

An excellent volume in the Home Study Series.

BIOCHEMISTRY

1. Bacon, J. S. D. *The Chemistry of Life: An Easy Outline of Biochemistry*. London: Watts and Co., 1944.

A popular, readable introduction.

2. Borek, Ernest. *Man the Chemical Machine*. New York: Columbia University Press, 1952.

This clear and authoritative book describes for the general reader some of the outstanding achievements of biochemistry.

3. Baldwin, Ernest. *An Introduction to Comparative Biochemistry*. Cambridge: Cambridge University Press, 1949.

A skillful, attractively written little volume bringing together material widely scattered throughout the literature. Sir Frederick Gowland Hopkins, in his preface, widely recommends this study of the chemical nature and functions of animals to students as well as to those "whose interest may be great but their leisure small."

4. Baldwin, Ernest. *Dynamic Aspects of Biochemistry*. Cambridge: Cambridge University Press, 2nd edition, 1952.

A first-class textbook of general biochemistry.

5. Tracey, N. V. *Principles of Biochemistry: A Biological Approach*. London: Isaac Pitman and Sons, Ltd., 1954.

An excellent book for the serious student about to begin the study of biochemistry. Though this may be regarded as an advanced work it is very readable.

6. Parsons, T. R. *Fundamentals of Biochemistry in Relation to Human Physiology*. Cambridge: Heffer and Sons, Ltd., 1933.

Although this book is now out of date and has not been revised, it is included on the strength of Baldwin's comment that it is "the best introductory textbook to the subject that has ever been written."

BIOLOGY

1. Allee, W. C. *Cooperation Among Animals, with Human Implications*. New York: Schuman, 1951.

A nontechnical account of the simpler, more direct evidence concerning the beginnings of co-operation among nonhuman animals. Dr. Allee also discusses certain implications of co-operation and their bearing on international relations. A book of exceptional interest and importance.

2. Allee, W. C., Emerson, A. E., Park, O., Park, T. and Schmidt, K. P. *Principles of Animal Ecology.* Philadelphia: Saunders, 1949.

This volume organizes and summarizes a large, complex field. Although primarily a technical monograph, many chapters are clearly and simply written and will appeal to the general reader. Chapter 23 on "Animal Aggregations," and Chapter 24 on "The Organization of Insect Societies" bear closely on the discussion in Dr. Allee's essay.

3. Bates, Marston. *The Nature of Natural History.* New York: Scribner's, 1950.

An excellent popular survey, mainly of animal biology, addressed to mature readers.

4. Beebe, William. *The Book of Naturalists, An Anthology of the Best Natural History.* New York: Alfred Knopf, 1944.

A fine collection of essays, selected and edited by a gifted biological writer.

5. Blum, Harold F. *Time's Arrow and Evolution.* Princeton: Princeton University Press, 1951. (See especially Chapter 10: "The Origin of Life.")

Somewhat technical, but suitable for those with a strong curiosity about the subject, who are not unwilling to concentrate while reading.

6. Buchsbaun, Ralph. *Animals Without Backbones.* Chicago: University of Chicago Press, 2nd edition, 1948.

Easy reading and accurate, with a wealth of superb illustrations; for intelligent persons with high school education.

7. Carr, Archie F. *High Jungles and Low.* Gainesville: University of Florida Press, 1953.

A rewarding book for the thoughtful, general reader.

8. *Encyclopedia Britannica,* printings since 1950.

The zoological articles have been recently carefully revised, or rewritten by eminent modern zoologists. This is a better source book of modern knowledge in the field than is generally realized. The material is usually presented in fairly elementary fashion. Particularly pertinent articles include: animal behavior, animal sociology, biology, comparative psychology, courtship of animals, marine biology, play in animals, social insects. The general articles on biology and zoology are also valuable for a quick survey and in giving leads to articles on other subjects.

9. Harden, Garrett. *Biology, Its Human Implications.* San Francisco: Freeman, 1949.

A well-written, comprehensive textbook for college freshmen.

10. Montagu, Ashley. *On Being Human*. New York: Henry Schuman, Inc., 1950.

Selected bits of the scientific data supporting the idea that co-operation, not conflict, is the basic principle of group living are presented in this small, palatable book.

11. Odum, Eugene P. *Fundamentals of Ecology*. Philadelphia: Saunders, 1953.

A relatively simple, direct, almost popular textbook for beginners in ecology.

12. Wheeler, William M. *Social Life Among the Insects*. New York: Harcourt, Brace Co., 1923.

A brilliant description of different insect societies. Accessible to the ordinary reader.

EVOLUTION AND GENETICS

1. Darlington, C. D. *The Facts of Life*. London: Allen and Unwin, 1953.

A fascinating and unconventional account of the development of man's ideas on reproduction and heredity. Controversial.

2. Darwin, Charles. *The Origin of Species*. London: Murray, 1859.

3. Darwin, Charles. *The Expression of the Emotions in Man and Animals*. London: Murray, 1872.

4. Ford, E. B. *Mendelism and Evolution*. London: Methuen, 1931.

A brief but illuminating book.

5. Goldschmidt, Richard D. *Understanding Heredity*. New York: John Wiley and Sons, Inc., 1952.

An excellent primer by a foremost geneticist. Can be read without special training but requires close attention.

6. Dobzhansky, Theodosius. *Genetics and the Origin of Species*. New York: Columbia University Press, 3rd edition, 1951.

Perhaps the outstanding textbook in the field but on a somewhat more advanced level than most of the other books suggested on this list.

7. Huxley, Julian S. *Evolution, the Modern Synthesis*. London: Allen and Unwin; New York: Harpers, 1942.

A comprehensive treatise containing numerous illustrative examples. Also a somewhat advanced work.

8. Huxley, Julian S. *Evolution in Action*. London: Chatto and Windus; New York: Harpers, 1953.

An admirable discussion of evolution as a process and man's place in it.

9. Scheinfeld, Amram. *The New You and Heredity*. Philadelphia, New York: J. B. Lippincott Company, 1950.

> One of the good popularizations of recent years, this comprehensive book offers the general reader a clearly written, fully illustrated survey of all aspects of the problem of human inheritance.

10. Simpson, George Gaylord. *The Meaning of Evolution*. New Haven: Yale University Press, 1949.

> The clearest semi-popular summary of the process of evolution and its implications for general thought.

11. Simpson, George Gaylord. *Horses*. New York: Oxford University Press, 1951.

> An interesting account of the best known single case of the evolution of a group.

12. Smith, Homer W. *From Fish to Philosopher*. Boston: Little, Brown, 1953.

> A lucid and original presentation of the course of vertebrate evolution. Professor Smith, an eminent physiologist and a fine writer, traces the evolution of man through the evolution of the kidney.

13. Wells, H. G., Huxley, J. S. and Wells, G. P. *The Science of Life*, especially books 3, 4 and 5. New York: Doubleday; London: Cassells, 1934.

> A primer of the actual course of evolution; together with a summary of genetics, reproduction and evolution theory. Though written a quarter of a century ago this book remains the best all round popularization of biology.

14. Tinbergen, N. *The Study of Instinct*. New York: Oxford University Press, 1951.

> An engrossing study of the mechanism underlying innate behavior. In this and other books Tinbergen shows himself a remarkable observer of animal behavior, from the stickleback to the herring gull.

15. Young, J. Z. *The Life of Vertebrates*. Oxford: Clarendon Press, 1950.

> A monumental survey of all phases of vertebrate life. This is an advanced textbook, but it can be read by anyone with a more than superficial desire to enlarge his biological knowledge.

PSYCHOLOGY

GENERAL TREATMENTS OF PSYCHOLOGY

1. Boring, E. G., Langfeld, H. S., and Weld, H. P., (Eds). *The Foundations of Psychology*. New York: John Wiley, 1948.

A thorough treatment of modern scientific psychology at a somewhat advanced textbook level, consisting of 25 chapters written by 19 experts. Clear, concise, full of facts.

2. Woodworth, R. S. *Experimental Psychology.* New York: Henry Holt, 1938.

A clear, straightforward, simple handbook of experimental psychology, written in a unitary style by a single author; somewhat more technical than Boring, Langfeld and Weld, but not nearly so difficult as the handbooks written for research workers.

HISTORY OF PSYCHOLOGY

3. Peters, R. S. (Ed). *Brett's History of Psychology.* New York: Macmillan, 1953.

An abridgement of G. S. Brett's three classical volumes (1919-1921) on the history of psychology from before Socrates down into the 20th century. This is the standard work on pre-scientific philosophical psychology, but for the scientific period since 1850 it is better to consult Murphy or Boring.

4. Murphy, Gardiner. *Historical Introduction to Modern Psychology.* New York: Harcourt, Brace, 2nd edition, 1949.

One of the best and broadest, as well as the most readable, histories of scientific psychology, its origin and development. More inclusive than Boring, though less detailed in respect of the topics treated.

5. Boring, E. G. *A History of Experimental Psychology.* New York: Appleton-Century-Crofts, 2nd edition, 1950.

A fine exposition of the origin of experimental psychology and philosoophy and sense-physiology and its subsequent development from 1850 to the present.

6. Garrett, H. E. *Great Experiments in Psychology.* New York: Appleton-Century-Crofts, 2nd edition, 1941.

An attractive, readable, elementary discussion of great experiments in psychology of the last 100 years: sensory measurement, sense-perception, learning, conditioned response, brain function, reaction time, instinct, emotion, intelligence testing, human abilities and personality.

SYSTEMS AND THEORIES OF PSYCHOLOGY

7. Woodworth, R. S. *Contemporary Schools of Psychology.* New York: Ronald Press, 2nd edition, 1948.

A small book, consisting of clear and felicitous accounts of five modern schools of psychology: the introspective, behavioristic, Gestalt, psychoanalytic and purposivist schools.

8. Heidbreder, Edna. *Seven Psychologies.* New York: Appleton-Century-Crofts, 1933.

Lucid summaries of seven systems of psychology which were modern in 1933: William James' psychology, Titchener's structural psychology, Chicago functionalism, Columbia dynamic psychology, behaviorism, Gestalt psychology and psychoanalysis. Out of date but still widely used because of its excellence.

9. Skinner, B. F. *Science and Human Behavior.* New York: Macmillan, 1953.

A brilliant modern polemic for the analysis and control of human behavior and conduct in respect to learning, thinking, social conduct, psychotherapy, government, religion, economics, education and the design of culture; the present culmination of a half century of behavioristic thought and effort.

FIELDS OF PSYCHOLOGY

10. Guilford, J. P., Ed. *Fields of Psychology.* New York: Van Nostrand, 1940.

Thirteen distinguished authors in 22 chapters describe the nature and content of 12 fields of modern psychology.

PHYSIOLOGICAL PSYCHOLOGY

11. Morgan, C. T. and Stellar, Eliot. *Physiological Psychology.* New York: McGraw Hill, 2nd edition, 1950.

A comprehensive text on the mechanisms of human and animal behavior, covering basic physiology and neurology, individual and evolutionary development, the senses, motor functions, learning, motivation and thought. The best book of its kind.

LEARNING, MEMORY AND THINKING

12. McGeoch, J. A. and Irion, A. L. *The Psychology of Human Learning.* New York: Longmans Green, 2nd edition, 1952.

A compendium of the results of the experimental research on human learning. Somewhat difficult and technical but at present the best single book in the field.

13. Wertheimer, Max. *Productive Thinking.* New York: Harpers, 1945.

A brilliant little volume by the distinguished founder of the school of Gestalt psychology; not a systematic text covering the subject, but an analysis of representative cases of creative thinking, including Galileo's, Gauss's, and Einstein's.

HUMAN ABILITIES AND INDIVIDUAL DIFFERENCES

14. Scheinfeld, Amram. *Women and Men.* New York: Harcourt, Brace, 1943.

> The simplest and also most thorough analysis of the evidence of the difference between the two sexes. Very easy reading.

MOTIVATION AND PERSONALITY, NORMAL AND ABNORMAL

15. White, R. W. *The Abnormal Personality.* New York: Ronald Press, 1948.

> An exceptionally clear discussion of the phenomena of the neuroses and psychoses, of dreams and hypnosis, of anxiety, defense and conflict, of phobias, obsessions and hysteria, and of psychosomatic disorders.

SOCIAL PSYCHOLOGY

16. Sargent, S. S. *Social Psychology.* New York: Ronald Press, 1950.

> An excellent text dealing with the relation of personality to culture, motives, frustration, egoism, communication, the interaction of social groups, leadership, public opinion, mass behavior, social change and movements, and social prejudice.

17. Newcomb, T. M. and Hartley, E. L. (Eds). *Readings in Social Psychology.* New York: Henry Holt, 1947.

> A comprehensive work consisting of 83 excerpts from the writings of 97 authors dealing with social and cultural effects on individual characteristics and on memory, judgment, perception and motivation, the development of socialization in the child, the effects of group situations, of social role and social status and of class structure, prejudice, language, suggestion, communication, propaganda, public opinion, frustration, morale, mass behavior, war and peace.

PSYCHOANALYSIS

1. Freud, Sigmund. *Introductory Lectures on Psychoanalysis.* London: Allen and Unwin, 1922.

> A systematic, yet simple and lucid presentation of Freud's main ideas and discoveries. Still the best primer of the subject.

2. ———. *New Introductory Lectures on Psychoanalysis.* New York: W. W. Norton Co., 1933.

> The New Introductory Lectures contain Freud's later discoveries and the changes from the original theories as expressed in the earlier lectures.

3. ———. *The Basic Writings of Sigmund Freud.* New York: The Modern Library, 1938.

> This excellent volume contains several of Freud's classical writings. *Psychopathology of Everyday Life* is a readable little book which deals with the causes of forgetting, why we make slips of the tongue, etc. *The Interpretation of Dreams*, Freud's most famous work, is fascinating, but large parts of it are not easy to follow. *The History of the Psychoanalytic Movement* is an interesting short survey of psychoanalysis and the deviations from it—seen from the partisan position of the founder of psychoanalysis.

4. Jung, Carl J. *The Psychology of the Unconscious.* New York: Dodd, Mead and Co., 1927.

> A detailed, fundamental presentation of his views by the foremost theoretician who broke away from Freud.

5. Adler, Alfred. *Understanding Human Nature.* New York: Greenberg Publishing Co., Inc., 1927.

> Another of Freud's well-known disciples (who later deviated from him) describes his system.

6. Mullahy, Patrick. *Oedipus—Myth and Complex.* New York: Hermitage Press, Inc., 1948.

> The theories of Freud, Jung, Adler, Rank, Horney, Fromm and Sullivan covered in clear, disinterested sketches.

7. de Forest, I. *The Leaven of Love.* New York: Harper Brothers, 1954.

> A well-rounded picture of the main factors in Ferenczi's therapy.

8. Alexander, Franz. *Fundamentals of Psychoanalysis.* New York: W. W. Norton and Co., Inc., 1948.

> Freud's basic concepts and how they have evolved in application. The author is director of the Chicago Institute for Psychoanalysis.

9. Horney, Karen. *The Neurotic Personality of our Time.* New York: W. W. Norton and Co., Inc., 1937.

> Horney's first work, presenting her main ideas on the essence of neurosis.

10. ———. *New Ways in Psychoanalysis.* New York: W. W. Norton and Company, Inc., 1939.

> The author explains how and why she departed from Freud's theories.

11. ———. *Our Inner Conflicts.* New York: W. W. Norton and Company, Inc., 1945.

> A further development of Horney's theoretical thought.

12. Sullivan, Harry Stack. *Conceptions of Modern Psychiatry.* Washington: The William Alanson White Foundation, 1947. Also,

The Theory of Interpersonal Relations. New York: W. W. Norton Co., Inc., 1951.

Together these books offer a full statement of Sullivan's theory of inter-personal relations.

13. Fromm, Erich. *Escape From Freedom.* New York: Farrar and Rinehart, Inc., 1941.

A study of the causes of authoritarianism and an analysis of modern man's ways of escaping from freedom and from himself. Fromm's best-known and most influential book.

14. ———. *Man For Himself.* New York: Rinehart and Co., Inc., 1947.

An inquiry into the psychology of ethics; an attempt to establish ethics on the basis of our knowledge of man's nature.

15. ———. *The Sane Society.* New York: Rinehart and Co., Inc., 1955.

A study of the pathogenic effect on man of contemporary industrial society, and suggestions for a society more conducive to mental health.

16. Dunbar, Flanders. *Emotions and Bodily Changes.* New York: Columbia University Press, 4th edition, 1954.

An enormous survey of literature on psychosomatic interrelationships. Dr. Dunbar's book, ideal for reference and for browsing, is an encyclopedia of what is known today about the effect of mental behavior on our bodies.

SCIENCE AS FORESIGHT

1. Ashby, W. Ross. *Design for a Brain.* New York: John Wiley and Sons, Inc., 1952.

A British psychiatrist who has performed important researches on the functioning of the brain explains the problem of designing a machine which will have some of the self-organizing and adaptive powers of the nervous system. The key, Ashby says, is the principle of "ultrastability"; and he has built the mechanism incorporating the principle. Half of Ashby's book is mathematical, half states its thesis in plain words but is difficult.

2. *Scientific American,* September 1952.

This issue of the leading U.S. science magazine has become famous for its comprehensive survey of automatic control. Eight contributors discuss various aspects of the subject: Ernest Nagel, the basic ideas and their social implications; Arnold Tustin, the theory of feedback and self-regulating processes; Gordon Brown and Donald Campbell, the application of feedback mechanisms; Eugene Ayres, an automatic chemical plant; William Pease, an automatic machine tool; Louis Ridenour, the role of the computer; Gilbert King, the nature of information and communication theory; Wassily Leontief, the potential economic effects—good and bad—of automatization. The articles are written for the general reader and there are many excellent illustrations.

3.   Bowden, B. V. (Editor). *Faster than Thought.* London: Sir Isaac Pitman and Sons, Ltd., 1953.

Twenty-four articles, many of general interest, on the history and theory of computers, on their uses in solving problems of logic, physics, astronomy, meteorology, ballistics, engineering, government administration, economics, business and commerce, and games.

4.   Shannon, Claude E. *A Chess-Playing Machine.* Scientific American, February, 1950.

Claude Shannon has done some of the most important fundamental work on the theory of communication. In this popular article he describes an electronic computer that can be set up to play a pretty strong game of chess.

5.   Shannon, Claude E. and Weaver, Warren. *The Mathematical Theory of Communication.* Urbana: The University of Illinois Press, 1949.

In this volume are presented Shannon's famous paper on the mathematical theory of communication, first published in 1948, and a largely expository and nonmathematical summary of the main concepts and results of Shannon's theory by the Director of the Division of the Natural Sciences in the Rockefeller Foundation. A condensation of Weaver's paper couched in popular language appears in *Scientific American,* July 1949.

6.   Sluckin, W. *Minds and Machines.* Penguin Books, 1954.

A clear, unpretentious, popular survey of modern automatic computing machines, cybernetics, information theory, and a discussion of how the study of these machines has influenced modern psychology.

7.   Berkeley, Edmund Callis. *Giant Brains or Machines That Think.* New York: John Wiley and Sons, Inc., 1949.

Berkeley's readable book gives unusually detailed but rather simple explanations of the operations of different types of calculating machines including punch-card calculators, differential analyzers, electronic calculators, logical-truth calculators. So swift are the developments in this field that the latest machines have already gone well beyond Berkeley's book, but his introduction retains its validity.

8.   Wiener, Norbert. *Cybernetics for Control and Communication in the Animal and the Machine.* New York: John Wiley and Sons, Inc., 1948.

A landmark in its field. While much of the discussion is technical and quite advanced there are sections which will fascinate almost any reader. Wiener's popular book (*The Human Use of Human Beings,* Houghton, Mifflin, New

York, 1950) is a rambling essay giving the author's views on almost any subject that popped into his head, but a few chapters are lively and enjoyable.

9. Walter, W. Grey. *The Living Brain*. New York: W. W. Norton and Company, Inc., 1953.

An account of the researches of the last twenty years on the mechanics of the brain. Overwritten, but an absorbing book.

10. Turing, A. M. *Computing Machinery and Intelligence*. Mind, October, 1950.

A brilliant essay which considers the question "Can a machine think?" Clear, original and profoundly interesting.

11. Jeffress, Lloyd A. (Editor). *Cerebral Mechanisms in Behavior* (The Hixon Symposium). New York: John Wiley and Sons, Inc., 1951.

This volume consists of six papers by different specialists concerned with the problem of the brain as a machine. The outstanding essay, by John von Neumann, on the general and logical theory of automata, considers the question whether it is possible to design and construct a machine capable of reproducing machines of its own kind. Von Neumann argues that it is possible.

Index

A

A-bombs, manufacture, 15
abnormal, definition, 344
absolute threshold, 301
acetaldehyde, 182
acetic acid, 182
acetyl-coenzyme, 212-213, 222
acetylene (ethyne), 181
Ach, N., 310
Achilles, race with tortoise, 29, 31
acids:
  halogens, 170
  hydrolysis, 215
  ionic compounds, 177
acquired characters, inheritance, 257, 258, 274
activities, constant and variable, 241
activity, physiological need, 311
adaptation and logic, 413-414
adaptive machines, 405-414
  adaptation and logic, 413
  experience in machines, 407
  exploring machine, 412
  goal-seeking strategy, 405
  unlimited foresight, 406
addition reaction, 181
adenosinediphosphate (ADP), 215-217
  formation, *diag.*, 216
adenosinetriphosphate (ATP), 215-217
Adler, Alfred (1870-1937), 377, 378
administration problems, dependent peoples, 354
adopted infant, adaptability, 331
ADP, *see* adenosinediphosphate
Adrian, Sir Edgar Douglas (1889-   ), *quoted*, 14
adrenalin, 210, 222
Africa, South, ape-men, 322, 323, 324, 330
Africa, tropical, toolmaking, 322

African culture, plough and wheel, 385
afterlife, denial, 344
age, galaxies, 95
age regression, 367
aggregation of matter, three states, 156
aggressiveness, animal, 243-244
agriculture:
  dependence on chemistry, 178
  soil exhaustion, 7, 8
air:
  chemical nature, 165
  combustion, 162, 163
  embodiment of qualities, *diag.*, 156
  movement, tropical forest, 239
airplane night flier, visual sensitivity, 303
a-keto acids, 208, 209
a-ketoglutaric acid, 209
alanine, 208; formula, 207
Alaska, artifacts, 326
albinism, 261
albumin, egg, 205
alchemical emblem, *illus.*, 161
alchemists, puffers, *illus.*, 158
alchemy:
  chemistry, 158
  end of, 162
  origin and tenets, 157
  traditional, 274
alcohol, 181-182; intoxication, 368
aldehyde group, organic chemistry, 182
Alexander, Franz, 378
algae, 235
algebra, Boolean, 49-50
algebraic geometry, 394
alkali metals, 170
alkaloids, 188
Allee, Warder Clyde (1885-1955), 228-230
alleles, 267-268
alloys, ancient knowledge of, 155

alpha particles:
  deflection, 125-126
  ejection from radium, 129
  polonium, interaction with, 130, 131,
    diag., 130
  summarized, 147-148
  transmutation, 174
  uranium, interaction with, 130, 131,
    diag., 130
alum, ancient knowledge, 155
aluminum, symbol, 169
American Indian:
  cultures, 330
  language similarities, 350
amino acids:
  deamination, 222
  essential, 206, 218
  formulae, 207
  glucogenic, 212
  ketogenic, 212
  metabolism, 212
  new tissue formation, 205
  proteins, 204, 205, 206, 207, 208,
    232
  surplus, 208, 209
  tyrosine, 222
ammonia:
  basis for life, 237
  components, 168
  derivatives, 182-183
  discovery, 164
  earth, early atmosphere, 232
  excretion, 209
  molecule, 174
  symbols, 168
  toxicity, 209
ammonites, fossil evidence, 280
amphibians:
  partial colonization, 281
  territorial defense, 243
amylase, 203
anabolic process, 200
anaerobic bacteria, 236
analogue machines, 389; *diag.*, 390
analysis into units, 428
anatomy, studies, 256
Anaximander (611?-?547 B.C.), 25
Andean culture, 328
Anderson, Carl David (1905-   ),
  104, 143, 146, 148
andromeda nebula, 81
Angel, J. L., 337

angle, tetrahedral, 192
aniline, 183, 185
animal behavior, Harvard law of, 238
animal breeds, outward appearance, 332
Animal Ecology, Principles of, 237
animals:
  adaptation to environment, 385
  animal-plant relation, 236
  behavior patterns, 233, 240, 405
  biochemistry, 199
  carnivorous, 218
  change in unfavorable surroundings,
    245
  communal reaction, 243
  community living, 247
  continuous transformation, 274
  diet experiments, 219-220
  domestication, 325, 326
  evolution, 246, 273
  experimental psychology, 308, 310
  fossil, 277
  genetic mechanism, 267
  group survival, 245-247
  herbivorous, 218
  induction, 433
  light, reactions to, 237
  mutation, 265
  nutritional requirements, 219, 220
  population regulation, 288
  protein diet, 208
  proto-co-operation, 247
  separate species, 279
  social rank responsibilities, 244
  sociality, 233
  stabilization, 282, 284
  synthetically deficient, 218
  telegony, 259-260
  tropical rain-forest, 239
anthracine, formulae, 184
anthropological Monroe Doctrine, 326,
  327
anthropological publication, 356
anthropologist, primary role, 354
anthropology, 319-357
  constitutional, 335, 353
  cultural, 319, 338, 340, 354, 356
  historical, 352
  human biology, comparative, 330-337
  human evolution, 321-322
  industrial, 354
  linguistics, 345-352
  man, history of, 322-329

anthropology (*cont.*)
  physical, 353
  psychoanalysis, 378, 379
  range of enquiry, 319-320
  techniques, 340
  uses, 352-357
  ways of men, 338-345
anti-proton, mass particle, 149
anti-vitamins, 224
antibiotics, 188, 222-224
antigen, Henshaw, 333
ants:
  fixed behavior, 405
  stabilization, 282
  tropical rain-forest, 239
anxiety, role of, 378
ape, introspection, 300
ape-men (Australopithecines), 322, 323, 324, 330
aptitude, 312
Aquinas, Saint Thomas (1225?-1274), 61
archaeology, 319; role in public adult education, 352
Archimedes (287?-212 B.C.), 15, 37, 44
Arctic area, early population, 326
Aristotle (384-322 B.C.):
  four elements, 155, 159, 161, 162
  logic, 52, 61
  matter, unity, 173
arithmetic, a new, 394-399
arithmetic continuum, 44
arithmetical machines, 389-391
arithmetical puzzles, 45
Arizona, cave cultures, 328
aromatic compounds, 183
art:
  function, 248
  libidinal forces, 372
  Paleolithic Age, 325
arthritic conditions, cortisone, 223
artifacts:
  Alaska, 326
  circumpolar region, 326
  dating, 328
artificial elements, 172
artistic creation, neurotic symptom, 377
artists and writers, great, cycles, 339
ascorbic acid (vitamin C), 218, 219
Ashby, Dr. Ross, 412, 413
association:
  axioms of, 36

association: (*cont.*)
  free, 368-369
  laws of, 307
assumptions, cosmology, 85-94
astrolabe, 386
astronomical space geometry, 31-33
astronomy, 66-96
  calculation, 58
  cosmology, 84-96
  galaxies, 81-84
  physical principles, 103
  reaction time, 305-306
  solar system, 66-69
  stars, 69-81
  tools, 386
asymmetric forms, 191, 192, 193
atmosphere, earth, 76
atomic:
  bomb, 140, 174
  energy, constructive application, 174, 288
  mechanics, 129
  nuclei, 105, 135, 140
  numbers, 135
  physics, 79, 415; particles summarized, 145-149
  power, replacing oil, 8
  power stations, 10
  reactions, code, 431
  structure, 103; *diag.*, 171
  theory, 102, 166, 167, 170
  weight, atoms, 168
Atomic Energy, U.S. Senate Special Committee on, 99
atomistic school, solid geometry, 29-30
atoms:
  arrangement, 144
  atomic weight, 168
  behavior, 104, 105
  chemical nature, 135, 172
  crystals, 124, 125
  Daltonian symbols, *illus.*, 168
  deflection, 125-126
  distance between, 391
  electronic constitution, 170
  ion, 137 *fn.*, 171
  light-emitting properties, 103, 127, 134
  molecules, 174
  motion of electrons, 127
  Newton's theory, 167
  nuclear, 126

atoms: (*cont.*)
  ratio of forces, 92
  self-linking, 180
  sodium, *diag.*, 172
  splitting, 170
  structures, *diag.*, 171
  valency, 175
ATP, *see* adenosinetriphosphate
attention degree, measuring, 306
attitude and need, concepts, 311
aureomycin, 223
Australia, fertility, 10
automatic pilot, 409, 412, 413, 422
automatic scanner, 386
automatic timer, 386
automatic voting machine, 387
Avogadro's hypothesis, 175, 177
axes, hand, 324 *fn.*
axioms:
  Euclid, 36
  Greek, 25-26
  mathematics, 39
  new views, 36-37
azo dyes, 189
Aztec civilization, 328

B

Babbage, Charles (1792-1871), 400,
  435
Babylonians:
  algebra and geometry, contributions
    to, 27 *fn.*
  hypotenuse, length, 26
  numerical problems, solving, 24, 45
  surveying and measuring, 25
background noise, 421
Bacon, Francis (1561-1626), 62
bacteria:
  anaerobic, 236
  experiments, 220
  genes, 267
  metabolism, 224
  nutritional requirements, 219, 220-
    221
  self-reproduction, 261
  toxins, 221
  vitamins, 220, 221
bacteriostatics, 222-224
Baldwin, Ernest (1909-   ), 196-197
Bally, Gustav, 378
barbarism, reversion to, 13

barrier leakage, natural radioactivity,
  134
bases, ionic compounds, 177
Basques, blood group gene, 333
Bateman, Harry, 20-21
Bateson, William (1861-1926), 264
beams, energy, 74
bees, spontaneously generated, 257
beetle, burying, 405
behavior:
  instinctive, 240-241
  linguistic, 350
  patterns, 233, 240-242, 338
  physique-behavior relation, 335
behaviorism, 299, 300, 301, 308
beliefs, needed changes in, 16
benzene ring, 183, 185, 430; *diag.*, 184
Bergson, Henri (1859-1941), 272
Bernoulli, James, 58
beryllium:
  symbol, 169
  transmutation, 174
Berzelius, Jöns Jakob (1779-1848), 168
Bessel, Friedrich Wilhelm (1784-1846),
  305
beta-emitters, 141-142
beta-processes, 147
beta-rays, 125
Bethe, Hans (1906-   ), 140
binary notation, *diag.*, 304
binary scale, 48
binary stars, motion, 69
biochemical quantum, 215
biochemistry, 198-225
  carbohydrate metabolism, 210-213
  carbohydrate storage, 204-205
  citric-acid cycle, 213-214
  digestion, 203-204
  energy metabolism, 214-218
  enzymes, 201-203
  fat metabolism, 210-213
  fat storage, 204-205
  hormones, antibiotics, bacteriostatics,
    222-224
  metabolism, 199-200
  organic chemistry, 178
  organic molecules, 193
  pharmacology, 222
  protein foods, 205-210
  therapeutics, 222
  vitamins, 218-222
biogeography, 233

biological:
  adaptation, 279
  constitution, effect on personality, 342
  evolution, 272, 277-280, 286
  genetics, 285
  organization, stabilization, 282
  panorama, 284
  problems, chemical methods, 198
  sciences, 154, 250
  substances, isolation, 223
  work, 200
biology, 231-252
  biology-religion relation, 233-234
  classification problems, 233
  divisions, 232
  organic chemistry, 178
  physical knowledge, 103
birds:
  crocodile, 385
  dominance on land, 281
  peck orders, 244
  stabilization, 282
  territorial defense, 243
birth difficulties, human, 331
birth trauma, 377
Black, Joseph (1728-1799), 163
Blake, William (1757-1827), *quoted*, 160
blood, glucose concentration, 210, 211
blood cells, sickling, 333
blood groups, variations, 333
blood poisoning, bacteria, 220-221
blue sky, 421
blue stars, 71, 81
bodies, large, mechanical motions, 102
bodily structure, evolution, 272
Bohr, Niels (1885-   ), 103, 126, 127, 128, 133, 171
Bondi, Hermann (1919-   ), 64-65
Boole, George (1815-1864), 49, 50, 52
Boring, Edwin G. (1886-   ), 292-293
Born, Max (1882-   ), 98, 103, 132
boron, symbol, 169
bottled gas, 180
Bouguer, Pierre (1698-1758), 295
Boyd, W. C., 333
Boyle, Robert (1627-1691), 159, 162, 164
brain:
  electronic, 404

brain: (*cont.*)
  expansion, 321, 323-324, 389
  human, visual portions, 303
  mind, interaction with, 298
  organ of psychological studies, 308, 309
breathing mechanism, insects, 283
Breit, Gregory, 138
Bridgman, Percy Williams (1882-   ), 300
bright stars, 72, 80, 84
Broglie, Prince Louis de (1892-   ), 103, 127, 128-129
Bronowski, Jacob (1908-   ), 382-384
Brouwer, L. E. J., 55
Bullard, Dexter (psychoanalyst), 374
burying beetle, 405
business and industry, anthropological techniques, 340
butane, formulae, 180
Butler, Samuel (1835-1902), 271
butterfly, protective coloring, 276

C

calcium, dietary, absorption, 221
calcium carbide, 182
calcium compounds, dimmed stars, 83
calculating machine, 389, 391
  logical machines, 435
  program tape, *diag.*, 402
  step-by-step approximation, 394; *diag.*, 402-403
calculation, reach of, 414
calorie requirements, calculations, 217
calx (oxide), 163, 166
camera, 386
cancer therapy, uranium reactors, 144
candle-meters, 238
carbohydrates:
  function, 186
  katabolism, 201
  metabolism, 205, 209, 210-213
  oxidation, 214
  storage, 204-205
  tissue requirements, 210
carbon:
  basis for life, 237
  compounds, chemistry of, 179
  dimmed stars, 83
  food cycle, *diag.*, 187

carbon: (*cont.*)
  symbols, 168, 169
  transmutation, 174
carbon atoms, 211, 212, 213, 214, 217
  asymmetric, 192
  linking, 179, 180, 183; *diag.*, 184
  valencies, 179, 191; *diag.*, 192
carbon dioxide, 163, 164
  formulae, *diag.*, 176
  symbols, 168
Carbon 14 technique, 329
carbon monoxide, 182
carbonic oxide, symbols, 168
carboxyl group, 182
cardinal numbers, 41, 42
carnivorous animals, 218
cash register, 391
catalyst:
  chemical reaction, 181
  enzymes, 201-203
  neutrons, 160
  philosopher's stone, 159
cattle, hornlessness, 261
causality, principle, 60
caustic soda, 170
cave cultures, 328
Cavendish, Henry (1731-1810), 165, 166
cells:
  chromosomes and genes, 267
  divisions, 260
  gametes, 260
cells, living:
  chemical changes, 200, 202
  composition, 199
cellulose, macromolecules, 190
censors, objection to useful knowledge, 12
census taker, 387
Chadwick, Sir James (1891-   ), 103, 135, 147
chalk, heated, 163, 164
chance, games based on, 415
character:
  changes, 11
  differences, 261-264
  Mendelian factors, 264
  neurotic, 373-374
character traits, organic inferiorities, 377
Chaucer, Geoffrey (1340-1400), *quoted*, 155
checkers, game, 406
chemical action, linking atoms, 430

chemical bonds, concept, 431
chemical elements, formation, 272
chemical energy, scale, 391
chemical equation, 177
chemicals, synthetic, 223
chemistry, 154-194
  alchemy, 157-162
  atomic theory, 166-178
  combustion, 162-166
  inorganic and organic, 178-194
  self-reproducing matter, 266
  space, 193
  use of modern physics, 103
chess-playing machine, 406, 409-410
chicken, high-ranking males, 244
child-relationships, 379
Child Training and Personality (Whiting and Child), 343
child training system, effect on personality, 342
childhood:
  experience significance, 378
  importance of first years, 369
chimpanzees, cranial capacity, 324
China:
  contacts with New World, 327
  epistemology, 351
Chippewa Indians, aboriginal culture influence, 342
Chittenden, Russell H. (1856-1943), 206, 208
chlorides, saliva, 202
chlorine:
  discovery, 165
  symbol, 169
chloromycetin, 223
chlorophyll green:
  development, 232
  plant pigment, 186
chloroprene, molecules, 190
chromophores, 189
chromosomes:
  cell organs, 260
  doubling, 276
  mutations, 265
  number of kinds, 267-268
  organs of heredity, 261
  self-reproducing system, 261
  sex, 260 *fn.*
  diags., 262, 263
chronoscopes, 305
Churchill, Sir Winston (1874-   ), *quoted*, 174

chymotrypsin, enzyme, 204
circuit as a counter, *diag.*, 392
citric-acid cycle, 213-214, 222; *diag.*, 213
citrus fruits, vitamin C, 219
civil defense, thermonuclear weapons, 13
civilization:
  classical, 326
  modern, 248
  rise and fall, 337
Clark, Colin, 399, 400
Clark, John, 435
Clifford, William Kingdon (1845-1879), *quoted*, 32
climate, tropical rain-forest, 238-239
clinics, psychoanalytic institutes, 375
clock, 387
  basis of modern life, 386
  digital machine, 389
clothes, fashion changes, 339
clouds:
  dust, 83, 88 *fn.*
  gas, 83-84
  radioactive, 13
"Coal Sack," Milky Way, 83
coal-tar:
  chemistry, 184
  dyes, 189
  primaries, formulae, 184
cocaine, natural, 189
Cockroft, Sir John, 103, 134, 136, 139
code:
  breaking, 436
  linguistic analysis, 352-353
  organization in, 426
  redundancy, 423
code of nature, breaking, 429
coin tossing, 60
  strategies, 416-417
colchicine, 276
cold, extreme, body responses, 335
cold gas, 83
collision, producing, 77-78
collision mechanics, laws of, 125
color-luminosity, stars, *diag.*, 71
Columbia University, psychoanalytic training, 376
Columbia, Christopher (1446?-1506), 15, 326, 327
Coma Berenices, nebula, *illus.*, 82
combustion:
  fat and carbohydrate, 210

combustion: (*cont.*)
  nature of, 161, 162
  theory, 166
common air, 163, 165
common notions, principles of logic, 26
communication:
  and information, theory, 388
  true speech, 284 *fn.*
communication needs, speakers and hearers, 349
communities, Mesolithic Age, 325
community, linguistic, 346 *fn.*
community living, animal, 247
competitiveness-aggressiveness, 372-373
Complex Variable, Theory of Functions of a, 47
complexions, tanning by sunlight, 257, 258
compound atoms, 167
compounds, molecules, 174
Compton, Arthur H. (1892-   ), 124, 125, 133
conditioned response, 307
Condon, Edward U. (1902-   ), 98-101
  wave theory for nuclear particles, 129
conflicts, unconscious, 374
congruence, axioms of, 36
conscious co-operation, animal, 243
consciousness, incorporeal events, 295
constant composition, atomic theory, 167
constants, physical, 92
constitutional anthropology, 335, 353
contents of the unconscious, 375
contiguity, frequency of, 307
control mechanisms, 387
convenient memory, 312
Cook, Captain James (1728-1779), 218
Coon, Carleton, 317
co-operation:
  beginning of, 233, 235
  natural, 244-245, 246, 247-248
Copernicus, Nicolaus (1473-1543), 362, 364
  model, 67, 68
copper, symbol, 169
corpses, disposal, 344
corpuscular theory of light, 115-117, 121-122; *diag.*, 116
correlation, theory of statistics, 59
cortisone, 223
cosmic rays, 143

cosmological phase, 279
cosmology, 84-96
  comprehensive theory, 90-96
  evolutionary approach, 278
  subject matter, 84-90
  see also astronomy
cosmos, early views, 155
Coulomb, Charles A. (1736-1806), 130
Coulomb barrier, *diag.*, 130
counters, scale, 391
Cours de Chymie (Lémery), 160
covalency:
  directional, 191
  nonpolar bond, 176
cows, hook orders, 244
cradle of mankind, 326
cranial capacities, 324
creation, myth of, 271
creation of matter, continual, 93
creative insight, unconscious, 298, 299
creative thinking, 297
crime detection, time reactions, 306
crocodile bird, 385
cross-staff, 386
cryptography, 432
crystals:
  atoms, 124, 125
  structure, 430
cubic equation, 46
cultural anthropology, 319, 338, 340, 354, 356
cultural development, organisms and stages, table, 323
cultural diffusion, 286
cultural divergence in man, 287
cultural evolution, acceleration, 285
cultural innovations, spread, 338-339
cultural realm, nature of proof, 357
cultural relativity, 343
cultural variation, 345
culture:
  growth, repetitive patterns, 337
  history, vocabulary analysis, 346 *fn.*
  influence on personality, 342
  medieval, 362
  sublimation, effect, 371
  technical term, 338
Culture, The Nature of (Kroeber), 339 *fn.*
cultures, high, mongrel, 337
cultures, Neolithic, spread, 326
cultures, similarity, 344

cumulative transmission of experience, 284
cure, psychoanalysts' method, 374
Curie-Joliot, Frédéric (1900-), 103
cybernetics, 9
cycles, culture growth and change, 339
cyclic molecular structures, 185
cyclotron, 139
cytology, 232
cytoplasmic inheritance, 261

D

Dalton, John (1766-1844), 166, 167, 168, 170, 430
Daltonian symbols, *illus.*, 168
Darlington, C. D., 257 *fn.*, 276
Darwin, Charles R. (1809-1882), 244, 246, 247, 259 *fn.*, 269, 271, 272, 274, 363; *quoted*, 436
dating:
  anthropological, 328
  linguistic, 329-330
  tree-ring, 329
Davis, Bergen, *quoted*, 132
Davisson, Clinton Joseph (1881-), 128
death:
  ceremonializing, 344
  drive for, 371
decimal system numeration, 47-48
decision by calculation, 415
decoding, scientific theories, *diag.*, 431-432
deduction, logic of, 404, 433
deductions, mathematics, 39
deductive machines, 388-404, 406
  analogue, 389; *diag.*, 390
  arithmetical, 389-391
  logic of the machines, 400-404
  new arithmetic, 394-399
  New Political Arithmetick, 399-400
  speed, problem of, 391-394
deficiency disease, 218
definitions, mathematics, 39
de Méré, Chevalier, 415
Democritus, 29, 166
Dempster, A. J., 136
density, stellar matter, 76
dentistry, physical anthropology contributions, 353
dependent peoples, administration problems, 354

dephlogisticated air, 165, 166
dermatology, physical anthropology contributions, 353
Desargues, Gérard (1593-1662), 37
Descartes, René (1596-1650), 106 *fn.*, 155, 298
deserts, environment for life, 237
desires, reasons for, 364
destinies, association with planets and metals, 155
destructiveness, role of, 371
determining tendency, 310
deuterium, discovery, 135
deuterium oxide, 173
deuteron, summarized, 147
de Valera, Eamon (1882-   ), 21
Devonian vertebrates, 281
de Vries, Hugo (1848-1935), 273
diabetes:
    diagnosis, 198
    insulin, 223
    metabolism, 210-212
diagnosis, chemical tests, 198
diagrams, geometrical proofs, 36
diet, influence on disease, 219
differential threshold, 301
diffraction:
    atom arrangement, 144
    light, 117; *illus.*, 118
    X rays, 124
diffusion, ideas and techniques, 339
digestion, enzymes, 202, 203-204
digital machines, 389
dimmed star, 83
dinosaurs:
    extinction, 6, 16
    fossil evidence, 280
diploid chromosomes, 260
Dirac, Paul A. M. (1902-   ), 98, 132, 146
"Directions for knowing all dark things," 45
disease, diet influence, 219
dissociation, states of, 366-367
distance, observable, 90
distant regions, Olber's assumptions, 85
divergent specialization, 280, 281
Dobzhansky, Theodore, 278
dog:
    cerebrum removal, 309
    conditioned response, 307
    emergency emotion, 309
    fight orders, 244

dominance hierarchies, 243
dominance orders, humans, 244
dominant groups, 281
dominant types, successions of, 282
Doppler, Christian Johann (1803-1853), 432
Doppler shift, 70 *fn.*
draughts, game, 406
dreams, wish fulfillment, 366
Drosophile (fruitfly), mutation, 265
drugs, expression of unconscious feelings, 368
Dunn, L. C., 262 *fn.*, 263 *fn.*
Dust Bowl, 16
dust clouds, 83, 88 *fn.*
dust shot, animal collecting, 239
dwellings, Paleolithic Age, 324
dyes:
    artificial, 189
    natural organic compounds, 188
dynamic psychology, 297
dynamo, 386

E

ear, sensitivity, 302, 303, 304
earth:
    atmosphere, 76, 232
    embodiment of qualities, *diag.*, 156
    environment for living organism, 237
    motion through ether, 110
Eastern Hemisphere, cradle of mankind, 326
Ebbinghaus, Hermann (1850-1909), 296, 307
eclipse, moon and sun, 69
ecology, 232, 236, 256
economic freedom, limitation, 10
economic life, Mesolithic Age, 325
economics, problems, 399
economy, food-producing, 325-326
Eddington, Sir Arthur Stanley (1882-1944), 21, 33
Edison, Thomas A. (1847-1931), 386
education:
    role of archaeology, 352
    world needs, 16
egg timer, 391
egg white, molecules, 205
ego and id, conflict between, 373
ego development, 378
Egyptians:
    four-elements theory, 155

Egyptians: (*cont.*)
  geometrical facts, 25
  numerical problems, 24, 45
  Ouroboros serpent, 183; *illus.*, 184
  pyramid-builders, 26
  surveying and measuring, 25
Ehrlich, Paul (1854-1915), 223
Einstein, Albert (1879-1955):
  electrons, liberated, 123
  gravitation theory, 33
  light velocity, 110
  mass-energy relation, 136, 138, 145
  motion, equations, 114-115
  quantum, 145
  relativity, theory of, 103, 108, 113,
    127, 274, 362
  space and time measurements, 111,
    112
  wave-particle duality, 132
Eisenhower, Dwight D. (1890-   ),
    100, 393
elastic solids, 106, 107, 108
election forecasts, UNIVAC, 393, 400
electoral seats, machine counting, 393-
    394
electric:
  conduction, 389
  current, topology, 35-36
  discharge, 215, 232
  forces, atom, 92
  motor, 387
electrical analogue, *diag.*, 390
electrical particles, behavior, 104
electricity:
  positive or negative, 142 *fn.*
  power generated by uranium fission,
    140
electrolytic dissociation, 177
electromagnetism:
  laws, 108, 113
  logical theory, 106-107
  mathematics, 111
electromagnets, 305
electron:
  atomic nucleus, 105
  behavior, 104
  code, 431
  crystal atoms, 124
  diffraction, 144
  discovery, 430
  ejection, 123
  energy in X-ray tube, 115
  helium, 127

electron: (*cont.*)
  localizing, 133
  motion in atoms, 127
  nuclear atom, 126
  positron, 142
  speed, 79
  spin, 106, 127
  summarized, 145-146
  unit of negative electricity, 170
  valency, 171, 172, 175, 176, 177
electronic brain, 387, 404
electronic machine:
  arithmetic, 393
  chess problems, 406
  problem of speed, 391-393
electrovalency:
  nondirectional, 191
  polar bond, 176
elements:
  artificial, 172
  material embodiment of qualities,
    diags., 156, 194
  modern table, 172
  molecules, 174
  periodic table, 169
  symbols and atomic weights, 136,
    168, 169
  transmutation, 103, 135, 156
elephants, fossil evidence, 280
"Elephants and Ethnologists," 327
elixir of life (*elixir vitae*), 158
Elliot-Smith, Grafton, 327
elliptic geometry, 34
embryology, 256, 272, 273
emergency theory of emotion, 309
Emerson, A. E., 230
emotional responses, eliciting, 367
emotions, mass, 12
Encyclopaedia Britannica, 233
endothermic chemical changes, 178
energy:
  alpha particle, 129, 131
  biological work, 200
  body requirements, 210
  cycle, *diag.*, 215
  electron, 123
  expenditure, 217
  helium, 139
  inertia, 114
  kev, 142
  light beam, 122
  metabolism, 214-218
  organic, 188

energy: (*cont.*)
  phosphate radicle, 216
  production, 78
  psychic, transforming, 380
  quantum, 145
  scale, 391
  solar, 140
  stellar, 77
  uranium atom split, 139
  X-ray quantum, 123
energy-mass relation, 136, 138, 145
energy-yielding processes, 201
entomology, 232
entrophy and information, 424-426
environment:
  acquired characters, 257
  adjustment to, 235, 236, 378
  biochemical adaptation, 210
  changes, 6-7, 16, 276
  exploring machine, 412
  fitness, 237
  genes mutation, 259
  influences, 334
  or heredity, 259
  uniform, 259
enzymes:
  biological catalyst, 201-203
  classes, 202
  coenzymes, 202
  competitive inhibition, 224
  digestive, 203
  formation, 200
  gas gangrene organisms, 221
  heat susceptibility, 202
  muscle, 215
  oxidizing, 222
  peptidases, 204
  separation, 203
  specificity, 202
  transaminases, 222
  transferring, 203
  zymase, 181
Epicurus (342?-270 B.C.), 166
equals added to equals, 26
equation, chemical, 177
Equidae, horse family, 280
equilibrium, nitrogenous, 206, 207, 208
erg, energy, 302
Eskimo culture, 328
Eskimos, Alaskan, contacts with China
    and Korea, 327
estrogens, synthetic, 223
ethane, formulae, 180

ether:
  all-pervasive, 106 *fn.*, 107, 108
  luminiferous, 115
ethics, private, affected by science, 16
ethyl alcohol:
  equations, 181
  production, 182
ethylamine, 183
ethylene:
  molecules, 189
  reactivity, 181
  symbols, 168
Euclid (fl. 300 B.C.):
  axioms, 36
  geometry definitions, 38
  parallel axiom, 30, 31
Euclid, *Elements* of, 27, 39, 61
Europe:
  Mesolithic Age, 325
  Neanderthaloid races, 323
  Neolithic Age, 325-326
  Paleolithic Age, 323-324
evaporation rate, tropical forest, 239
evolution, 271-289
  animals, 246
  artificially directed, 276
  biological, 272, 277-280, 286
  change, 269, 271, 273, 275
  Darwin's theory, 244, 363
  defined, 278
  human, 321-322
  natural selection, 246-247
  progress, 283
  studies, 256
  transformation, 274
  universal process, 272
  virus, 234
  see also genetics
Evolution (journal), 278
exact calculation, distrust of, 394
exceptional individual, importance, 287
exclusion principle, atomic physics, 79
excretory products, deamination and
    formation, *diag.*, 209
existence, struggle for, 244, 251
existence-theorems, mathematics, 39
exothermic reactions, equation, 177
exotic languages, study, 353
expanding-universe theory, 33
experience:
  cumulative transmission, 284, 285
  fossilization, 406
  in machines, 407-412

experience: (*cont.*)
  interpreting, 350
experimental psychology, 295, 296, 298,
  301, 308, 310
  Germany, 299
experimental sciences, 433
experiments:
  physics, new, 104-105
  use of, 432
exploring machine, 412-413
explosives, organic, 188
eyes:
  insects, 283 *fn.*
  sensitivity, 301-302, 303, 304

F

factitious airs, 165
factorial analysis, 313
factors, interaction between, 264
faint stars, 71, 72, 80, 85
falcon, eyes, 279, 283
family, differences in, 268-269
fat men, professional, 204
fathers, effect on nature of offspring,
  261
fats:
  carbohydrate, 204, 213
  katabolism, 201, 211
  metabolism, 210-213
  oxidation, 214
  storage, 204-205
Fechner, Gustav Theodor (1801-1887),
  294, 295, 298, 301, 314
Ferenczi, Sandor, 377
Fermat, Pierre de (1601-1665), 560
fermented liquors, ancient knowledge,
  155
Fermi, Enrico (1901-1954), 103, 147
fertilizers:
  enemy corpses, 8
  food production, 7
fight orders, dogs, lizards, mice, 244
figures, similarity, 26
file, cutting teeth, 387
finger game, strategy, 417; *diag.*, 418
Finlay-Freundlich, E., 33
fire:
  discovery, 386
  embodiment of qualities, *diag.*, 156
  sulphur-mercury theory, 158
fireflies, light, 214
Fisher, R. A., 266, 274, 275

fishes:
  electric organs, 214
  intercrossing, 270
  nip orders, 244
  territorial defense, 243
fission, 139-140, 391
Fitzgerald, George Francis, 21, 111;
  quoted, 33
fixed air (carbon dioxide), 163
fixed proportions, law of, 167
fixed stars, 66
flakes, flint, 324
Fleming, Sir Alexander (1881-1955),
  223
flies:
  genes, number, 267
  spontaneously generated, 257
flint flakes, 324
flower-color, differences, 261
fluorine, symbol, 169
fog, better vision in, 421
food:
  absorption, 204
  cycles, *diag.*, 187
  energy yields, 217
  molecules, 203, 214
  production, 7
  protein, function, 205-210
  raising, planned, 325
  vital need, 311
forces, electromagnetic, 103, 107
forces behind observal phenomena, 362-
  363
forecasting machine, 387
foreign tongue, reproducing sounds, 347
foresight:
  and insight, 427
  strategy, 388
  unlimited, 406-407
forest, climate changes, 239
formation, process, 75
formula, molecular, 175
Forsyth, Andrew Russell (1858-1942),
  21
fossilization of experience, 406
fossils:
  animal groups, 277
  biological evolution, 280
  hominids, 273
  human, dating, 328
  primate, 322
four-dimensional manifold, 40
fowls, comb changes, 264

Frankland, Edward (1825-1899), 175
Franklin, Benjamin (1706-1790), 385
free association, 368-369
free assortment, genetic law, 268
freedom, limiting, 10
freedom of choice, illusion, 364
French Revolution, new explosives, 15
frequency of contiguity, 307
Freud, Sigmund (1856-1939), 297, 298, 299, 310, 363, 364, 372
Fricker, Peter Racine, 384
frogs, spontaneously generated, 257
Fromm, Erich (1900-   ), 360-361, 378
Fromm-Reichmann, Frieda, 374
fundamental qualities, elements embodiment of, *diag.*, 156
furan ring, *diag.*, 186
future, anticipation of, 427

G

galaxies:
    aging, 95
    arrangement, 66
    condensation, 94
    evolutionary process, 278
    observable properties, 96
    recession, 86, 90, 91
    spiral, 81, 83; *illus.*, 82
    stars, 66, 81, 85, 95
    systematic motions, 89
    uniformity in distribution, 89
Galileo (1564-1642), 15, 62, 67, 102, 415, 430
gall wasp, 405
game-playing machines, 406-407, 409
games:
    based on chance, 415-420
    models for purposeful activities, 405
gametes, 260-261
gamma rays, 125, 145, 146
Gamow, George (1904-   ), 94, 129
Gardner, E., 148
gas:
    atmosphere, 170
    clouds, 83-84
    cold, 83
    gangrene organisms, enzyme, 221
    interstellar, 83
    isolating, 163, 164
    molecules, 122, 175
    pressure, 79
    specific gravity, 165

gas: (*cont.*)
    terrestrial, 76
gasoline, 180
gastric juice, pepsin, 204
Geiger counter, automatic record, 391
general relativity, 33
genes:
    artificially induced, 276
    bacteria, 267
    behavior, 264
    chemical nature, 266
    frequencies, 333
    functional interrelation, 273
    gene-complex, 265, 266, 271, 273-274, 276
    geographical restrictions, 333
    hereditary constitution, 258
    mapping genetic system, 266, 268
    molecular weight, 267
    mutation, 259, 265
    new, effect of, 334
    organization, 267
    recessive mutant, 275
Genesis, myth of creation, 271
genetics, 257-271
    analysis, quantitative, 332
    biological, 285
    effect of cultural beliefs, 337
    evolutionary implications, 256
    genetic drift, 334
    mutations, 267
    outbreeding, 276
    raising desirable qualities, 286
    variation, two kinds, 269
    see also evolution
Genetics, Principles of (Sinnott and Dunn), 262 *fn.*, 263 *fn.*
Genghis Khan (1167-1227), 287
geographical distribution, 273
geology:
    inorganic chemistry, 178
    physical principles, 103
geometry:
    astronomical space, 31-33
    atomistic school, 29-30
    elliptic, 34
    hyperbolic, 34
    irrational numbers, 28
    large-scale regions, 88 *fn.*
    logic, place in, 25-27
    non-Archimedean, 37
    non-Desarguesian, 37
    non-Euclidean, 34-35

geometry: (*cont.*)
  rational, 26-27
  rigorous, 38-39
  theorems, 37
  see also mathematics
germanium, semi-conductor, 134
Germany:
  experimental psychology, 299
  idealism, philosophy, 300
Germer, Lester Halbert (1896-   ),
  128
giant calculators, 387-388
gibbons, variation, 331
glass, ancient knowledge of, 155
Glauber, Johann Rudolf (1604-1670),
  161, 431
glottochronology, 330
glucogenic amino acids, 208
glucose:
  alcohol, 181
  blood, 210, 211
  chemical changes, 200
  glycogen, 205
  katabolic breakdown, 216
  molecules, 203-204
  stored energy, 187
glutamic acid:
  formula, 207
  molecules, 209
glycerol, discovery, 165
glycine, 208; formula, 207
glycogen:
  carbohydrate, 204, 205
  molecules, 203
  production, 200
  stored in liver, 210
glycogenolysis, 210
glycolysis, 212, 217
glycosuria, 211
goal-seeking strategy, 405-406
God, variety of meanings, 249
Gödel, Kurt (1906-   ), 53
Goethe, Johann Wolfgang von (1749-
  1832), 409; *quoted*, 158
goiter, iodine lack, 257
gold:
  atoms, 125-126
  medieval alchemy, 159
  symbol, 169
Gold, Dr. Mitchell, 367
Gold, Thomas, 64, 65
Goldschmidt, Richard B. (1878-   ),
  270 *fn.*

gorillas, cranial capacity, 324
Gorki, Maxim (1868-1936), 3
government agencies, work of anthropologists, 354-355
gravitation:
  constant of, 92
  Einstein theory, 33
  law of, 69, 74, 75
  Newton's theory, 67, 68
gravitational mass, 430
Greeks:
  alchemical reasoning, 158
  geometry, 25-26
  irrational numbers, 28
  language, Western science related to,
    351
  material universe, 35
  mathematics and physics, distinction,
    62
  natural co-operation, 247
  Ouroboros serpent, 183; *illus.*, 184
  parallel axiom, 30
  proving of theorems, 24, 39
  psychology, 295
  quadratic equation, 46
  whole number, 27
green leaves, plant, 186
Gregory, James (1638-1675), 22
Grimm's Laws, 347
group habits, language reflection, 345-
  346
group preservation, animal, 247
group survival, 245, 246
growth, living things, 235
growth factors, 220
Gulliver's Travels (Swift), 414
Gurney, Ronald W., 98, 139

H

habits, inviolability of political and social, 7
Hahn, Otto (1879-   ), 139
hair, amino acids, 205
Haldane, J. B. S. (1892-   ), 255,
  274
Hales, Stephen (1677-1761), 164
halogens, 170
Hamilton, Sir William Rowan (1805-
  1865), 21
hand-axes, 324 *fn.*
haploid gametes, 260, 261

Hardy, Sir Godfrey Harold (1877-1947), 20
Hartman (psychoanalyst), 378
Hawkins, Thomas, 435
H-bombs, manufacture, 15
heat:
  energy, 215
  enzymes, 202
  hydrocarbons, 188
  principle of the maximum, 236
heath hen, extinction, 245
heavy hydrogen, 103
Heisenberg, Werner (1901-   ), 98, 133
helium:
  atomic structure, *diag.*, 171
  electrons, 127
  energy, 139
  hydrogen conversion, 78, 80, 95
  nuclei, 135, 141, 148, 174
  symbol, 169
Helmholtz, Herman L. von (1821-1894), 295, 304
hemoglobin, composition, 201
hemophilia, 265
Henderson, Lawrence (1878-1942), 237
hens, social orders of dominance, 243, 244
Henshaw antigen, 333
herbalist, change to pharmacist, 160
herbivorous animals, 218
heredity:
  basis for scientific theory, 260
  chromosomes, 261
  mechanism, 256, 267
  or environment, 259
  primary function, 258
  self-reproducing gene-units, 266
  uniform, 259
  variations, effect on cultures, 337
Hertzsprung-Russell diagram, 71, 80
Hesse, R., 230
heterocyclic ring systems, 185; *diag.*, 186
heterogenesis, 274
hidden parameters, 60
Hilbert, David (1862-1943), 53; *quoted*, 102
Hippocrates (460?-?377 B.C.), 218
historical anthropology, 352
Hitler, Adolf (1889-1945), 299
Hobbes, Thomas (1588-1679), 372

Hodge, W. V. D., 22
Hollerith, Dr. H., 401
hominids, fossil, 273
homo sapiens, see man
homocyclic ring systems, 185
homologous series, organic compounds, 179-180
hook orders, cows, 244
Hooke, Robert (1635-1703), 106 *fn.*, 162
Hooton, Earnest A. (1887-1954) 317
Hopi Indians, language, 351
Hopkins, Sir Frederick Gowland (1861-1947), 219
hormones:
  carcinogenic, 223
  diabetogenic, 210, 211
  discovery, 222
  formation, 200
  natural organic compounds, 188
  sex, 223
  synthetic production, 201
Horney, Karen (1885-1952), 378
horses:
  fossil evidence, 280
  molars, pattern, 283
  stabilized, 280
horseshoe crab, reaction to light, 238, 240
hostility, role, 371
Hoyle, Fred, 64
Hubble, Edwin Powell (1889-1953), 32
Huggins, Sir William (1824-1900), 21
human:
  affairs, rate of change, 285
  biology, comparative, 330-337
  evolution (Washburn), 321-322
  existence, philosophical and anthropological problems, 378, 379
  life, recent changes, 6
  organs, association with planets and metals, 155
  sciences, progress, 16
  values, variability, 343
Human Relations Area Files, 340 *fn.*
humans, *see* man
hunting, collective, Paleolithic Age, 324
Huxley, Julian (1887-   ), 235, 254-255
Huxley, Thomas Henry (1825-1895), 254, 281; *quoted*, 272

Huygens, Christian (1629-1695), 106
   fn., 116
hyperbolic geometry, 34
hydrocarbons, 179-182, 185, 188
hydrogen:
   acceptor, 203
   atom, 127; *diag.*, 171
   atomic number, 126
   atomic weight, 168
   created matter, 93
   deuterium, 135
   earth, early atmosphere, 232
   fused to form helium, *diag.*, 432
   heavy, 103, 135
   inflammable air, 165
   interstellar, 83
   isotopic form, *diag.*, 173
   material of stars, 76, 79
   molecules, 174, 175, 178
   nucleus, 129, 135-136
   symbols, 168
   transmutation, 78, 80, 95, 135, 139,
      234
   valency, 175, 176
hydrogen chloride, discovery, 164
hydrogen peroxide, 167
hydrolysis:
   acid, 215
   digestive, 203
   processes, 202
hydroxy-ethane, 181
hyperon, particles, 149
hypnosis, state of dissociation, 367
hypotheses, chemistry, 155

I

iatrochemistry, 160
ice, dimmed stars, 83
iceberg, conscious and unconscious
   comparison, 365
id and ego, conflict, 373
idealism, philosophy, 300
ideas, language shaper of, 351
imaginary quantities, 45
inbreeding, 276
Inca civilization, 328
India:
   four elements theory, 155
   judgment of guilt, 309
individual evolution, 272
Indo-European language:
   laryngeals, 348
   statistics available, 350

induction, test, 433-434
industrial anthropology, 354
Industrial Revolution, 9, 386
inertia, energy content, 114
inertial mass, 430
infant prodigies, 409
infants, language, 347
infinitesimal calculus, 62
inflammable air, 165
information:
   communication, 388
   entropy, 424-426
   organization, 420-426
   system, 424
   theory, 426
infrared radiations, 103, 117
inheritance:
   acquired characters, 258
   blending, 274
   cytoplasmic, 261
   environmental effects, 272
   instinct, 233
   mechanism, 271, 284
   mendelian, 261-264
   particulate, 266
   results of will and effort, 272, 274
   tendencies, 240
   see also evolution
inner psychophysics, 298
inorganic chemistry, 178
inorganic sector, evolutionary process,
   278-279
insanity, dreaming while awake, 367-
   368
insects:
   breathing mechanism, 283
   restriction of evolutionary possibili-
      ties, 284
   stick, 385
insight and foresight, 427
instinct, inherited, 233
instinctive behavior, 240-241
instinctual wishes, unconscious, 373
insulin, 210, 211, 430
integral calculus, 394
intellectual honesty, maintaining, 251
intelligence, concept, 312
intelligence tests, 313
intensity, weakening with distance, 74
interbreeding:
   humans, 331, 332, 334
   incompatibility, 270
interferometer, 109, *diag.*

intergalactic space, evolutionary process, 278
internal-combustion engine, 386
international agencies, work of anthropologists, 354-355
international relations:
  based on war, 251
  use of anthropology, 355
interpersonal relations, 379; linguistic uses, 346 *fn.*
interstellar gas, 83
intonation patterns, mental disorders, 345
intoxication, alcohol, 368
introspection:
  behavior, 300, 301
  method, 299
intuition, dangers, 37-38
intuitionists, mathematics and logic, 55
ion:
  atom, 137 *fn.*, 171
  shifting location, 234
ionic compounds, 177
Iraq, stratigraphy sites, 325
iron, symbol, 169
irrational numbers, 27-28, 39, 43-44
Isaiah (prophet), *quoted*, 186
isobutane, 180
isolationism, archaeological, 327
isomerization, 203
isomers, 180
isotopes, 135, 139, 173
isotropic space, 108 *fn.*
Italy, cubic equation, 46

J

Jacob, prenatal influence, 257
James, William (1842-1910), 309
Java man, cranial capacity, 324
Jeans, Sir James Hopwood (1877-1946), 20
Jefferson, Thomas (1743-1826), 409
Jericho, stratigraphy site, 325
Johnson, Samuel (1709-1784), 22, 197
Jung, Carl J. (1875-   ), 376

K

Kant, Immanuel (1724-1804), 38, 52, 300
Kapitza, Peter L. (1894-   ), 15
Kardiner, Abram, 378

katabolism, 200, 214, 216, 217
Kekulé, Friedrich August (1829-1896), 185, 191, 192, 193; *quoted*, 179, 183
Kelvin, Lord (William Thomson) (1824-1907), 21, 35
Kepler, Johannes (1571-1630), 67, 102
ketogenic amino acids, 208
ketone bodies, 211, 212
ketonuria, 211
kev, energy, 142
kidney disease, diagnosis, 198
killing prohibition, understanding, 345
kinetic energy, 129
kinship terms, 336
Klein, Felix (1849-1925), 21
Kluckhohn, Clyde (1905-   ), 316-318
knots, topology, 35
knowledge:
  disinterested pursuit, 15
  fear of, 12
Krebs, H. A., 213
Kris, Ernest (psychoanalyst), 378
Kroeber, Alfred Louis (1876-   ), 340
Külpe, Oswald (1862-1915), 298, 299, 310

L

lactic acid, forms, 191; *diag.*, 192
lactic dehydrogenase, 203
Lagrange, Joseph Louis (1736-1813), 166
Lamarck, Chevalier de (1744-1829), 258, 271, 387
land vertebrates, extinction, 281
language:
  change, orderliness, 347
  culture paradigm, 346, 347, 350
  dating, 329
  epistemological, 351
  linguistic community, 346 *fn.*
  logical relation system, 350
  patterns, 351
  reflection of group habits, 345
  scientific study, 349-350
  social stratification, 346 *fn.*
  sound classes, 336
Larmor, Sir Joseph (1857-1942), 21
laryngeals, 348 *fn.*
latency period, 370

Lattes, C. M. G., 148
Lavoisier, Antoine L. (1743-1794), 163, 165, 166
law, evolutionary study, 272
Lawrence, Ernest (1901-   ), 139
lead:
    medieval alchemy, 159
    symbol, 169
leaders, social rank, 244
learning:
    experimental study, 307
    measurements, 296
leather, ancient knowledge, 155
Le Bel, Joseph Achille (1847-1930), 190, 192
Leibniz, Gottfried W. von (1646-1716), 48, 391, 429
Lemaître, Abbé Georges Edouard (1894-   ), 94
Lémery, Nicolas (1645-1715), 160
length measurements, space, 111-112
Lenin, Nikolai (1870-1924), 3, 287
Leucippus, 166
lexico-statistic dating, 330
liberty, limitations, 10-11
libido:
    general psychic energy, 377
    sexual energy, 370, 379
Liebig, Baron Justus von (1803-1873), *quoted*, 158
life:
    basic facts, 275
    definition, 235
    drive for, 371
    early kind, 234
    environment fitness, 237
    nature of, 267
    origin, 231-235
    possibilities realized, 284
    produced on other planets, 279 *fn.*
    studies, 256
    tactics and strategy, 377
    temperature of existence, 237
    unicellular level, 279
Life, The Facts of (Darlington), 257 *fn.*
Life Force, 272
light:
    colored, wave length, 117
    corpuscular theory, 115-117, 121-122; *diag.*, 116
    diffraction, 117; *illus.*, 118
    emission and absorption, 122, 126

light: (*cont.*)
    intensity, 121-122; tropical forest, 239
    nature, 103
    night sky, 93
    passage through rectangular opening, *illus.*, 120
    passage through slits, *diag.*, 119
    production, 215
    quantum, 103, 122, 145
    reactions to, 237-238
    receding source, 89
    rectilinear propagation, 74
    signals, velocity of propagation, 113
    speed, 114
    stars, 70-73, 76, 77, 78, 80-81, 85, 87; *diag.*, 86
    velocity, 86, 88, 89, 90, 96
    wave-particle duality, 121, 127
    wave theory, 108-110, 115-116, 118-119, 121; *diag.*, 117
likeness between things, 427
lime, slaked, 182
linguistics, 319
    anthropological, 346, 352
    evolutionary study, 272
    see also language
linkage, genetic law, 268
literature, scientific, 194
lithium:
    symbol, 169
    transmutaton, 135, 139
Littlewood, J. E., 21
liver:
    carbohydrate storage, 204
    glycogen, 210
living matter:
    genetics, 256
    material transmission, 257
lizards:
    collecting, 239
    fight orders, 244
    territorial defense, 243
Lockyer, Sir Joseph Norman (1836-1920), 21
Lodge, Sir Oliver (1851-1940), 21; *quoted*, 106 *fn.*
logarithmic scale, 424
logarithms, Napier invention, 389
logic:
    and adaptation, 413-414
    deductive, 433, 434
    place in geometry, 25-27

logic: (*cont.*)
  symbolic, 48-50, 54
  see also mathematics
logic of science, 427-436
  analysis into units, 428
  code, implication, 430
  experiments, use of, 432
  induction, test, 433-434
  insight and foresight, 427
  likeness, 427
  units, finding, 429-430
logical calculus, 48
logical machines, 435
logical positivism, Vienna school, 300
Lorentz, Hendrik Antoon (1853-1928), 111
Lorentz-Fitzgerald concept, 112
loyalty to human race, 14
lubricating oils, 180
luck, role in human life, 341
Lucretius (96?-55 B.C.), *quoted*, 194
luminiferous ether, 115
luminosity, sun, 77
luminosity-temperature diagram, 71
Lysenko (scientist), 272
lysine, formula, 207
Lyttleton, R. A., 64

M

Mach, Ernst, 303
machines:
  adaptive, 405-414
  deductive, 388-404
  evolution, 386
  experience in, 407-412
  exploring, 412-413
  game-playing, 406-407, 409
  injury, adaptation to, 413
  logic, 400-404
  procedures, *diag.*, 395-398
  substitution for human labor, 9
Maclaurin, Colin, 22
macroevolution, 270 *fn.*
macromolecules, 189
macromutation, 270 *fn.*
maggots, meat, 257
magic, Paleolithic Age, 324-325
magnesium, symbol, 169
magnetic field, stars, 81
main sequence stars, 71-72, 76-81
maize:
  early production, 328

maize: (*cont.*)
  zein, protein, 207
males, territorial defense, 243
maltase, enzyme, 204
maltose, starch, 204
mammalogy, 232
mammals:
  dominance on land, 281
  higher, divergent specialization, 280
  territorial defense, 243
man:
  activation, 296
  apelike ancestors, 272
  basic inner forces, 379
  behavior, science of, 355
  central cravings, 379
  cerebral cortex, 308-309
  common characteristics, 235
  co-operative drives, 248
  cultures, identical values, 344
  dominance orders, 244
  domination, 385
  entry into New World, 326
  environmental control, 385
  evolution, 282, 288-289, 321-322, 330, 352
  extermination, 6, 7, 8, 13
  fine perception, 302
  foresight, 427
  freak of nature, 379
  genes, number, 267
  heat output, 78
  history, 322-330
  ideological divergence, 287
  interdependence, 247, 340
  introspection, 300
  long-range task, 289
  modern, cranial capacity, 324
  modern, first appearance, 323
  needs, 311-312
  olfactory capacity, 302
  overspecialized, 331
  peoples, constancies and variations, 357
  single unit, 287
  striving, main source, 377
  stultifying effects of society, 380
  variation, 331-332
  virtues, biological basis for, 251
  visual space perception, 303
manufacturing industries, dependence on chemistry, 178
marble, heated, 163

marine forms, separate sexes, 246
Marx, Karl (1818-1883), 363
Masères, Francis (1731-1824), 47
mass, nature, 430
mass-energy relation, 136, 138, 145
mass-luminosity, stars, 72; *diag.*, 73
mass protection, 245
mass spectograph, 136; *diag.*, 137
material-spiritual relation, 294-295, 314
maternal impressions, 257, 261
mathematical physics, 106
mathematicians, the first, 24-25
mathematics, 24-62
   astronomical space, geometry, 31-33
   atomistic school, solid geometry, 29-
     30
   axioms, new views, 36-37
   electric discharges, opposite, 142 *fn.*
   electromagnetism, 111
   imaginary quantities, 45-47
   intuition, dangers, 37-38
   intuitionists, 55
   irrationals, discovery, 27-28
   logic, place in geometry, 25-27, 48-
     52, 415
   mathematicians, first, 24-25
   non-Euclidian geometries, 34-35
   numbers, 40-42
   numeration, system, 47-48
   paradoxes of Zeno, 28-29
   parallel axiom, 30
   Peano's symbolism, 50-51
   philosophy, 61-62
   physical chemistry, 178
   probability, 55-58
   quantum mechanics, 102, 132
   relativity, general, 33
   rigorous geometry, 38-39
   Russell's paradox, 53-55
   short cuts, discovery, 394
   space time, 39-40
   statistics, 58-59
   stochastic systems, 60
   symbolic logic, 48-50
   three-dimensional space, 45
   topology, 35-36
   transfinite numbers, 42-45
   ultimate realities, 173
   Whitehead-Russell developments, 51-
     53
matter:
   aggregation, 156

matter: (*cont.*)
   atomic constitution, 166-167
   continual creation, 93
   discontinuous, 166
   extended substance, 298
   four elements, *diag.*, 156
   granular structure, 349
   heat and thermal properties, 103
   law of conservation, 167
   living and nonliving, 235
   mind, association with, 155
   nature, 154
   study, 154
   unity, 158, 194
   wave and probability properties, 103
mauveine, 184, 185
maximum, principle, 236
Maxwell, James Clerk (1831-1879),
   111
Maya pottery, wheel-made, 327
Mayow, John (1641-1679), 162, 164
Mayr, Ernst, 278
measurement and observation, psychology, 296
measurements, space and time, 111-112
meat, maggots, 257
mechanical aptitude, 313
mechanical energy, 215
mechanics, laws of, 113
mechanism, life studies, 256
medicine:
   chemistry applied to, 160
   cultural anthropology, applications,
     354
   physical anthropology, contributions,
     353
medieval culture, 362
medium-bright stars, 85
meiosis, reduction, 260
Meitner, Lise (1878-   ), 139
memories, storing, 309
memory test, reaction times, 306
men, the ways of, 338-345
Mendel, Abbé Gregor Johann (1822-
   1884), 261, 264, 268, 273
Mendel, Lafayette Benedict (1872-
   1935), 207
Mendeléeff, Dmitri Ivanovich (1834-
   1907), 169, 170
mendelian inheritance, 261-264, 273
Mendel's laws, 268
Menninger Clinic, 374

mental disorders:
connection with social norms, 342
speech aid in diagnosis, 345
therapy, 373
mental health, 379-380
mental phenomena, measuring, 295
mental philosophy, 295
mental possibilities, advance, 284
mercaptan, 302
mercury:
chemical and mystical significance, 160
symbol, 169
Mercury (planet), orbit, 33
mercury-sulphur theory, 158, 160
Mesoamerica, archaic horizon, 328
Mesolithic Age, 325
mesons:
particles, 143
summarized, 148
Mesozoic, reptilian supremacy, 281
message symbols, checking, 423
metabolic changes, enzymes, 201
metabolism:
abnormalities, 210
amino acids, 212
bacterial, 220, 224
carbohydrate, 205, 209, 210-213
derangement of normal, 222
diabetic subjects, 210-212
energy, 214-218
fat, 210-213
nitrogen, 206
protein foods, 205-210
summary of main lines, *diag.*, 212
metallurgy, inorganic chemistry, 178
metals:
alkali, 170
ancient knowledge, 155
association with human organs and destinies, 155
burning, 163
photoelectric effect, 122-123
sulphur-mercury theory, 158
transmutation, 159
metamathematics, 53
methane (marsh gas):
earth, early atmosphere, 232
formulae, 176
model, 191; *diag.*, 192
molecular, 174
paraffin series, 180

MEV, million electron volts, 129, 145
Mexico, National University, psychoanalytic training, 376
Mexico, pre-Columbian horizon, 327
mice:
fight orders, 244
spontaneously generated, 257
Michelson, Albert Abraham (1852-1931), 109 *fn.*
Michelson-Morley experiment, 109, 111, 112; *diag.*, 109
Michurin, J. V., 272
Micrographia (Hooke), 162
microorganisms:
nutritional requirements, 219-220
pathogenic, checking, 223, 224
unicellular, 277
microscope, electron, 144
microscopy, 198-199
mileage counter, 391
military, aided by constitutional anthropology, 353
milk:
importance in diet, 219
souring organisms, 220
Milky Way, 81, 83
Miller, Stanley, 231
Millikan, Robert Andrews (1868-1953), 145
mind:
and behavior, 272
brain, interaction, 298
matter, association, 155
self-reproduction, 285
unextended substance, 298
mines, ventilation, 390
minimax strategy, 417-419
minimum, principle of, 236
mitochondria, particles, 199
mitosis, 260
Mittag-Leffler, G., 21
models, astronomers', 67, 75-76
Abbé Lemaître, 94
modern alchemy, 157
modifications of the individual, 259
molecular formula, 169, 175
molecules:
atom combinations, 174
Avogadro's hypothesis, 175
behavior, 104
changes, 175
compound atoms, 167

molecules: (*cont.*)
   configuration, 190, 191; *diag.*, 192
   deamination, 209
   energy-content, 188
   food digestion, 203, 214
   gas, 122
   genes, 267
   glucose, 200, 203-204
   glutamic acid, 209
   ions, shifting location, 234
   lifelike, 231, 232
   light-emitting properties, 134
   multiple, 190
   natural organic, 186
   nitrogenous part, 208
   rearrangement, 203
   simple, 190
   standard patterns, 189
   structure, 193
   superfluous amino-acid, 209
   symmetry, 191-193
   tetrahedral angle, 192
   weight, 175
monkeys:
   high-ranking males, 244
   territorial defense, 243
monocyclic ring systems, 185; *diag.*, 186
monomer, simple molecule, 190
Monroe Doctrine, anthropological, 326, 327
moon, 69
Morley, Edward Williams (1838-1923), 109 *fn.*
morphological structure, exploration, 198
morphology, 232, 256, 273
Morse Code, 386
mortality tables, 133 *fn.*
moths, melanic, 275 *fn.*
motion:
   Einstein's equations, 114
   laws of, 115, 429
   Newtonian view, 114
motivation, 298, 299, 306, 310-312
   dynamic psychology, 297
   unconscious, examples, 364-365
motor reaction, 306
mule, interbreeding, 270
Muller, Hermann Joseph (1890-   ), 265, 276
multiple proportions, law, 167
muons, summarized, 148
Murdock, G. P., 340

Murray, Henry Alexander, 317
muscles:
   carbohydrate storage, 204
   enlargement, 257-258
   enzyme, 215
   protein, necessity for, 206
mustard gas, mutations, 277
mutation:
   artificially induced, 265
   discovery, 265
   genes, 259, 267
   hereditary material, 273
   inexact copying, 269
   new hereditary traits, 333
mythology, expression of human wisdom, 377
myths, interpersonal relations stabilizing, 341

N

naphthalene, formulae, 184
Napoleon I (1769-1821), 287
national planning, problems, 399
national statistics, 400
nationalistic development cycles, 339
nationality, liberal doctrine, 10
natural:
   co-operation, 244
   organic compounds, 179, 188
   philosophy, 295
   selection, 246, 247, 271-276, 280, 281, 286, 334, 363
Natural Selection, Genetical Basis of (Fisher), 266, 274
nature:
   based on mathematical plan, 173
   understanding, 428
Navaho, kinship terms, 336
navigation, study of astronomy, 386
Nazism, morally acceptable, 343
Neanderthal Man, 323; cranial capacity, 324
Near East, planned food raising, 325
near stars, 84
Neddermeyer, S., 148
need and attitude concept, 311
negative numbers, 46
Negroes, African, serological genes, 333
Neolithic Age, 325-326
neon:
   atomic structure, *diag.*, 171
   symbol, 169

neoprene, molecules, 190
nerve-muscle components, behavior complex, 240
neurosis, 374
neurotic character, 373-374
neurotic symptoms, artistic creation, 377
neutretto, 149
neutrino, 141-142; summarized, 147
neutron:
    atomic nucleus, 105
    catalyst, 160
    code, 431
    discovery, 103, 135
    summarized, 146-147
New Mexico, cave cultures, 328
New Political Arithmetick, 399-400
Newlands, John (chemist), 169, 172
Newton, Isaac (1642-1727):
    atom, 167
    gravitation theory, 33, 67
    light, corpuscular theory, 116
    mechanics, laws of, 113-114, 115, 127
    metal transmutation, 159
    motion, laws of, 102, 429, 430
    philosophy, 62
    solar system, work on, 68-69
nicotinic amide, 222
Nietzsche, Friedrich Wilhelm (1844-1900), *quoted*, 365
night blindness, 218
night sky, darkness, 88, 93
Nile, riv. Africa, flooding, 386
Nim, game, 407; *diag.*, 408
nineteenth century, degree of repression, 372
nip orders, fish, 244
nitric oxide, 168
nitrobenzene, 185
nitrogen:
    atom, valency, 175
    food cycle, 187
    protein source, 206
    symbols, 168, 169
    transmutation, 174
nitrogen-rich soils, excessive growth, 257
nitrogenous equilibrium, 206, 207, 208
nitroglycerine, 188
nitrous gas, symbols, 168
noisy line, 421-423
non-Archimedean geometry, 37
non-Desarguesian geometry, 37

non-Euclidean geometries, 34-35
nonluminous matter, dimmed stars, 83
nonpolar bond, covalency, 176
normal behavior, predictable, 345
normal butane, 180
nose, smelling sensitivity, 302
nose form, cold climates, 335 *fn.*
noughts-and-crosses machine, 406
novocaine, 189
nuclear atom:
    model, 126
    structure, 103
nuclear energy:
    power, main source, 8
    reaction, 77
    scale, 391
nuclear fuels, 386
nuclear particles, wave theory, 129
nuclear physics, 103
nuclear pile, 387
nuclear reactions, 77-78, 138; code, 431
nuclear research, 144
nucleic acid, chemical template, 266
nucleon, 140; summarized, 146
nucleus:
    analyzed into unit concepts, 431
    cohesive forces, 140
    distance between parts, 391
    positive and negative electrical units, 171
number-squaring machine, procedure, 394; *diag.*, 395-398
numbers:
    atomic, 135
    cardinal, 41-42
    irrational, 27-28, 39, 43-44
    negative, 46
    ordinal, 41
    rational, 42
    real, 44
    transfinite, 42-45
numeration, system, 47-48
nylon, macromolecules, 190

O

oat seedlings, reaction to light, 238
object constancy, 304
obscurantism, fighting, 14
observable phenomena, 362-363
observation, instruments, 387
observation and measurement, psychology, 296

obstetricians, contributions of physical anthropology, 353
octaves, law of, 169, 172
octonory system, numeration, 47-48
Oedipus complex, 370
Ohm, Georg Simon (1787-1854), 389
Ohtsuki, Dr. Kenji, 378
oil, exhaustion, 8
Olbers, Heinrich (1758-1840), 84
    assumptions, 85-94
    paradox, 87, 88, 89, 92; *diag.*, 86
olefiant gas (ethylene), symbols, 168
Ommaney, Erasmus, 21
ontogeny, 272
oögenesis, *diag.*, 263
open-chain compounds, 183
open-chain structures, 185
opposites, pairs, 157
optical phenomenon, content, 108
optically active organic matter, 191, 193
optimum, principle of, 236
order, axioms, 36
ordinal numbers, 41
organic chemistry:
    "Big Four," 179
    biochemistry, 199
    division of chemistry, 178
    molecular, 186
organic compounds, homologous series, 179
organic compounds, natural, 188
organic defects, psychological significance, 377
organic energy, 188
organic explosives, 188
organic materials, radioactive disintegration, 329
organic molecules:
    structure, 179
    tetrahedral angle, 192
organisms:
    diverse, 279
    earliest, 279
    genetic mechanism, 267
    living, evolution, 232
    living, similarity, 199
    lower, co-operation, 244
    oxygen intolerant, 236
    self-reproducing chromosomes, 261
organization:
    in a code, 426
    main steps, 286
    rise in level, 279

organization: (*cont.*)
    simple types, 233
organization and information, 420-426
    information and entropy, 424-426
    information in a system, 424
    noisy line, 421-422
    organization in a code, 426
    redundancy, 423
    signal and noise, 420
organs, disuse, 257
Origin of Species (Darwin), 272
orthogenesis, 272, 274
orthopedic surgeons, contributions of physical anthropology, 353
Osborne, Thomas Burr (1859-1929), 207
osteomalacia, 221
Ouroboros Serpent, 183; *illus.*, 184
ova, 260
overcrowding, dangers, 245
oxaloacetate, 214
oxidation:
    biological, 201, 203
    chemical change, 182
    fat, 214
oxide, 163
oxygen:
    atom, valency, 175
    discovery, 164-165
    first production, 236
    nitrogen transmutation, 174
    symbols, 168, 169
    vital need, 311

P

Paleolithic Age, 323-324, 329, 330
paleontology, 272, 273, 277
p-aminobenzoic acid, 221, 224
pancreas:
    amylase, 203
    insulin, 210
pangenesis, 259 *fn.*
pantothenic acid, 222
Paracelsus, Philippus Aureolus (1493?-1541), 160
paradox:
    Olbers', 87, 88, 89, 92; *diag.*, 86
    Russell's, 53-54
paraffin hydrocarbons, 180, 181, 192
paraffin wax, 180
parallel axiom, 30-31, 34, 37
parasites, modern viruses, 234

parent relationships, 369
parental attitudes, effect on personality, 343
Park, O., 230
Park, T., 230
parthenogenesis, 269
particles:
  atomic physics, summarized, 145-149
  behavior, 132
  electrical, 104
  light, theory, 116, 121
  mechanics, 129
  subcellular, 199
  velocity, 79
particulate inheritance, 266
Pascal, Blaise (1623-1662), 55, 391, 415; *quoted*, 414
Pascal-Leibniz machine, 391
Pasteur, Louis (1822-1895), 166, 190, 191, 430; *quoted*, 193
patterns, standard molecular, 189
Pauli, Wolfgang, 79, 147
Pavlov, Ivan Petrovich (1849-1936), 307
Peano, Giuseppe (1858-1932), 3; symbolism, 50-51
pebble tools, 322, 323
peck orders, birds, 244
pediatrics, growth study contributions, 353
Peking man, 323; cranial capacity, 324
penicillin, 223
penicillium, mold, 277
Pennsylvania, petroleum, 180
pepsin, enzyme, 204
peptidases, enzymes, 204
perception, 304-305
perfect cosmological principle, 85 *fn.*, 91, 92-93, 94, 95, 96
perfumes, natural organic compounds, 188
periodic table of elements, 169
Perkin, Sir William Henry (1838-1907), 183, 185
Perkin's mauve, 184
perpetual motion machine, 274
personal equations, 305
personality, influence of culture, 342-343
personality type, 380
personnel problems, anthropological techniques, 340
petro-chemicals, 185

petroleum:
  derivatives, 188
  hydrocarbons, 180, 183, 185, 188
pharmacist, herbalist's change to, 160
pharmacology, 222
phenol, formulae, 184
phenomena, recurring, 107
philosopher's stone, 158, 159
philosophical principles, languages built on, 350
philosophy:
  function, 248
  libidinal forces, 372
Philosophy, International Congress of, Paris (1900), 3, 51
phlogiston, 163, 166
phonemes (sound classes), 336, 348, 348 *fn.*, 349
phosphate, enzyme-catalyzed reaction, 216
phosphorus, symbols, 168, 169
photoelectric cell, 386
photoelectric effect, light emission and absorption, 122-123, 126
photography, light, 238
photon quantum, 145
physical anthropology, 319, 335, 353
physical chemistry, 178
physical constants, 92
physical sciences, 154; experimental data, 399-400
physical types, human, rceognizable, 332
physicists:
  analyzing experiment records, 431
  work in two worlds, 105
physics, 102-149
  atomic, 79, 134-144, 415
  atoms, 125-131
  light, 115-125
  major discoveries, 103
  mathematical, 106
  motion, 108-115
  Olbers' assumption, 85-92
  particles, atomic, summarized, 145-149
  terrestrial, 67-75
  wave mechanics, 131-134
physiological chemistry, 198
physiological genetics, 266
physiological psychology, 295, 296
physiology, 232
  evolution of, 272

physiology (*cont.*)
  organic chemistry, 178
  studies in, 256
physique-behavior relation, 335
pigeons, learning, 296, 308
pigments:
  formation, 200
  natural organic compounds, 188
  retinal, 221
  synthetic production, 201
pilot, automatic, 409, 412, 413, 422
pions, summarized, 148
piperidine ring, *diag.*, 186
pituitary gland, 210
plague, spread throughout Eastern
  Hemisphere, 16
Planck, Max (1858-1947), 103, 145
Planck's constant, 123
planets:
  association with human organs and
    destinies, 155
  motion, 67
  outer, living matter on, 237
plants:
  animal-plant relation, 236
  behavior patterns, 240
  change in unfavorable surroundings,
    245
  continuous transformation, 274
  domestication, 325, 326
  genetic mechanism, 267
  green, leaves, 186
  green, synthesis, 218
  group stabilization, 282
  intercrossing, 270, 276
  light, reactions, 237
  mutation, 265
  one-celled, 235
  polysaccharides, 205
  proteins, amino acids, 207
  separate species, 279
platinum black, catalyst, 202
Plato (427?-347 B.C.), mathematics,
  173
play, animals, 405
pneumatic trough, 164
Poincaré, Jules Henri (1854-1912), 21
polar bond, electrovalency, 176
political behavior, affected by science,
  16
political philosophy, changes in, 9
political systems, libidinal forces, 372

politicians, professional skill, 12
politics, psychoanalytic knowledge, 379
polonium, interaction with alpha particle, 130-131
polycyclic ring systems, 185; *diag.*, 184
polymer, multiple molecule, 190
Polynesian languages, sound classes, 336
polyploidy, chromosome-doubling, 276
polysaccharide, 205
polysaccharide glycogen, 200
polythene, molecule, 189
Pope, William Jackson (1870-1939),
  152
population:
  constant average, 95
  differentiation, 334
  distinctive human problem, 288
  effect on evolution, 246-247
positron-electron, 142
positron, generation and annihilation,
  143
positron, summarized, 146
posture, adopting upright, 331
potassium, symbol, 169
pottery, early production, 328
Powell, C. F., 104
power, striving for, 377
power-hungry machines, 386
power-stations, atomic, 10
power tools, 386-387
pragmatism, 300
predisposition, 306
pressure, compressed matter, 79
pressure, stellar matter, 76
Priestley, Joseph (1733-1804), *quoted*,
  164-165
primary needs, 311
primitive concepts, mathematics, 39
Principia Mathematica (Whitehead
  and Russell), 52, 53
principle, cosmological, 85 *fn.*, 91, 92-93
principles, three, *diag.*, 194
printing, invention, 285
printing press, 387
probability, theory of, 55-58, 415
process, explaining, 428
process, life studies, 256
production levels, maintaining, 9
productive orientation, 379-380
progress, resistance to, 9
propane, formulae, 180
properties, galaxies, 96

prosthetic group, protein, 201
proteins:
  amino acids, 204, 205, 206, 232
  animal, 208-209
  carbohydrate, 213
  daily requirement, 206
  energy providing, 186
  enzymes, 201
  fat, 213
  foods, function and metabolism, 186, 205-210
  gene-units of heredity, 266
  insulin, 222
  macromolecules, 190
  nitrogenous equilibrium, 206, 207, 208
  oxidation, 214
  plant, 208
  protoplasm, living, 232
  synthetic production, 201
  tissue building, 186, 205
proto-co-operation, 233, 244; animals, 247
proton-electron pairs, 171
protons:
  atomic nucleus, 105, 126
  behavior, 104
  code, 431
  scattered, 129
  summarized, 146
protoplasm, growth and destruction, 235
protoplasm, living, protein, 232
protozoans, 235
  evolution, 246
  learned behavior, 242
protozoology, 232
psychic energy, transforming, 380
psychoanalysis, 362-380
  Asiatic philosophic concepts, 378
  neo-Freudian theories, 378-380
  theory, 364-373
  therapy, 373-376
psychoanalyst, objective observer, 377
psychic juice, saliva secretion, 307
Psycholinguistics, 349 *fn.*
Psychological Association, American, 300
psychologists, handling of psychic difficulties, 376
psychology, 294-314
  ability, 312-313

psychology (*cont.*)
  emotion, 309
  learning, 307-309
  motivation, 310-312
  perception, 304-305
  psychophysics, 301-304, 314
  reaction, 305-306
psychophysics, 301-304, 314
Psychophysics, Elements of (Fechner), 295
psychoses, 374, 378
psychosocial evolution, 284-289
psychosomatic diseases, 378
Ptolemy, Claudius, model, 67
Pueblo Indians, classic civilization, 328
puffers, alchemists, *illus.*, 158
pyridoxal, 222
pyrrole, ring, *diag.*, 186
pyruvate, 213, 222
pyruvic acid, 212
Pythagoras, 26, 27, 28, 44

Q

quadrant, 387
quadratic equation, 46
qualitative chemistry, 164, 165, 177
quantum:
  energy, 145
  mechanics, 102, 129, 131-133
quartz, atoms, 124
quicklime, chalk decomposition, 163, 164

R

rabbits, color-types, 267
race mixture, 334
race prejudice, witchcraft substitute for, 341-342
races, major human, 333
radio waves, interstellar gas atoms, 83
radioactive clouds, 13
radioactive elements, 125
  measuring disintegration, 328
radioactivity:
  barrier leakage, 134
  spontaneous, 77
radiography, X-ray quanta, 145
radiometer, 302
radium:
  atom, spontaneous breakup, 60

radium: (*cont.*)
   radiations, 125
   radioactivity, 129, 173
Rank, Otto (psychoanalyst), 377
rare-earth elements, 172
rational geometry, 26-27
rational numbers, 42
rationalization, concept, 365-366
rats:
   appearance changes, 264
   diet experiments, 219
   future lies with, 7
   introspection report, 300
   learning ability, 299, 308
   visual brain areas removal, 309
raw materials:
   allocation, 10
   dependence on chemistry, 178
   exhaustion, 7-8
Rayleigh, Lord (1842-1919), 21
reaction, nuclear, 77-78, 138, 431
Read, Arthur Hinton, 153
Read, John (1884-   ), 152-153
real numbers, 44
reasoning, alchemical, 158
reciprocal proportions, law of, 167
red-displacement, spectrum, 33
Red Star, The, 13
red stars, 71, 72, 80, 81
red shift, spectra of galaxies, 91
Redi, Francesco (1626?-1697?), 257
reduction, chemical change, 182
redundancy, 423
relatives, categories, 336
relativistic cosmology, 92
relativity:
   cultural, 343
   general, 33
   theory, 40, 90, 93-94, 103, 108, 113,
      127, 274, 430
religion:
   contribution of anthropology, 341
   evolutionary study, 272
   expression of human wisdom, 377
   learning from science, 248-249
   libidinal forces, 372
   scientifically oriented, 233
repressed ideas, time reactions, 306
repressed wishes, 297
repressions, sublimation, 371
reproduction:
   incompatibility, 270
   living beings, 235

reproduction: (*cont.*)
   sexual, 260
reptilians, extinction, 281, 282
resistance, concept, 365
resonance, nuclear reactions, 138
restriction of evolutionary possibilities,
   283
retina, human, sensitivity, 302, 304
rhesus monkeys, high-ranking males,
   244
riboflavin, 220, 222
rickets, 221
rigorous geometry, 38-39
ring-atoms, 185; *diags.*, 184, 186
ring-systems, 185, 192
rituals, stabilizing interpersonal relations, 341
rocks, age estimate, 107-108
rocksalt, atoms, 124
rod, measuring, contraction in motion,
   111
Rohheim, Geza (psychoanalyst), 378
rubber, natural and synthetic, 189-190
Rubner, Max (1854-1932), 206, 208
Russell, Bertrand (1872-   ), 2-5
   mathematical developments, 51-53
   paradox, 53-54
Rutherford, Ernest (1871-1937), 15,
   21, 103, 125-126, 157, 171, 173

S

Saccheri, parallel axiom, 31, 32
sage grouse, high-ranking males, 244
Sahara desert, rain, 10
saline conditions, succulence of plants,
   257
saliva secretion, psychic juice, 307
salivary amylase, enzyme, 202, 203
salt:
   chemical and mystical significance,
      160
   salivary amylase cofactor, 202
salts, formation, 170
Sanskrit languages, sound system, 347
Sapir, Edward (1884-1939), 349 *fn.*
saturated substances, 181
scale of values, 419
Sceptical Chymist, The (Boyle), 162
Scheele, Karl Wilhelm (1742-1786),
   quoted, 165
schizophrenia, 374, 378, 379
Schmidt, K. P., 230

Schrödinger, Erwin (1887-   ), 98, 103, 128
Schuster, Sir Arthur (1851-1934), 21
science:
  analytic method, 429
  association with war, 15
  Chinese lack of development, 351
  continuous refinement of calculations, 415
  liberator, 17
  logic, 427-436
  of leftovers, 320
  procedure, 429
  religion learning from, 248-249
Science, British Association for the Advancement of, 14
science as foresight, 385-436
  adaptive machines, 405-414
  deductive machines, 388-404
  organization and information, 420-436
  strategy and its safeguards, 414-419
Science Awakening (Van der Waerden), 27 *fn.*
sciences, experimental, 433
scientific age, 314
scientific knowledge, dangers, 16
scientific revolution, 17th century, 161
scientific theories, purpose, 67, 73
scientists, social duty, 11-17
scurvy, deficiency disease, 218
sea-urchin eggs, divisions, 246
secret code deciphering, linguistic analysis, 352-353
seeds, exposure in a vacuum, 236
segregation, genetic law, 268
selection, culture influences, 334
self-assertion, anarchic, 11
self-preservation, animal, 247
self-reproduction, mechanism, 267
self-transformation, 286
semi-conductors of electricity, 134
Semitic language, statistics available, 350
sensations, difference between intensities, 294-295
sense-physiologists, 296
senses, thresholds, 301-302
sensory discrimination, improvement, 258
sensory perceptions, linguistic patterns, 351
sensory reaction, 306

separate species, formation, 280
servomechanisms, 412
sex:
  chromosomes, 260 *fn.*
  genetical knowledge, 269
  hormones, use of, 223
sexual:
  choice, social laws, 340
  desire, physiological need, 311
  reproduction, 260
  strivings, 370
shadow, light theory, 116; *diags.*, 116, 117
Shakespeare, William (1564-1616), 409
Shaw, George Bernard (1856-1950), 272, 423
Sheldon, W. H., 335
shift, Doppler, 70 *fn.*
shortfall, 422
Shortley, George H., 98
Siberia, fertility, 10
sibling relationships, 369
signal-to-noise ratio, 420-421
silicon:
  basis for life, 237
  semi-conductor of electricity, 134
  symbol, 169
silver:
  medieval alchemy, 159
  symbol, 169
similar processes, theory, 412
similarity in figures, 26
Simpson, George Gaylord, 278
Sino-Tibetan language, statistics avail able, 350
sins, seven capital, 251-252
size constancy, 304-305
size variation, human stature, 264
skin, amino acids, 205
slavery, morally acceptable, 343
sleep:
  dissociation, 366
  vital need, 311
slide rule, 389
slim figure, acquisition, 204-205
smoking, process of rationalization, 365
snakes, evolution, 281, 282
soap, ancient knowledge, 155
social anthropology, evolutionary study, 272
social life, adhesions of certain features, 340

social organization, 340, 341
social peck order, animals, 244
social psychology, 297
social relations, needed changes, 16
— social science, problems, 399
social stratification, linguistic usages, 346 *fn.*
social structure, changes, 340
social systems, determination, Marx's theory, 363
sociality, animals, 233
socially patterned defect, 380
society, interdependence, 9-10
socioeconomic structure, role, 380
— sociology, psychoanalytic knowledge, 379
sodium:
    atomic structure, *diags.*, 171, 172
    symbol, 169
sodium hydroxide (caustic soda), 170, 177, 182
sodium ion, *diag.*, 172
sodium nitrate and water, equation, 177
soil, exhaustion, 7, 8
solar system, *see* astronomy; stars; sun
solid geometry, atomistic school, 29-30
solids:
    elastic, 106, 107, 108
    electrical properties, 134
somatypes, 335
souls, transmigration, 271
sound:
    change, 347, 349
    classes (phonemes), 336, 348, 348 *fn.*, 349
    speed, 393
South America, early population, 326
space:
    absolute motion in, 110
    astronomical geometry, 31-33
    homogeneity and isotropy, 108
    measurements, 111, 112
    popular notions, 336
    theory, 190, 191, 193
    three-dimensional, 45
    time, 39-40
spagyric chemistry, 160
spatial visualization, 313
species:
    extinction, 245
    origin of new from old, 269

species: (*cont.*)
    related, separate biological entities, 270
specificity, enzymes, 202
spectrograph, mass, 136, *diag.*, 137
spectroscope, 386
    inferences, 74
    value, 70-71
spectrum:
    light emitted by atoms, 127
    red displacement, 33
    wave lengths, 121
speech:
    discovery, 386
    information conveyed by, 345
    true, 284 *fn.*
    see also language
spermatogenesis, *diag.*, 263
spermatozoon, 260
sperms, 260
Spinoza, Baruch (1632-1677), 364
spiral galaxies, 81; *illus.*, 82
spiritualistic philosophy, 314
spiritual-material relation, 294, 295, 314
sponges, mass protection, 245
spontaneous generation, 259
spontaneous mutation, 265
spores, exposure in a vacuum, 236
spread of discoveries, 338-339
squaring a number, machine procedure, 394; *diag.*, 395-398
stabilization, evolutionary, 280-284
Stahl, Georg Ernst (1660-1734), 163
starch:
    green chlorophyll, 232
    maltose, 204
    molecules, 203
    photosynthesis, 236
    production, 200
    stored energy, 187
starchy food, digestion, 202
stars:
    age, 80
    binary, 69
    blue, 71, 81
    bright, 72, 80, 84
    changes, 75
    constitution, 69-70, 73, 75, 76, 80
    dimmed, 83
    faint, 71, 72, 80, 85
    fixed, 66
    galaxies, 66, 95

stars: (*cont.*)
  gravitational forces, 76
  interaction with gas and dust, 84
  life history, 272, 278
  light, 69, 70-73, 76, 77, 78, 80-81, 85, 87; *diag.*, 86
  line-of-sight velocity, 70
  magnetic field, 81
  main sequence, 71-72, 76-81
  measurement, *diag.*, 70
  medium bright, 85
  near, 84
  origin, 84
  partially dimmed, 83
  receding, 432
  red, 71, 72, 80, 81
  structure, 74-76
  sub-dwarf, 81
  surface area, 71
  temperature, 71, 72, 76-77, 78, 79
  velocity, 86, 89
  white, 71, 72, 80
  yellow, 71
starvation, nitrogen, 206
states, limitations on liberty, 10-11
statesmen, duty, 16
statistical accounting, 399
statistics, theory of probability, 58-59
steam-driven machines, 386
stereochemistry, 193
stereoscopic color vision, 276, 321
stereoscopic movies, 3-D perception, 304
sterile hybrid, 276
Stern, Otto, 129
Stevenson, E. C., 148
stick insect, 385
stilbestrol, 223
stochastic systems, 60-61
stock ticker, 386
Stokes, Sir George Gabriel (1819-1903), 21
Stone Age, 323-325
stone implements:
  polished, 325
  unpolished, 324
stoneware, ancient knowledge, 155
Stoney, George Johnstone (1826-1911), 145
strategy:
  goal-seeking, 405
  minimax, 417

strategy: (*cont.*)
  of foresight, 388
strategy and its safeguards, 414-419
  games based on chance, 415-417
  larger choices, 417
  minimax strategy, 417-419
  scale of values, 419
stratigraphy, earliest sites, 325
Street, J. C., 148
streptococci, 221, 223
streptomycin, 223
strikers, atomic power-stations, 10
structural isomerism, 180
struggle for existence, 244, 251
subatomic things, discovery, 103
sublimation, 371
substances, studies of, 154
substitution reaction, 181
succinate, oxidation, 217
succinic acid, 214
sucrose, stored energy, 187
suffering, an end in itself, 344
sugar:
  alcohol, 181, 182
  glucose, stability, 200
  green chlorophyll, 232
  photosynthesis, 236
  stored energy, 187
sulfanilamide, 224
Sullivan, Harry Stack, 374, 378
sulphur:
  chemical and mystical significance, 160
  symbols, 168, 169
sulphur dioxide, discovery, 164
sulphur-mercury theory, 158, 160
sun:
  Copernicus' discovery, 67, 68, 362, 364
  eclipse, 69
  energy, 78, 140
  hydrogen store, 80
  luminosity, 77
  main sequence band, 72
  size, 69
  ultraviolet rays, 231
superconductivity, 144
supergiant stars, 72, 80
superstitions, heredity, 257
supranational authority, 11
swamps, drying, 6
Swift, Jonathan (1667-1745), 414

switch and fuse, 386
syllogisms, logic, 61
symbolic logic, 48-50, 54
Symbolic Logic, Journal of, 53
symbolism, Peano's, 50-51
symbols, Daltonian, *illus.*, 168
symbols, elements, 136
symmetry, 191, 192, 193
symptoms, neurotic, 373
synthetic chemicals, 223
synthetic rubbers, 190
systematic motions, distant regions, 85, 89
systematics, studies, 256

T

tachina fly, unlearned behavior, 241-242
Tait, Peter G. (1831-1901), 35
tape recorder, 386
tartaric acid, forms, 191
Taylor, Sir Geoffrey, 21
techniques, anthropological, 340
technology, 386; Paleolithic Age, 324
teeth, loss of wisdom teeth, 330
telegony, 259-260
telegraph, 386
telephone, 386
telescope, 386
    aperture, doubling, 90
television receivers, electrons, 115
temperature:
    birds and mammals, regulation, 281, 283, 284
    stars, 71, 72, 76-77, 78, 79
    tropical forest, 239
tendons, growth, 258
Tennyson, Alfred (1809-1892), *quoted*, 193
terramycin, 223
terrestrial gas, 76
terrestrial observation, 67
territorial defense, 243
tetrahedral angle, 192
thalassemia, 333
Thales (640?-546 B.C.), principle, 25, 27
theology, semi-science, 249
theorems, proving, 24, 37
theories, chemistry, 155
theories, disproof, 84, 88
therapeutics, 189, 222
therapy, psychoanalytic, 363, 373-376

thermochemistry, 178
thermodynamics, second law, 425
thermonuclear reaction, 78
thermonuclear warfare, 13
thermostat, 409, 412, 413, 422; *diag.*, 410-411
thiamine, 222
thinking:
    unconscious, 298, 299
    wishful, 312
thiophen ring, *diag.*, 186
Thomas, D. G. A., 384
Thomson, Sir George Paget
    (1892-   ), 128
Thomson, Sir Joseph John (1856-1940), 21, 145, 170, 171
Thomson, William, *see* Lord Kelvin
thorium, radioactive disintegration, 129
Thought, An Investigation of the Laws of (Boole), 49
thought processes, language influence, 352
thoughts, products of fears and desires, 363
3-D perception, 304
three-dimensional space, 45
thresholds, determination, 301
thyroxin, 222
time:
    mathematical variable, 107
    measurements, 111-112
    space, 39-40
tin:
    heated, 163
    medieval alchemy, 159
    symbol, 169
tissue formation, amino acids, 205
tissues:
    food storage, 200
    protein necessity, 206
tobacco-mosaic disease, 234
toe, loss of little, 330
Tolstoy, Leo (1828-1910), 314
toluene, formulae, 184
tongues of men, 345-352
tools:
    evolution, 324
    oldest-known, 322, 323
    reorganizing matter, 385
topology, 35-36
toxins, bacterial, 221
toys, wheeled, 327 *fn.*
training, psychoanalysts, 375

transaminases, enzymes, 222
transference, concept, 369
transfinite numbers, 42-45
transmigration of souls, 271
transmission of experience, 284, 285
transmutation:
artificial, 173-174
elements, 103, 135, 156
hydrogen, 234
induced, 77
metals, 159
tree rings, dating by, 329
tria prima (three hypostatical principles), 160, 162; *illus.*, 161
trial-and-error machine, 394, 409, 410
trilobites, fossil evidence, 280
triolein, stored energy, 187
trip hammer, 387
tritium:
hydrogen, 136
isotope, 173
tropical rain forest, climate changes, 238-239
Trotsky, Leon (1877-1940), 3
trypsin, enzyme, 204
tryptophan, formula, 207
tungstic acid, discovery, 165
Turnbull, H. W., 21
"Two Contraries, Doctrine of the," 157, 173
Tyndall, John (1820-1893), *quoted*, 421
typewriter, 386
tyrosine, amino-acid, 222

U

ultraviolet radiations, 103, 117, 231
genes mutation, 259, 277
unconscious:
becoming conscious of, 368
concept, 364
conflicts, 374
contents, 375
inference, 304
motivation, examples, 364-365
wishes, psychology of, 310
unconsciousness, discovery, 298
undefined notions, geometry, 39
undercrowding, dangers, 245
understudies for workers, 10
unicellular microorganisms, research, 277

unit-character, 264
unit factors, identified as material particles, 266
United States:
experimental psychology development, 299-300
General Classification Test, army, 313
language teaching methods, government, 352
units:
analysis, 428
finding, 429
unity of matter, 158, 194
UNIVAC, 413; election forecasts, 393, 400
universe:
birth, 94
consistent picture, construction, 351
destruction, 13
expansion, 33, 91, 93 *fn.*, 94
observable, 90
uniformity, 85, 88, 89-90, 91, 93, 95
youth, 92
unlimited foresight, 406-407
unsaturated substances, 181
upright posture, adoption, 331
uranium:
atomic number, 126
fission, 139-140
interaction with alpha particle, 130-131
isotopes, 139; *diag.*, 173
race for, 8
radioactivity, 129, 173
separation, 174
transmutation, 160
urea, formation, 209
Urey, Harold C. (1893-   ), 103, 135, 147
uric acid, formation, 209
Ursa Major nebula, *illus.*, 82
U.S.S.R., scientists' loyalty, 15
Uttley, A. M., 412

V

vacuum, living processes, 236
valency electrons, 171, 172, 175, 176, 177, 431
value system, essence of culture, 343-344
values, scale of, 419

Van der Waerden, B. L., 27 *fn.*
van't Hoff, Jacobus H. (1852-1911), 190, 192
variants, differential survival, 275
variation, sources, 270
variations, human social importance, 331-332
vegetation:
  acquired characters, 257
  reproduction, 269
velocity:
  light, 86, 88, 89, 90, 96
  light signals, propagation, 113
  particles, 79
  proportional to distance, 89, 90
  recession, 70 *fn.*, 91
  stellar, 86, 89
ventilation, mines, 390
verbal aptitude, 313
Versailles, Treaty of, 10
vertebrate, units of vision, 283
Victorian age, moral code, 372
Vinci, Leonardo da (1452-1519), 15, 387
violin string, vibrations, *diag.*, 128
viruses:
  crystallized, 234, 236
  evolutionary degeneration, 234
  genetics, 277
  modern, 279
  submicroscopic, self-reproducing, 261
vision:
  maximal sensitivity, 303
  threshold for light, 301-302
visual acuity, 283 *fn.*, 284
visual purple, retinal pigment, 221
visualization, spatial, 313
vitamins:
  antagonists, 224
  bacterial, 220, 221
  daily requirement, 218
  functions, 221-222
  natural organic compounds, 188
Von Laue, Max, 124
Von Neumann, John, 132

W

Wälder (psychoanalyst), 378
Walton, Ernest, 103, 134, 136, 139
War:
  international relations based on, 251

War: (*cont.*)
  preventing, 13-14, 288
  risks, 11
  science associated with, 15
warfare, scientific, 8-9, 13
Waring, Edward, *quoted*, 24
Washburn, S. L., 321
wasp:
  gall, 405
  unlearned behavior, 241-242
water:
  constitution, 165, 166, 167, 168
  dissolved oxygen content, 236
  embodiment of qualities, *diag.*, 156
  molecule, 174, 175
  product of combustion, 163
  sulphur-mercury theory, 158
  symbols, 168, 169
  vital need, 311
  wave motion, 116
water clock, 391
water-driven machines, 386
Watson, G. N., 21, 23
Watson, John B. (1878-   ), 299, 300, 308
Watt, James (1736-1819), 16
wave length:
  colored light, 117
  spectrum, 121
  X-ray, 123, 124
wave mechanics, 131-132, 133
wave motion, electrons, 127-128
wave-particle duality, 121, 127, 132, 134
wave propagation, mathematics, 129
waves:
  light, 115-116, 118-119, 121; *diags.*, 117, 122
  water, 116
weather forecasters, 400
Webb, Sidney and Beatrice, 3
Weber, Ernst Heinrich (1795-1878), 294, 295
weight:
  loss in burning, 163
  molecular, 175
Wells, H. G. (1866-1946), 255
Werner, Alfred (1866-1919), 152
Western Hemisphere, first settlers, 326
Weyl, Hermann (1885-   ), 55
wheel, 327
white stars, 71, 72, 80

Whitehead, Alfred North (1861-1947), 2, 3
  imaginary quantities, 47
  mathematics, developments, 51-53
Whitehead-Russell doctrine, 55
Whittaker, Sir Edmund Taylor (1873-   ), 20-23
Whittaker, J. M., 22
whole is greater than its parts, 26
Whorf, B. L., 350, 351
Wiener, Norbert, 9, 407
Wigner, Eugene, 138
William of Ockham (1300?-1349), 400
Wilson, Woodrow (1856-1924), 10
wind vane, 387
Wisconsin glaciation, 326
wishful thinking, 312
wishing, psychology of, 297
witchcraft, functional significance, 341-342
"Women's Dress Fashions, Three Centuries of," 339 *fn.*
workers, atomic power-stations, 10
world, reshaping, 385, 387
world history, understanding processes, 352
World War I, psychological tests, 299
World War II:
  psychology, demands for, 300
  sensitivity, maximal, 302-303
  U.S. Army General Classification Test, 313
Wright, Sewall, 274

writing, invention, 285, 386
written language, progress, 426
Wundt, Wilhelm (1832-1920), 295

X

X rays:
  artificial mutations, 265
  diffraction, 124
  electrons, 115
  genes, mutation, 258-259, 276, 277
  positron-electron pairs, 143
  quanta, 145
  scattering, 124, 125
  study, 103
  wave length, 123, 124

Y

Yarborough problem, 57
yeasts, 182
yellow stars, 71
Yukawa, Hideki, 104, 143, 148

Z

zein, maize protein, 207
Zeitgeist, 298
Zeno, paradoxes, 28-29
zoology, subdivisions, 232
zygote, 260
zymase, 181

About the Editor

JAMES R. NEWMAN *was born in New York City in 1907 and was educated there. He took his law degree from Columbia University and became a member of the New York bar, practicing in New York from 1929 to 1941. During and after World War II he held several government positions, including that of Chief Intelligence Officer at the United States Embassy in London, Special Assistant to the Under Secretary of War, and counsel to the United States Senate Committee on Atomic Energy.*

He is a contributor to many publications and has been a member of the board of editors of SCIENTIFIC AMERICAN *since 1948. Mr. Newman has been a visiting lecturer at Yale Law School and a Guggenheim Fellow. He is the author or co-author of several books, among them* The Tools of War, The Control of Atomic Energy, *and a standard work in the popular scientific field,* Mathematics and the Imagination, *on which he collaborated with Edward Kasner.*